PRINCIPLES OF STRUCTURAL STABILITY THEORY

CIVIL ENGINEERING AND ENGINEERING MECHANICS SERIES

N. M. Newmark and W. J. Hall, *editors*

PRINCIPLES OF STRUCTURAL STABILITY THEORY

ALEXANDER CHAJES

Department of Civil Engineering
University of Massachusetts

Prentice-Hall, Inc., Englewood Cliffs, New Jersey

Library of Congress Cataloging in Publication Data

CHAJES, ALEXANDER,
  Principles of structural stability theory.

  (Civil engineering and engineering mechanics)
  Includes bibliographical references.
  1.–Structural stability. 2.–Buckling
(Mechanics) I.–Title.
TA656.2.C47   624′.171   73-19895
ISBN 0-13-709964-9

10 9 8 7 6 5

Printed in the United States of America

PRENTICE-HALL INTERNATIONAL, INC., London
PRENTICE-HALL OF AUSTRALIA, PTY., LTD., Sydney
PRENTICE-HALL OF CANADA, LTD., Toronto
PRENTICE-HALL OF INDIA PRIVATE LIMITED, New Delhi
PRENTICE-HALL OF JAPAN, INC., Tokyo

To *Diane, Susan, and Michael*

CONTENTS

2.   APPROXIMATE METHODS OF ANALYSIS   75

3.   BEAM COLUMNS   145

4.   BUCKLING OF FRAMES   174

PREFACE

This is an introductory book on the subject of structural stability. Its aim is to provide a detailed treatment of the buckling characteristics of various structural elements and to present the different analytical methods used in the solution of stability problems.

The first chapter deals with the buckling of columns. It begins with the linear elastic theory and goes on to treat initial imperfections, large deformations, and inelastic behavior. The chapter concludes by relating theoretical results to actual engineering materials. In Chapter 2 various approximate methods used to solve buckling problems are considered. Numerical techniques that can be used in conjunction with high speed electronic computers, as well as traditional methods, are included. The remaining chapters deal with the buckling of beams, frames, plates, and shells. These chapters serve a dual purpose. They present the buckling characteristics of various structural elements in a manner similar to the treatment of columns in Chapter 1. They also demonstrate how the various approximate methods introduced in Chapter 2 can be applied to different structural systems. Although the book is primarily concerned with analysis, an attempt is made to relate theoretical conclusions to current design practices.

An effort has been made to limit the book to fundamentals and to treat these in considerable detail. Therefore, it is felt that the text can easily be followed by persons not already familiar with the subject of structural stability, including both upper level undergraduate or graduate students and practicing structural engineers. If the book is used as a textbook, it will be evident that most chapters contain more examples of applications of the theory than can be covered in class. It may be desirable to assign some of these examples, in addition to the problems at the ends of the chapters, as home assignments by the students.

The basis of the book is a course on the buckling of structures, taught by Dr. George Winter at Cornell University, which the author was privileged to take when he studied under Dr. Winter. The author wishes to express his appreciation and gratitude to Dr. Winter for inspiring him to write the book and for the help given by Dr. Winter in preparing the book.

Acknowledgment is made also to Dr. Robert Archer and other colleagues and students at the University of Massachusetts for their help and useful suggestions and to Dr. Merit P. White for providing the kind of atmosphere conducive to scholarly work.

Finally, the author thanks Mrs. Michaline Ilnicky for the fine job she did in typing the manuscript.

ALEXANDER CHAJES

Amherst, Massachusetts

PRINCIPLES OF
STRUCTURAL
STABILITY
THEORY

1
BUCKLING OF COLUMNS

1.1 INTRODUCTION

Slender columns are subject to a type of behavior known as buckling. As long as the load on such a member is relatively small, increases in the load result only in an axial shortening of the member. However, once a certain critical load is reached, the member suddenly bows out sideways. This bending gives rise to large deformations, which in turn cause the member to collapse. The load at which buckling occurs is thus a design criterion for compression members.

Tension members as well as short stocky columns fail when the stress in the member reaches a certain limiting strength of the material. Once this limiting strength of the material is known, it is a relatively simple matter to determine the load-carrying capacity of the member. Buckling, however, does not occur as a result of the applied stress reaching a certain predictable strength of the material. Instead, the stress at which buckling occurs depends on a variety of factors, including the dimensions of the member, the way in which the member is supported, and the properties of the material out of which the member is made. The determination of the buckling stress is thus a relatively complex problem. It is the solution of this problem that will be our main concern in this book.

If buckling does not take place because a certain strength of the material is exceeded, then why, one may ask, does a compression member suddenly buckle? Although it is not possible to answer this question directly, one can make certain observations about the buckling phenomenon and thus explain at least partially what is taking place. One such observation, which elucidates in an excellent manner the phenomenon of buckling, is given in the following paragraph quoted from *Structure in Architecture* by Salvadori and Heller (Ref. 1.1): "A slender column shortens when compressed by a weight applied to its top, and, in so doing, lowers the weight's position. The tendency of all weights to lower their position is a basic law of nature. It is another basic law of nature that, whenever there is a choice between different paths, a physical phenomenon will follow the easiest path. Confronted with the choice of bending out or shortening, the column finds it easier to shorten for relatively small loads and to bend out for relatively large loads. In other words, when the load reaches its buckling value the column finds it easier to lower the load by bending than by shortening."

The buckling load thus appears to be the limiting load under which axial compression in an unbent configuration is possible. It will be assumed here and proved later that the transition from the straight to the bent configuration at the buckling load occurs because the straight configuration ceases to be stable. In Article 1.2 the idea that the buckling load marks the limit of stability of the unbent configuration will be developed into a procedure for evaluating the buckling load.

1.2 METHOD OF NEUTRAL EQUILIBRIUM

The concept of stability is frequently explained by considering the equilibrium of a rigid ball in various positions, as depicted in Fig. 1-1 (Refs. 1.2 and 1.3).

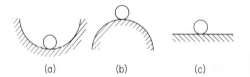

(a)   (b)   (c)

Fig. 1-1 Stability of equilibrium (Adapted from Ref. 1.2).

Although the ball is in equilibrium in each position shown, a close examination reveals the existence of important differences among the three situations. If the ball in part (a) is displaced slightly from its original position of equilibrium, it will return to that position subsequent to the removal of the disturbing force. A body that behaves in this manner is said to be in a state of *stable equilibrium*. By comparison, the ball in part (b), if it is displaced slightly from its position of rest, does not return, but instead continues to move farther away from the original equilibrium position. The equilibrium of the ball in part (b) is a very precarious one. It is called *unstable equilibrium.* Part (c) depicts yet another possible type of equilibrium. Here the ball, after being displaced slightly, neither returns to its original position nor continues to move farther away. Instead, it remains at the position to which the small disturbance has moved it. This behavior is referred to as *neutral equilibrium.*

The ball in Fig. 1-2 is in equilibrium at any point along line *ABC.* In the

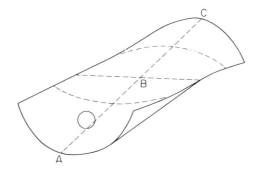

Fig. 1-2   Stability surface.

region between *A* and *B* the equilibrium is stable, and in the region between *B* and *C* it is unstable. At point *B*, the transition between the two regions, the ball is in a state of neutral equilibrium. In Article 1.1 it was pointed out that a column buckles at a certain load because the straight configuration becomes unstable at that load. The behavior of the column is thus very similar to that of the ball in Fig. 1-2. The straight configuration of the column is stable at small loads, but it is unstable at large loads. If it is assumed that a state of neutral equilibrium exists at the transition from stable to unstable equilibrium in the column, similar to that present for the ball in Fig. 1-2, then the load at which the straight configuration of the column ceases to be stable is the load at which neutral equilibrium is possible. This load is usually referred to as the *critical load.*

To determine the critical load of a column, one must find the load under which the member can be in equilibrium both in the straight and in a slightly bent configuration. The technique that uses this criterion for evaluating critical loads is called the *method of neutral equilibrium.*

1.3   CRITICAL LOAD OF THE EULER COLUMN

Even as simple a structural element as an axially loaded member behaves in a fairly complex manner. It is therefore desirable to begin the study of columns with a very idealized case, the Euler column.* The axially loaded member shown in Fig. 1-3a is assumed to have a constant cross-sectional area and to

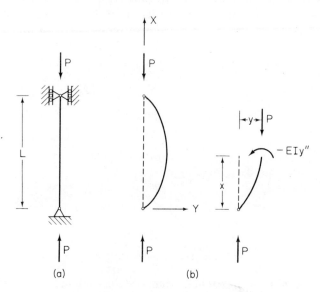

Fig. 1-3   Euler column.

be made of a homogeneous material. In addition, four assumptions are made:

1. The ends of the member are simply supported. The lower end is attached to an immovable hinge, and the upper end is supported so that it can rotate freely and move vertically but not horizontally.
2. The member is perfectly straight, and the load is applied along its centroidal axis.
3. The material obeys Hooke's law.
4. The deformations of the member are small enough so that the term $(y')^2$ is negligible compared to unity in the expression for the curvature $y''/[1 + (y'^2)]^{3/2}$. Hence the curvature can be approximated by y''.†

In accordance with the criterion of neutral equilibrium established in Article 1.2, the critical load is that load for which equilibrium in the slightly

---

*The Euler column takes its name from the man who, in the year 1744, presented the first accurate stability analysis of a column. Although it is customary today to refer to a simply supported column as an Euler column, Euler in fact analyzed a member fixed at one end and free at the other in his famous treatise, which can be found in Ref. 1.4.

†The attention of the reader is drawn to the fact that the symbols y'' and y' are used to denote the second and first derivatives of y with respect to x.

bent configuration shown in Fig. 1-3b is possible. If the coordinate axes are taken as shown in the figure, the internal resisting moment at any section, a distance x from the origin, is

$$M_x = -EIy''$$

Equating this expression to the externally applied bending moment, Py, gives

$$EIy'' + Py = 0 \tag{1.1}$$

Equation (1.1) is a linear differential equation with constant coefficients. As such, its solution is readily obtained. However, before considering this solution, let us digress somewhat and see what form Eq. (1.1) takes if the foregoing simplifying assumptions are not made. If the assumptions of elastic behavior and small deflections are not made, the modulus E in Eq. (1.1) becomes a variable, and curvature y'' is replaced by $y''/[1 + (y')^2]^{3/2}$. The equation then has neither constant coefficients nor is it linear; as a result its solution is difficult to obtain. If the assumptions of concentric loading and hinged supports are not made, there are additional terms on the right-hand side of the equation. This makes the equation nonhomogeneous, but does not make the task of obtaining a solution difficult.

The solution of Eq. (1.1) will now be obtained. Introducing the notation

$$k^2 = \frac{P}{EI} \tag{1.2}$$

Eq. (1.1) becomes

$$y'' + k^2 y = 0 \tag{1.3}$$

The solution of homogeneous linear differential equations with constant co-efficients is always of the form $y = e^{mx}$. Substitution of this expression into Eq. (1.3) leads to $m = \pm ik$. Hence the general solution of Eq. (1.3) is

$$y = C_1 e^{ikx} + C_2 e^{-ikx}$$

Making use of the relation

$$e^{\pm ikx} = \cos kx \pm i \sin kx$$

and the fact that both the real and imaginary parts of a complex function that satisfies Eq. (1.3) must also satisfy the equation, the general solution can be rewritten in the form

$$y = A \sin kx + B \cos kx \tag{1.4}$$

To evaluate the arbitrary constants A and B, we make use of the boundary conditions

$$y = 0 \quad \text{at } x = 0$$
$$y = 0 \quad \text{at } x = l \tag{1.5}$$

The first of these conditions when substituted into Eq. (1.4) leads to

$$B = 0$$

Consequently,

$$y = A \sin kx \tag{1.6}$$

From the second condition one obtains

$$A \sin kl = 0$$

This relation can be satisfied in one of two ways; either

$$A = 0$$
or $$\sin kl = 0$$

If $A = 0$, k and consequently P can have any value. This result is known as the trivial solution, because it confirms what is already known, that a column is in equilibrium under any axial load P as long as the member remains perfectly straight. If $\sin kl = 0$, then

$$kl = n\pi$$

where $n = 1, 2, 3 \dots$. Substitution of this expression into Eqs. (1.2) and (1.6) leads to

$$P = \frac{n^2 \pi^2 EI}{l^2} \tag{1.7}$$

and $$y = A \sin \frac{n\pi x}{l} \tag{1.8}$$

At the loads given by Eq. (1.7) the column can be in equilibrium in a slightly bent form. The shape of the deformation is given by Eq. (1.8). However, its amplitude is indeterminate, since A can have any value when $\sin kl = 0$.

The value of P, obtained by setting n equal to 1, is

$$P = \frac{\pi^2 EI}{l^2} \tag{1.9}$$

This load is known as the Euler load. It is the smallest load at which a state of neutral equilibrium is possible. Hence it is also the smallest load at which the column ceases to be in stable equilibrium.

The behavior of the Euler column, represented graphically in Fig. 1-4,

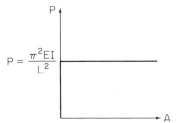

Fig. 1-4 Behavior of Euler column.

can be summed up as follows. Up to the Euler load the column must remain straight. At the Euler load there exists a bifurcation of equilibrium; that is, the column can remain straight or it can assume a deformed shape of indeterminate amplitude. This behavior signifies that a state of neutral equilibrium exists at the Euler load and that the Euler load, therefore, marks the transition from stable to unstable equilibrium.

Equation (1.7) indicates that for values of n greater than 1, there exist other loads larger than the Euler load at which neutral equilibrium is possible. Without going into any detail at this point in the book, these larger loads will be assumed to be valid mathematical solutions to Eq. (1.1), but devoid of significance as far as the physical phenomenon of stability is concerned.

The Euler load obtained in the foregoing analysis is sometimes referred to as the critical load and sometimes as the buckling load. Regarding these two terms, it has been suggested by Hoff (Ref. 1.5) that they not be used interchangeably. He advocates that the load under which an actual imperfect column suddenly bows out laterally be referred to as the buckling load and that the term critical load be reserved for the load at which neutral equilibrium is possible for a perfect member according to a linear analysis. In other words, buckling is something that can be observed when a real column is loaded during a test, whereas the term critical load refers to the solution of an idealized theoretical analysis. The Euler load obtained in this article should thus be referred to as the critical load of the column.

1.4 LINEAR COLUMN THEORY— AN EIGENVALUE PROBLEM

The small-deflection column theory presented in Article 1.3 is based on a linear differential equation and is, therefore, known as the linear column theory. By comparison, the large-deflection theory of columns to be studied later is based on a nonlinear differential equation and is referred to as a nonlinear column theory. Although the small-deflection column theory can be considered linear when contrasted with large-deflection theories, it is not linear in the same sense of the word as simple beam bending theory. In the latter, equilibrium is based on undeformed geometry and deflections are proportional to the applied loads, which is certainly not true for the Euler column.

Thus linear column theory is evidently different from both simple-flexure and large-deformation column theory. As a matter of fact, it does belong to an entirely different class of problems known as eigenvalue problems. These problems are characterized by the fact that nonzero solutions for the dependent variable exist only for certain discrete values of some parameter. The values of the parameter, for which nonzero solutions exist, are known as eigenvalues, and the solutions as eigenvectors. Only the shape and not the amplitude of the eigenvector can be determined in an eigenvalue problem. In a stability problem such as the axially loaded column, the loads $n^2 \pi^2 EI/l^2$ at which nonzero deflections are possible are the eigenvalues, and the deflected shapes that can exist at these loads are the eigenvectors. The smallest eigenvalue is the critical load and the corresponding eigenvector is the buckling mode shape.

1.5 BOUNDARY CONDITIONS

The first step toward generalizing the results obtained in Article 1.3 is to consider boundary conditions other than hinged-hinged supports.

Case 1. Both ends fixed

If a column is built in at both extremities, it can neither translate laterally nor rotate at these points. As a result, bending moments, M_0, are induced at each end of the member, as shown in Fig. 1-5a, when the column is deflected slightly. Equating the external moment to the internal moment, at a section a distance x from the origin (Fig. 1-5b), one obtains

$$EIy'' + Py = M_0$$

or
$$y'' + k^2 y = \frac{M_0}{EI} \tag{1.10}$$

where $k^2 = P/EI$.

The solution to Eq. (1.10) consists of a complementary and a particular part. The former is the solution of the homogeneous equation. It is given by Eq. (1.4). The particular solution is any solution to the entire equation, such

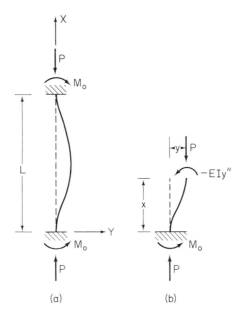

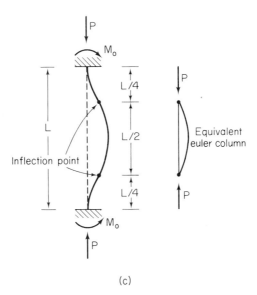

Fig. 1-5   Fixed-fixed column.

as $y = M_0/EIk^2$. Thus the entire solution is

$$y = A \sin kx + B \cos kx + \frac{M_0}{P} \qquad (1.11)$$

where A and B are arbitrary constants to be evaluated using the boundary conditions

$$y' = 0, \qquad y = 0 \quad \text{at } x = 0$$
$$y = 0 \quad \text{at } x = l$$

The first two conditions are satisfied if

$$A = 0 \quad \text{and} \quad B = -\frac{M_0}{P}$$

Hence
$$y = \frac{M_0}{P}(1 - \cos kx)$$

The last condition leads to the transcendental equation

$$\cos kl = 1.0$$

The smallest nonzero root to this equation is

$$kl = 2\pi$$

from which

$$P_{cr} = \frac{4\pi^2 EI}{l^2} \qquad (1.12)$$

and
$$y = \frac{M_0}{P}\left(1 - \cos \frac{2\pi x}{l}\right) \qquad (1.13)$$

Equation (1.12) indicates that the critical load of a column with fixed ends is four times as large as the critical load of a hinged–hinged column.

Using Eq. (1.13), it can be shown that inflection points, that is, points of zero moment, exist at $x = l/4$ and $x = 3l/4$. The central portion of the member, between the quarter points, is thus equivalent to a hinged-hinged column of length $l/2$ (Fig. 1-5c), whose critical load is

$$P_{cr} = \frac{\pi^2 EI}{(l/2)^2} \qquad (1.14)$$

The critical load of the pseudo hinged-hinged column that exists between the inflection points of the fixed-fixed column is thus equal to the critical load of the fixed-fixed column. It will be demonstrated in the succeeding pages that the critical load of any column can be obtained from an equivalent Euler column. The length of this equivalent Euler column is called the *effective length* of the member.

Case 2. One end fixed and one end free

The column shown in Fig. 1-6a is built in at the base and free to translate and rotate at its upper end. A small lateral deflection gives rise to a displacement δ at the upper end of the member and a moment $P\delta$ at the base. Equating the internal moment to the external moment, at a section a distance x from the base (Fig. 1-6b), leads to

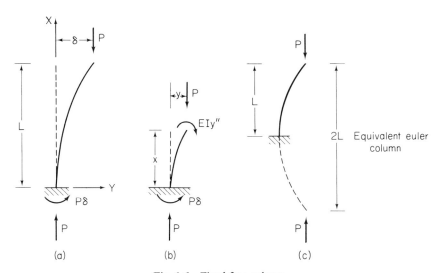

Fig. 1-6 Fixed-free column.

$$EIy'' + Py = P\delta$$

or
$$y'' + k^2 y = k^2 \delta \tag{1.15}$$

where $k^2 = P/EI$. The solution to Eq. (1.15) is

$$y = A \sin kx + B \cos kx + \delta \tag{1.16}$$

The boundary conditions at the base of the member are

$$y = 0 \quad \text{and} \quad y' = 0 \quad \text{at } x = 0$$

They are satisfied if

$$B = -\delta, \qquad A = 0$$

Hence
$$y = \delta(1 - \cos kx)$$

The boundary condition at the upper end of the member

$$y = \delta \quad \text{at } x = l$$

is satisfied if

$$\cos kl = 0$$

The smallest nontrivial root of this equation is

$$kl = \frac{\pi}{2}$$

which leads to

$$P_{cr} = \frac{\pi^2 EI}{4l^2} \qquad (1.17)$$

and
$$y = \delta\left(1 - \cos \frac{\pi x}{2l}\right) \qquad (1.18)$$

Equation (1.17) indicates that the critical load of a column fixed at one end and free at the other is one fourth the Euler load.

From Eq. (1.18) it can be shown that the deflection curve of the fixed-free column consists of one quarter of a sinewave or one half the deflection curve of a hinged-hinged column (Fig. 1-6c). The effective length of the equivalent Euler column is therefore equal to $2l$, and the critical load of a fixed-free column can be expressed in the form

$$P_{cr} = \frac{\pi^2 EI}{(2l)^2} \qquad (1.19)$$

Case 3. One end fixed and one end hinged

The column shown in Fig. 1-7 is hinged at the base and built in at its upper end to a support that is constrained to move along the axis of the member. A small lateral deflection gives rise to a moment M_0 at the fixed end, and shear forces of magnitude M_0/l at each end of the member. Equating the internal and external moment, at a section a distance x from the base, leads to

$$EIy'' + Py = \frac{M_0 x}{l}$$

or
$$y'' + k^2 y = \frac{M_0}{EI}\frac{x}{l} \qquad (1.20)$$

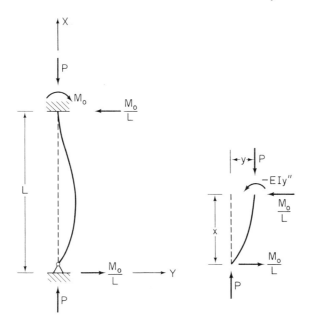

Fig. 1-7 Fixed-hinged column.

where $k^2 = P/EI$. The solution to Eq. (1.20) is

$$y = A \sin kx + B \cos kx + \frac{M_0}{P} \frac{x}{l} \qquad (1.21)$$

The boundary conditions

$$y = 0 \quad \text{at } x = 0$$

and

$$y' = 0 \quad \text{at } x = l$$

are satisfied if

$$B = 0 \quad \text{and} \quad A = -\frac{M_0}{P} \frac{1}{kl \cos kl}$$

Hence

$$y = \frac{M_0}{P} \left(\frac{x}{l} - \frac{\sin kx}{kl \cos kl} \right)$$

The boundary condition

$$y = 0 \quad \text{at } x = l$$

leads to the transcendental equation

$$\tan kl = kl$$

The smallest nonzero root of this equation is

$$kl = 4.49$$

which leads to

$$P_{cr} = \frac{20.2EI}{l^2} \tag{1.22}$$

and

$$y = \frac{M_0}{P}\left[\frac{x}{l} + 1.02 \sin\left(4.49\frac{x}{l}\right)\right] \tag{1.23}$$

Equation (1.22) gives the critical load of a column hinged at one end and fixed at the other. The corresponding deflection curve has an inflection point at $x = 0.7l$. Hence the effective length is $0.7l$, and the critical load can be given in the form

$$P_{cr} = \frac{\pi^2 EI}{(0.7l)^2} \tag{1.24}$$

Case 4. Elastically restrained end

In most actual structures the ends of columns are neither hinged nor fixed. Instead the columns are usually rigidly connected to other members, which permits a limited amount of rotation to occur at the ends of the columns. Supports of this type are referred to as *elastic restraints*. They are so named because the restraint that exists at the end of the column depends on the elastic properties of the members into which the column frames.

Let us consider a column that is hinged at the base and elastically restrained by a beam at its upper end, as shown in Fig. 1-8a. The beam is assumed to be fixed to a rigid support at its far end. For simplicity, the length and stiffness of the beam are taken as equal to the length and stiffness respectively of the column.

In order to linearize the problem, it is assumed that there is no bending in the horizontal member prior to buckling. However, when the critical load is reached, the bending deformation of the column will induce bending in the beam. Due to its stiffness, the beam resists being bent by the column and exerts a restraining moment M, as shown in Fig. 1-8b, on the column. In calculating the critical load the forces produced by the bending deformations as well as the deformations themselves are assumed to be infinitesimal. The shear forces Q acting on the beam are therefore negligible compared to P, and it is reasonable to assume that the axial force in the column remains equal to P during buckling.

Taking the coordinate axes as shown in the figure, moment equilibrium for a segment of the column gives

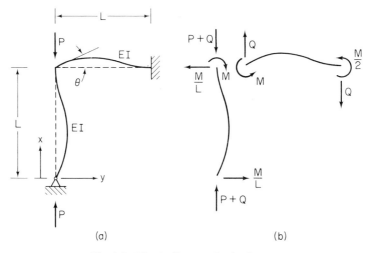

Fig. 1-8 Elastically restrained column.

$$-EI\frac{d^2y}{dx^2} - Py + \frac{Mx}{l} = 0$$

or

$$\frac{d^2y}{dx^2} + k^2y = \frac{M}{EI}\frac{x}{l} \qquad (1.25)$$

where $k^2 = P/EI$. The solution of Eq. (1.25) is

$$y = A \sin kx + B \cos kx + \frac{M}{P}\frac{x}{l} \qquad (1.26)$$

The boundary condition at the lower end of the member

$$y = 0 \quad \text{at } x = 0$$

is satisfied if

$$B = 0$$

and the condition at the upper end

$$y = 0 \quad \text{at } x = l$$

requires that

$$A = -\frac{M}{P}\frac{1}{\sin kl}$$

Hence

$$y = \frac{M}{P}\left(\frac{x}{l} - \frac{\sin kx}{\sin kl}\right)$$

Since the column is rigidly connected to the beam, the rotation of the column at its upper end must be equal to the rotation of the left-hand end of the beam. For the column, the slope at $x = l$ is

$$\frac{dy}{dx} = \frac{M}{P}\left(\frac{1}{l} - \frac{k \cos kl}{\sin kl}\right)$$

or
$$\frac{dy}{dx} = \frac{M}{kEI}\left(\frac{1}{kl} - \frac{1}{\tan kl}\right) \tag{1.27}$$

The rotation θ of the left-hand end of the beam is obtained from the slope–deflection equation. Thus

$$M = \frac{2EI}{l}(2\theta)$$

from which

$$\theta = \frac{Ml}{4EI} \tag{1.28}$$

Equating the expressions in (1.27) and (1.28) gives

$$\frac{Ml}{4EI} = -\frac{M}{kEI}\left(\frac{1}{kl} - \frac{1}{\tan kl}\right)$$

or
$$\frac{kl}{4} = -\left(\frac{1}{kl} - \frac{1}{\tan kl}\right) \tag{1.29}$$

The negative sign in front of the right-hand side of the equation is needed because the slope as given by (1.27) is negative, whereas θ is positive.

Equation (1.29) is the stability condition for the column being studied. It is convenient to rewrite the equation in the form

$$\tan kl = \frac{4kl}{(kl)^2 + 4}$$

The smallest root satisfying this expression is $kl = 3.83$ from which

$$P_{cr} = \frac{14.7EI}{l^2} \tag{1.30}$$

If the upper end of the column were hinged, the critical load would be $\pi^2 EI/l^2$, and if the upper end were fixed, it would be $20.2EI/l^2$. It is not surprising that the critical load for the elastically restrained end, given by Eq. (1.30), should fall between the two limiting cases of hinged and completely fixed ends.

Completely rigid, hinged or free and conditions are rarely found in actual

engineering structures. However, as demonstrated, the solutions corresponding to these idealized end conditions are useful because they provide upper
and lower bounds between which the critical loads of most actual columns
fall.

1.6 EFFECTIVE-LENGTH CONCEPT AND DESIGN CURVE

Figure 1-9 depicts the deflection curve and the effective length for several of

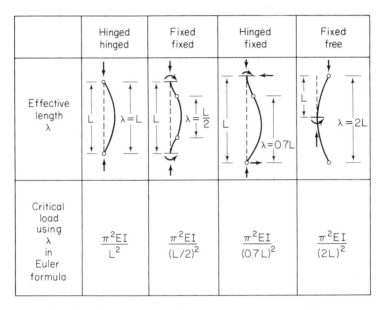

	Hinged hinged	Fixed fixed	Hinged fixed	Fixed free
Effective length λ	$\lambda = L$	$\lambda = \dfrac{L}{2}$	$\lambda = 0.7L$	$\lambda = 2L$
Critical load using λ in Euler formula	$\dfrac{\pi^2 EI}{L^2}$	$\dfrac{\pi^2 EI}{(L/2)^2}$	$\dfrac{\pi^2 EI}{(0.7L)^2}$	$\dfrac{\pi^2 EI}{(2L)^2}$

Fig. 1-9 Effective length of for various boundary conditions.

the boundary conditions considered in Article 1.5. For each case, it is shown
that the Euler formula can be used to obtain the critical load of the member,
provided the correct effective length is used. The effective-length concept is
equally valid for any other set of boundary conditions not included in the
figure. Thus

$$P_{cr} = \frac{\pi^2 EI}{\lambda^2} \tag{1.31}$$

gives the critical load for any column, regardless of the boundary conditions,
provided λ is the effective length of the member, that is, the length of the
equivalent Euler column.

For design purposes, it is convenient to have a graphical representation of

Eq. (1.31). Making use of the relation

$$I = Ar^2$$

in which A is the cross-sectional area and r the radius of gyration, Eq. (1.31) can be rewritten in the form

$$\sigma_{cr} = \frac{\pi^2 E}{(\lambda/r)^2} \tag{1.32}$$

For the elastic range of a given material, that is, a fixed value of E, Eq. (1.32) can be used to obtain a curve of critical stress versus slenderness ratio, λ/r. This has been done for steel ($E = 30 \times 10^6$ psi), and the resulting curve is shown plotted in Fig. 1-10. The curve in Fig. 1-10 is known as a column

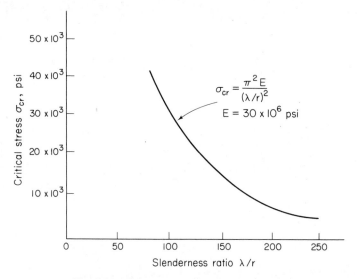

Fig. 1-10 Column curve for structural steel.

design curve. One of the great advantages derived from the effective–length concept is that one can obtain the critical load of any column, of a given material, regardless of the boundary conditions, from a single design curve.

1.7 HIGHER-ORDER DIFFERENTIAL EQUATION FOR COLUMNS

In Article 1.5 buckling loads were obtained for columns with various boundary conditions. In each case, a second-order differential equation, valid only for the member being analyzed, was used. However, as shown by Timoshenko and Gere (Ref. 1.2), a single fourth-order equation applicable to any column regardless of the boundary conditions can also be employed. This equation will be introduced now, and its solution obtained for two specific sets of end restraints.

For the general case of a column with unspecified boundary conditions, there exists a moment and a shear at each end of the member (Fig. 1-11a). By

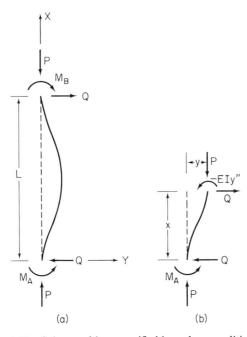

Fig. 1-11 Column with unspecified boundary conditions.

choosing appropriate values for these moments and shears, any desired set of boundary conditions can be satisfied. Equating the external moment to the internal moment, at a section a distance x from the origin (Fig. 1-11b) leads to

$$EIy'' + Py = -Qx + M_A \qquad (1.33)$$

Differentiating twice with respect to x, one obtains

$$EIy^{iv} + Py'' = 0 \qquad (1.34)$$

and introducing the notation

$$k^2 = \frac{P}{EI}$$

the equation becomes

$$y^{IV} + k^2 y'' = 0 \tag{1.35}$$

This fourth-order differential equation is applicable to any set of boundary conditions. Its general solution is

$$y = C_1 \sin kx + C_2 \cos kx + C_3 x + C_4 \tag{1.36}$$

The arbitrary constants in the solution are determined from the boundary conditions of the specific case under investigation.

Case 1. Hinged-hinged

For the hinged-hinged column (Fig. 1-12) the deflection and bending moment are zero at both ends of the member. Hence

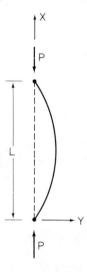

Fig. 1-12   Hinged-hinged column.

$$\begin{aligned} y = 0, \qquad y'' = 0 \quad \text{at } x = 0 \\ y = 0, \qquad y'' = 0 \quad \text{at } x = l \end{aligned} \tag{1.37}$$

Substitution of the two conditions at $x = 0$ into Eq. (1.36) leads to

$$C_2 + C_4 = 0, \qquad C_2 = 0$$

Hence
$$C_2 = 0, \qquad C_4 = 0$$

From the remaining two conditions one obtains

$$C_1 \sin kl + C_3 l = 0, \qquad -C_1 k^2 \sin kl = 0$$

Since k^2 is not identically equal to zero, these relations are satisfied either if $C_1 = C_3 = 0$ or if $\sin kl = C_3 = 0$. The first alternative leads to the trivial solution of equilibrium at all loads, provided the member remains straight. From the second conditions, one obtains

$$kl = n\pi, \qquad n = 1, 2, 3 \ldots$$

which for $n = 1$ leads to the critical load

$$P_{cr} = \frac{\pi^2 EI}{l^2} \tag{1.38}$$

Case 2. Fixed-free

For the fixed-free column (Fig. 1-13), the deflection and slope are zero at

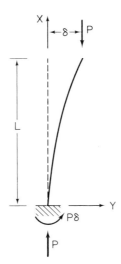

Fig. 1-13   Fixed-free column.

the base. At the free end, the moment vanishes and the shear is equal to the component Py' of the applied load. Thus

$$y = 0, \qquad y' = 0, \qquad \text{at } x = 0$$
$$y'' = 0, \qquad y''' + k^2 y' = 0, \quad \text{at } x = l$$

The conditions at the fixed end lead to

$$C_2 + C_4 = 0, \qquad kC_1 + C_3 = 0$$

and from the conditions at the free end one obtains

$$C_1 \sin kl + C_2 \cos kl = 0, \qquad C_3 = 0$$

Combining these results gives

$$C_1 = C_3 = 0, \qquad C_2 = -C_4, \qquad C_2 \cos kl = 0$$

As in the previous example, there are two solutions, the trivial one, obtained by letting $C_2 = 0$, and the nontrivial solution, $\cos kl = 0$. The latter leads to

$$kl = \frac{(2n - 1)\pi}{2}, \qquad n = 1, 2, 3, \ldots$$

from which, for $n = 1$,

$$P_{cr} = \frac{\pi^2 EI}{4l^2} \tag{1.39}$$

For both of these cases, the results obtained using the fourth-order equation are the same as those obtained previously by means of the second-order equations. The disadvantage of using second-order equations is that each different set of boundary conditions considered requires the setting up of a new equation. This is obviously not necessary when using the fourth-order equation, since the latter is equally applicable to all boundary conditions. However, there are instances, such as the case of the fixed-fixed column, where the evaluation of the four arbitrary constants needed in the fourth-order equation solution is considerably more involved than the determination of the two constants required in the second-order equation solution.

1.8   LARGE-DEFORMATION THEORY
FOR COLUMNS

In the preceding articles the behavior of columns was studied using a linear differential equation. The linear equation was obtained by employing an approximate expression, d^2y/dx^2, for the curvature of the member. Since this approximation is valid only when the deformations are small, the results obtained from the linear equation are limited to small deflections. In this article the limitation of small deflections will be removed by using an exact expression for the curvature.

Consider the simply supported column shown in Fig. 1-14. Aside from the assumption of small deflections, which is no longer being made, all the other idealizations made for the Euler column are still valid. The member is initially assumed to be perfectly straight and loaded along its centroidal axis, and the material is assumed to obey Hooke's law.

If the x-y coordinate axes are taken as shown in the figure and the column is in equilibrium in a bent configuration, then the external moment, Py, at any section, is equal to the internal resisting moment $-EI/R$. Thus

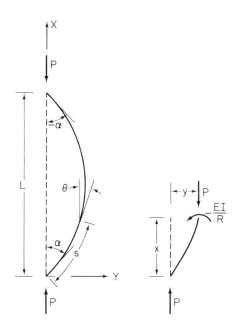

Fig. 1-14 Large deflections of a column (Adapted from Ref. 1.6).

$$Py = -\frac{EI}{R} \tag{1.40}$$

in which $1/R$ is the curvature.

The solution of the equation is facilitated if the curvature is expressed as the rate of change of the slope. Letting the slope at any point be given by θ and the distance along the curve from the origin to the point by s, the curvature is

$$\frac{1}{R} = \frac{d\theta}{ds}$$

Substitution of this expression in Eq. (1.40) leads to

$$EI\frac{d\theta}{ds} + Py = 0 \tag{1.41}$$

Equation (1.41) can be used to study the behavior of columns at large as well as at small deformations. Because $d\theta/ds$ is used in place of d^2y/dx^2, Eq. (1.41) is nonlinear, and its solution is a good deal more difficult to obtain than that of Eq. (1.1), the linear equation of the small-deformation theory. The analysis presented here follows the general outline of the solution given by Wang in Ref. 1.6.

Introducing the notation $k^2 = P/EI$, Eq. (1.41) takes the form

$$\frac{d\theta}{ds} + k^2y = 0 \tag{1.42}$$

If the equation is differentiated with respect to s, and dy/ds is replaced by sin θ, one obtains

$$\frac{d^2\theta}{ds^2} + k^2 \sin \theta = 0 \tag{1.43}$$

Multiplying the first term by $2(d\theta/ds)\,ds$ and the second term by the equivalent expression $2d\theta$ and integrating both terms gives

$$\int \left(\frac{d^2\theta}{ds^2}\right) 2\frac{d\theta}{ds}\, ds + \int 2k^2 \sin \theta \, d\theta = 0 \tag{1.44}$$

Since

$$2\left(\frac{d\theta}{ds}\right)\left(\frac{d^2\theta}{ds^2}\right) ds = d\left(\frac{d\theta}{ds}\right)^2$$

and

$$\sin \theta \, d\theta = -d(\cos \theta)$$

Eq. (1.44) can be written in the form

$$\int d\left(\frac{d\theta}{ds}\right)^2 - 2k^2 \int d(\cos \theta) = 0 \tag{1.45}$$

Carrying out the integration leads to

$$\left(\frac{d\theta}{ds}\right)^2 - 2k^2 \cos \theta = C \tag{1.46}$$

The constant of integration, C, is evaluated from the condition that $\theta = \alpha$ and $d\theta/ds = 0$ at the origin. Hence

$$C = -2k^2 \cos \alpha$$

and Eq. (1.46) becomes

$$\left(\frac{d\theta}{ds}\right)^2 = 2k^2(\cos \theta - \cos \alpha)$$

Taking the square root of both terms gives

$$\frac{d\theta}{ds} = \pm\sqrt{2}\, k \sqrt{\cos \theta - \cos \alpha}$$

or

$$ds = -\frac{d\theta}{\sqrt{2}\, k \sqrt{\cos \theta - \cos \alpha}} \tag{1.47}$$

The negative sign denotes that θ decreases as s increases.

If ds is integrated from 0 to L, one obtains the total length of the column.

Thus

$$L = \int_0^L ds = \int_{-\alpha}^{\alpha} \frac{d\theta}{\sqrt{2k}\sqrt{\cos\theta - \cos\alpha}} \tag{1.48}$$

The minus sign in front of the equation has been eliminated by reversing the limits of integration.

Making use of the identities

$$\cos\theta = 1 - 2\sin^2\left(\frac{\theta}{2}\right), \qquad \cos\alpha = 1 - 2\sin^2\left(\frac{\alpha}{2}\right) \tag{1.49}$$

in Eq. (1.48) leads to

$$L = \frac{1}{2k} \int_{-\alpha}^{\alpha} \frac{d\theta}{\sqrt{\sin^2(\alpha/2) - \sin^2(\theta/2)}} \tag{1.50}$$

To simplify this integral, let

$$p = \sin\frac{\alpha}{2} \tag{1.51}$$

and introduce a new variable ϕ defined by

$$p \sin\phi = \sin\frac{\theta}{2} \tag{1.52}$$

The integral in Eq. (1.50) can be expressed in terms of ϕ if one obtains $d\theta$ as a function of ϕ and determines the limits on ϕ corresponding to the given limits on θ. Taking the differential of both sides of Eq. (1.52), gives

$$d\theta = \frac{2p\cos\phi\,d\phi}{\cos(\theta/2)}$$

and using the identity

$$\cos\frac{\theta}{2} = \sqrt{1 - \sin^2\frac{\theta}{2}}$$

one obtains

$$d\theta = \frac{2p\cos\phi\,d\phi}{\sqrt{1 - p^2\sin^2\phi}} \tag{1.53}$$

Rewriting Eq. (1.52) in the form

$$\sin\frac{\alpha}{2}\sin\phi = \sin\frac{\theta}{2}$$

it is evident that as θ varies from $-\alpha$ to α, $\sin \phi$ varies from -1 to 1, and ϕ varies from $-(\pi/2)$ to $\pi/2$. In view of Eq. (1.53), and noting that

$$\sqrt{\sin^2 \frac{\alpha}{2} - \sin^2 \frac{\theta}{2}} = p \cos \phi \tag{1.54}$$

Eq. (1.50) can be rewritten in the form

$$L = \frac{2}{k} \int_0^{\pi/2} \frac{d\phi}{\sqrt{1 - p^2 \sin^2 \phi}} \tag{1.55}$$

or

$$L = \frac{2K}{k} \tag{1.56}$$

in which

$$K = \int_0^{\pi/2} \frac{d\phi}{\sqrt{1 - p^2 \sin^2 \phi}} \tag{1.57}$$

This integral is known as the complete elliptic integral of the first kind. Its value can be obtained from a table of integrals, which tabulates K for various values of p.

Equation (1.56) can also be written in the form

$$L = \frac{2K}{\sqrt{P/EI}}$$

or

$$\frac{P}{P_{cr}} = \frac{4K^2}{\pi^2} \tag{1.58}$$

in which $P_{cr} = \pi^2 EI/L^2$.

If the deflection of the member is very small, α and consequently p are very small, and the term $p^2 \sin^2 \phi$, in the denominator of K, is negligible. The value of K then approaches $\pi/2$, and from Eq. (1.58)

$$P = P_{cr} = \frac{\pi^2 EI}{L^2}$$

The nonlinear theory thus leads to the same critical load as the linear theory. This is to be expected, since both theories are accurate for small deformations.

It is now desirable to determine how the load varies as the deflection of the member becomes large. Using Eq. (1.56), a curve of load versus α can be plotted, or the more commonly employed relation between load and mid-height deflection, δ, can be obtained as follows.

Noting that $dy = \sin \theta \, ds$ and making use of Eq. (1.47) gives

$$dy = -\frac{\sin \theta \, d\theta}{\sqrt{2} \, k \sqrt{\cos \theta - \cos \alpha}}$$

The midheight deflection δ is obtained by integrating dy from 0 to δ. Hence

$$\delta = -\int_\delta^0 dy = \int_0^\alpha \frac{\sin \theta \, d\theta}{\sqrt{2}\,k\,\sqrt{\cos \theta - \cos \alpha}}$$

The limits for the integral on the right-hand side of the equation were obtained by noting that θ varies from α to 0 as y varies from 0 to δ. Using the relations in (1.49) gives

$$\delta = \frac{1}{2k} \int_0^\alpha \frac{\sin \theta \, d\theta}{\sqrt{\sin^2 (\alpha/2) - \sin^2 (\theta/2)}}$$

Except for the term $\sin \theta$, this integral is similar to the one in Eq. (1.50). As before, a change in variable from θ to ϕ is therefore made, and in view of Eqs. (1.51), (1.52), (1.53), and (1.54), one obtains

$$\delta = \frac{1}{2k} \int_0^{\pi/2} \frac{\sin \theta (2p \cos \phi \, d\phi)}{\sqrt{1 - p^2 \sin^2 \phi}\,(p \cos \phi)} \tag{1.59}$$

It can also be shown that

$$\sin \theta = 2p \sin \phi \sqrt{1 - p^2 \sin^2 \phi}$$

Substitution of this relation in Eq. (1.59) leads to

$$\delta = \frac{2p}{k} \int_0^{\pi/2} \sin \phi \, d\phi = \frac{2p}{k}$$

from which

$$\frac{\delta}{L} = \frac{2p}{\pi \sqrt{P/P_{\mathrm{cr}}}} \tag{1.60}$$

Using Eqs. (1.58) and (1.60), it is possible to compute for various values of α the corresponding values of P/P_{cr} and δ/L. The results of such calculations are summarized in Table 1-1 and plotted graphically in Fig. 1-15.

As indicated previously, large-deflection theory leads to the same critical load as linear theory. In addition, large-deformation theory predicts a very slight increase in load with increasing deflection during the early stages of bending and a more pronounced increase in load after considerable deformation has occurred. When the lateral deflection is one tenth the span, a very sizeable deflection, the load is only 1% greater than P_{cr}, and at $\delta/L = 0.2$, $P/P_{\mathrm{cr}} = 1.06$. It is evident from these results that the prediction of bending at constant load made by the linear theory is valid for a considerable range of deformations.

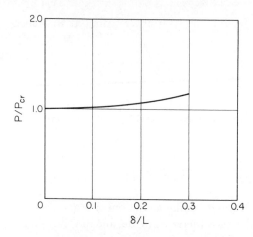

Fig. 1-15 Column load–deflection curve for large deflections.

Table 1-1   Load-deflection data for large-deflection column theory (Adapted from Ref. 1.6)

α	0°	20°	40°	60°
K	$\pi/2$	1.583	1.620	1.686
p	0	0.174	0.342	0.500
P/P_{cr}	1	1.015	1.063	1.152
δ/L	0	0.110	0.211	0.296

For most actual columns, as bending increases, the combined axial and bending stress will exceed the proportional limit of the material long before the deviation of the linear from the nonlinear theory becomes significant. Consequently, within the range of elastic behavior, the results obtained from the large-deformation analysis in no way invalidate any of the results obtained from the linear analysis.

1.9   BEHAVIOR OF IMPERFECT COLUMNS

In the derivation of the Euler load, the member is assumed to be perfectly straight and the loading is assumed to be concentric at every cross section. These idealizations are made to simplify the problem. However, perfect members do not exist in actual engineering structures. Both minor imperfections of shape and small eccentricities of loading are present in all real columns. It is therefore desirable to investigate the behavior of an imperfect column and compare it with the behavior predicted by the Euler theory.

1.10 INITIALLY BENT COLUMNS

In this article the behavior of an imperfect column is studied by considering a member whose centroidal axis is initially bent. It is assumed that the material obeys Hooke's law and that the deformations are small. Hence, of the idealizations made in the Euler theory, only the one that assumes the member to be initially straight has been omitted.

Consider the hinged column in Fig. 1-16, whose centroidal axis is initially

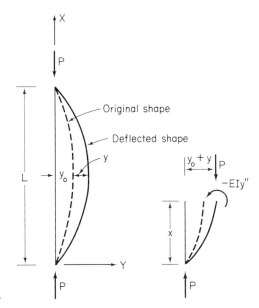

Fig. 1-16 Initially bent column.

bent. Let the initial deformation of the member be given by y_0 and the additional deformation due to bending by y. The solution of the problem can be simplified, without impairing the generality of the results, if the initial deformation is assumed to be of the form

$$y_0 = a \sin \frac{\pi x}{l} \qquad (1.61)$$

Since bending strains are caused by the change in curvature, y'', and not by the total curvature, $y_0'' + y''$, the internal resisting moment at any section is

$$M_x = -EIy''$$

Equating this moment to the extermally applied bending moment, $P(y + y_0)$, gives

$$EIy'' + P(y_0 + y) = 0 \qquad (1.62)$$

By substituting Eq. (1.61) for y_0 and making use of the notation $k^2 = P/EI$, one obtains

$$y'' + k^2y = -k^2a \sin \frac{\pi x}{l} \qquad (1.63)$$

The solution of Eq. (1.63) consists of a complementary function and a particular function. Thus

$$y = y_c + y_p$$

The complementary function is the general solution of the homogeneous equation obtained by setting the left-hand side of Eq. (1.63) equal to zero. It has already been shown that this is

$$y_c = A \sin kx + B \cos kx \qquad (1.64)$$

The particular function is any solution of the entire nonhomogeneous equation. When the right-hand side of the equation consists of a sine or cosine term, the particular function is of the form

$$y_p = C \sin \frac{\pi x}{l} + D \cos \frac{\pi x}{l} \qquad (1.65)$$

Substituting Eq. (1.65) into Eq. (1.63) and combining terms gives

$$\left[C\left(k^2 - \frac{\pi^2}{l^2}\right) + k^2a \right] \sin \frac{\pi x}{l} + \left[D\left(k^2 - \frac{\pi^2}{l^2}\right) \right] \cos \frac{\pi x}{l} = 0$$

This equation can be satisfied for all values of x only if both the coefficients of the sine and cosine terms are made to vanish. Hence

$$C = \frac{a}{(\pi^2/k^2l^2) - 1}$$

and either $D = 0$ or $k^2 = \pi^2/l^2$.

If one lets $k^2 = \pi^2/l^2$, the solution for y becomes limited to $P = \pi^2 EI/l^2$. This is not the case to be investigated, and D must therefore vanish. Hence $D = 0$.

Introducing the notation

$$\alpha = \frac{P}{P_E}$$

where $P_E = \pi^2 EI/l^2$, the expression for C can be rewritten in the form

$$C = \frac{a}{(1/\alpha) - 1} = \frac{a\alpha}{1 - \alpha}$$

Consequently,

$$y_p = \frac{a\alpha}{1 - \alpha} \sin \frac{\pi x}{l} \tag{1.66}$$

and

$$y = A \sin kx + B \cos kx + \frac{\alpha}{1 - \alpha} a \sin \frac{\pi x}{l} \tag{1.67}$$

The arbitrary constants in (1.67) are evaluated from the boundary conditions. The condition

$$y = 0 \quad \text{at } x = 0$$

leads to

$$B = 0$$

and from the condition

$$y = 0 \quad \text{at } x = l$$

one obtains

$$0 = A \sin kl$$

Thus either A or $\sin kl$ must vanish. Letting $\sin kl = 0$ again limits the solution for y to $P = P_E$. As before, this is undesirable, and consequently

$$A = 0$$

Substitution of $A = 0$ and $B = 0$ into Eq. (1.67) leads to the bending deflection

$$y = \frac{\alpha}{1 - \alpha} a \sin \frac{\pi x}{l} \tag{1.68}$$

The total deflection from the vertical is obtained by adding this expression to the initial deflection. Thus

$$y_T = y_0 + y = \left(1 + \frac{\alpha}{1 - \alpha}\right) a \sin \frac{\pi x}{l}$$

or

$$y_T = \frac{a}{1 - \alpha} \sin \frac{\pi x}{l} \tag{1.69}$$

The total deflection at midheight is

$$\delta = \frac{a}{1 - \alpha} = \frac{a}{1 - (P/P_E)} \tag{1.70}$$

Figure 1-17 gives a graphical representation of Eq. (1.70). The variation

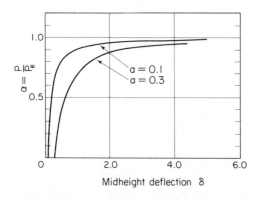

Fig. 1-17   Load–deflection curves of initially bent columns.

of the midheight deflection with the load ratio P/P_E is shown plotted for two different values of initial imperfection. Based on these curves, the behavior of the imperfect column can be summed up as follows. Unlike the perfect column, which remains straight up to the Euler load, the initially deformed member begins to bend as soon as the load is applied. The deflection increases slowly at first and then more and more rapidly as the ratio of the applied load to the Euler load increases. The larger the initial imperfection, the larger the total deflection at any load. However, as the applied load approaches the Euler load, the deflection increases without bound regardless of the magnitude of the initial imperfection. The carrying capacity of an imperfect column is thus always smaller than the Euler load, regardless of how small the initial imperfection is. If the initial distortion is sizeable, the column experiences fairly large deformations at loads considerably below the Euler load. A carefully constructed column that is fairly straight to begin with does how-ever not deflect appreciably until the applied load is quite close to the Euler load. Although the failure mechanism of columns has not yet been discussed, one can surmise that large deflections produce inelastic strains, which in turn lead to collapse. Members with large initial imperfections can thus be expected to fail at loads considerably below the Euler load, while relatively straight columns will support axial loads only slightly less than P_E.

1.11   ECCENTRICALLY LOADED COLUMNS

In Article 1.10 an initially bent member was used to investigate the behavior of an imperfect column. The effects of imperfections on column behavior can also be studied by considering the straight but eccentrically loaded member shown in Fig. 1-18. It is assumed that the member is initially straight, that the material obeys Hooke's law, and that deformations remain small. Equating

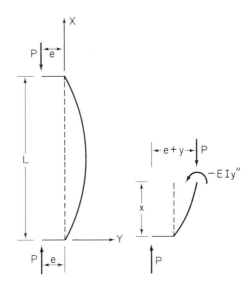

Fig. 1-18 Eccentrically loaded column.

the internal resisting moment $-EIy''$, at any section, to the corresponding applied moment $P(e + y)$ gives

$$EIy'' + P(e + y) = 0 \qquad (1.71)$$

Letting $k^2 = P/EI$, one obtains

$$y'' + k^2 y = -k^2 e \qquad (1.72)$$

The general solution of this equation is

$$y = A \sin kx + B \cos kx - e \qquad (1.73)$$

The arbitrary constants are evaluated from the boundary conditions. Thus the condition

$$y = 0 \quad \text{at } x = 0$$

leads to

$$B = e$$

and from the condition

$$y = 0 \quad \text{at } x = l$$

one obtains

$$A = e \frac{1 - \cos kl}{\sin kl}$$

Substitution of these results in Eq. (1.73) gives

$$y = e\left(\cos kx + \frac{1 - \cos kl}{\sin kl} \sin kx - 1\right) \tag{1.74}$$

An expression for the midheight deflection $y = \delta$ is obtained by letting $x = l/2$. Thus

$$\delta = e\left(\cos \frac{kl}{2} + \frac{1 - \cos kl}{\sin kl} \sin \frac{kl}{2} - 1\right) \tag{1.75}$$

Introducing the identities

$$\cos kl = 1 - 2 \sin^2 \frac{kl}{2}$$

and

$$\sin kl = 2 \sin \frac{kl}{2} \cos \frac{kl}{2}$$

Eq. (1.75) can be reduced to

$$\delta = e\left(\sec \frac{kl}{2} - 1\right)$$

or

$$\delta = e\left[\sec\left(\frac{\pi}{2}\sqrt{\frac{P}{P_E}}\right) - 1\right] \tag{1.76}$$

where $P_E = \pi^2 EI/l^2$.

Figure 1-19 gives a graphical representation of Eq. (1.76). The variation

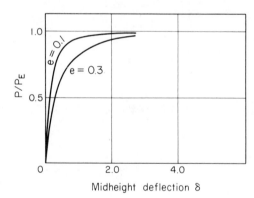

Fig. 1-19 Load–deflection curves of eccentrically loaded columns.

of δ with P/P_E is shown plotted for two values of the eccentricity e. Comparison of these curves with those of initially curved columns, given in Fig. 1-17, indicates that the behavior of an eccentrically loaded column is essentially the same as that of an initially bent column. In both cases, bending begins as soon as the load is applied. The deflection increases slowly at first and then more and more rapidly as P approaches P_E. At $P = P_E$ the deflection increases without bound. Columns with large eccentricities deflect considerably at loads well below the Euler load, whereas columns with very small eccentricities of loading do not bend appreciably until the load is fairly close to the Euler load. It will later be shown that excessive bending causes a column to collapse. A column with relatively small eccentricities of loading can therefore be expected to support loads only slightly less than the Euler load. On the other hand, a member with large eccentricities will collapse at loads considerably below P_E.

1.12 SUMMARY OF IMPERFECT COLUMN BEHAVIOR

It has been shown that a slightly imperfect column begins to bend as soon as the load is applied, that the bending remains relatively insignificant until the load approaches the Euler Load, and that the bending then increases very rapidly. Several important conclusions can be reached from these observations. First and foremost, the Euler theory, which is based on the fictitious concept of a perfect member, provides a satisfactory design criterion for real imperfect columns, provided the imperfections are relatively minor. The Euler load is thus a good approximation of the maximum load that a real imperfect column can support without bending excessively. Second, the foregoing results form the basis of a useful method of stability analysis. Up to now, the critical load has been determined exclusively by finding the load at which a perfect system can be in equilibrium in a slightly bent configuration, that is, the load at which neutral equilibrium is possible. Now, a second criterion for finding the critical load can be stated as follows:

The critical load is the load at which the deformations of a slightly imperfect system increase without bound. To apply this criterion, one gives the structural member or system to be investigated a small initial deformation and then determines the load at which this deformation becomes unbounded.

A third conclusion drawn from the foregoing analyses is that the behavior of an imperfect system can be simulated either by giving the system some initial crookedness or by applying the load eccentrically. The essential difference between a perfect and an imperfect compression member is that the former must be disturbed to produce bending, whereas bending stresses are present in the latter as a direct consequence of the applied load. It is therefore not surprising that either eccentricity of loading or initial crookedness, both of which cause bending, can be used with equal success to simulate the behavior of an imperfect system.

1.13 INELASTIC BUCKLING OF COLUMNS

In each of the investigations presented heretofore, the assumption has been made that the material behaves according to Hooke's law. For this assumption to be valid, the stresses in the member must remain below the propor-

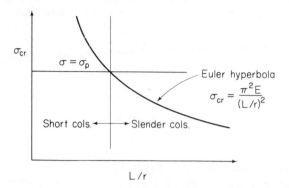

Fig. 1-20   Column curve.

tional limit of the material. Figure 1-20 shows the Euler curve and a horizontal line representing the proportional limit of the material. It is evident from the figure that, for slender columns, the applied load reaches the Euler load before the axial stress exceeds the proportional limit. The linear elastic analysis is therefore valid for slender columns, and the Euler load represents the correct buckling load of such members. One the other hand, the axial stress in a short column will exceed the proportional limit of the material before the applied load reaches the Euler load. Consequently, the results of the elastic analysis are not valid for short columns, and the buckling load of short columns must be determined by taking inelastic behavior into account.

Before considering the theory of inelastic column behavior, let us briefly review its historical development. The Euler formula was first derived by Leonhard Euler in 1744 (Ref. 1.4). It was, at the time, mistakenly assumed that the formula applied to short as well as slender columns. When test results during the nineteenth century indicated that the formula was unconservative for short columns, Euler's work was believed to be completely erroneous and was discarded for a lengthy period of time. Finally, in 1889 two men, Considère (Ref. 1.7) and Engesser (Ref. 1.8), reached the conclusion that the Euler load as presented by Euler was valid, but only for slender columns. They also realized that Euler's formula could be applied to short columns if the constant modulus E is replaced by an effective modulus that depends on the magnitude of stress at buckling. Engesser believed the tangent modulus to be the correct effective modulus for inelastic column buckling. Considère did not reach any specific conclusions regarding the value of the effective modulus. He did, however, suggest that as a column begins to bend at the critical load there is a possibility that stresses on the concave side increase in accordance with the tangent modulus and that stresses on the convex side decrease in accordance with Young's modulus. This line of reasoning is the basis of the *double modulus theory*, according to which the effective modulus is a function of both the tangent modulus and the elastic modulus. As soon as Engesser became aware of Considère's theory, he acknowledged its validity and went on to derive the first correct value of the effective modulus based on the double modulus theory (Ref. 1.9). However, it was not until von Kármán in 1910 (Ref. 1.10) independently rederived the double modulus theory that it gained widespread acceptance.

For roughly the next 30 years, the double modulus theory, or reduced modulus theory as it is sometimes called, was accepted as the correct theory for inelastic buckling. Then, in 1947, Shanley reexamined the mechanism of inelastic column behavior and concluded that the tangent modulus and not the double modulus is after all the correct effective modulus (Ref. 1.11). The double modulus theory is based on the assumption that the axial load remains constant as the column passes from a straight to a slightly bent configuration at the critical load. Only if this assumption is made does bending necessarily cause a decrease in strain on the convex side of the member while strains on the concave side are increasing. Shanley points out that it is possible for the axial load to increase instead of remaining constant as the column begins to bend, and that no strain reversal need therefore take place at any point in the cross section. If there is no strain reversal, the tangent modulus governs the behavior of all fibers in the member at buckling.

The tangent modulus theory leads to a lower buckling load than the double modulus theory and agrees better with test results than the latter. It has therefore been accepted by most engineers as the correct theory of inelastic buckling. Nevertheless, discussions regarding the merit of each of the theories continue.

The succeeding articles are devoted to a detailed study of inelastic buckling. First, the critical load of an initially perfect member is determined, using infinitesimal deformation theory. Then, initial imperfections and finite deformations are introduced in order to determine whether or not the maximum carrying capacity of an inelastic column coincides with the critical load, as is the case for elastic columns. Finally, the theoretical findings are used to develop design criteria for real engineering materials.

1.14 DOUBLE MODULUS THEORY

In this article the critical load of a column whose axial stress exceeds the proportional limit prior to buckling is obtained by means of the double modulus theory. The analysis involves the following assumptions:

1. The column is initially perfectly straight and concentrically loaded.
2. Both ends of the member are hinged.
3. The deformations are small enough for the curvature to be approximated by y''.

4. The same relation exists between bending stresses and bending strains as exists between stress and strain in simple tension and compression.

5. Plane sections before bending remain plane after bending; hence longitudinal strains vary linearly as their distance from the neutral surface.

The critical load is obtained by means of the concept of neutral equilibrium. Accordingly, the critical load is defined as the axial load at which equilibrium is possible both in the original undeformed position and in an adjacent slightly bent configuration. This definition implies that the axial load remains constant as the member moves from the straight to the deformed position.

Consider the column shown in Fig. 1-21a. The final deformed configuration of the member is reached by applying an axial force to the initially

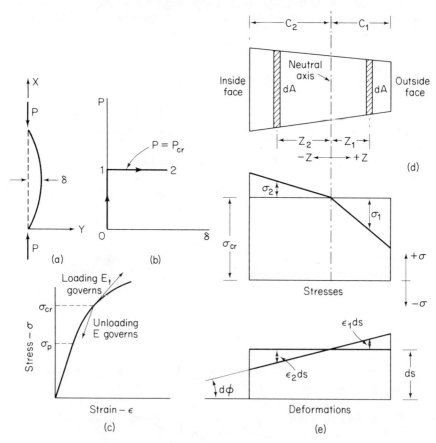

Fig. 1-21 Reduced modulus theory (Adapted from Ref. 1.12).

straight column, letting the force increase until it reaches the critical load, and then letting the member bend slightly while the axial force remains constant. In other words, the behavior of the column follows curve 0-1-2 in Fig. 1-21b. The axial stress, $\sigma_{cr} = P_{cr}/A$, that is present when bending begins is assumed to be above the proportional limit of the material (Fig. 1-21c). During bending, there occurs a small increase in the stress on the concave side of the column and a slight decrease in the stress on the convex side of the member. The final stress distribution on a typical cross section of the bent column is shown in Fig. 1-21d. At any point in the cross section, the total stress consists of a uniform axial stress, σ_{cr}, and a variable bending stress. The deformation corresponding to this bending stress distribution is shown in Fig. 1-21e.

The elastic modulus E always governs the relation of stress to strain when a fiber unloads. Hence the decrease in stress, σ_1, on the convex side of the column, which occurs as the member bends, is related to the corresponding decrease in strain, ϵ_1, by the relation

$$\sigma_1 = E\epsilon_1 \tag{1.77}$$

On the concave side, bending causes an increase in the total stress, and the instantaneous relation of the bending stress σ_2 to the corresponding strain ϵ_2 is therefore governed by the tangent modulus. Since deformations beyond the critical load are assumed to be infinitesimally small, bending stresses are very small compared to σ_{cr}, and the tangent modulus E_t corresponding to σ_{cr} can be assumed to apply over the entire part of the cross section where the stress is increasing. Hence

$$\sigma_2 = E_t\epsilon_2 \tag{1.78}$$

where E_t is the slope of the stress–strain curve at $\sigma = \sigma_{cr}$. Noting that the curvature is given by $d\phi/ds$ (Fig. 1-21e), the bending strains ϵ_1 and ϵ_2 located at distances z_1 and z_2 from the neutral axis are

$$\epsilon_1 = -z_1\frac{d\phi}{ds} \tag{1.79}$$

$$\epsilon_2 = -z_2\frac{d\phi}{ds} \tag{1.80}$$

Stresses and strains are positive when compressive and z is positive when measured to the right of the neutral axis. Approximating the curvature by $-y''$, Eqs. (1.79) and (1.80) become

$$\epsilon_1 = z_1 y'' \tag{1.81}$$

$$\epsilon_2 = z_2 y'' \tag{1.82}$$

Equilibrium between the external load and the stresses on any section will now be considered. It has been assumed that the axial load remains constant during bending. The resultant of the tensile and compressive stresses due to bending must therefore vanish. Thus

$$\int_0^{c_1} \sigma_1 \, dA + \int_0^{c_2} \sigma_2 \, dA = 0 \tag{1.83}$$

In view of Eqs. (1.77), (1.78), (1.81), and (1.82), Eq. (1.83) becomes

$$Ey'' \int_0^{c_1} z_1 \, dA + E_t y'' \int_0^{c_2} z_2 \, dA = 0 \tag{1.84}$$

Introducing the notation

$$Q_1 = \int_0^{c_1} z_1 \, dA, \qquad Q_2 = \int_0^{c_2} z_2 \, dA \tag{1.85}$$

for the moments of the area on either side of the neutral axis about this axis, Eq. (1.84) can be written in the form

$$EQ_1 + E_t Q_2 = 0 \tag{1.86}$$

Equation (1.86) is used to determine the location of the neutral axis. Since $E_t \neq E$, $Q_1 + Q_2 \neq 0$, and the neutral axis does not coincide with the centroidal axis for inelastic bending.

A second condition of equilibrium is that the bending stresses balance the externally applied moment Py. Thus

$$\int_0^{c_1} \sigma_1 z_1 \, dA + \int_0^{c_2} \sigma_2 z_2 \, dA + Py = 0 \tag{1.87}$$

Making use of Eqs. (1.77), (1.78), (1.81), and (1.82), one obtains

$$y'' \left(E \int_0^{c_1} z_1^2 \, dA + E_t \int_0^{c_2} z_2^2 \, dA \right) + Py = 0 \tag{1.88}$$

The two integrals inside the parentheses are equal to the moments of inertia of the areas on either side of the neutral axis about this axis. Representing these quantities by

$$I_1 = \int_0^{c_1} z_1^2 \, dA \quad \text{and} \quad I_2 = \int_0^{c_2} z_2^2 \, dA \tag{1.89}$$

Eq. (1.88) takes the form

$$y''(EI_1 + E_t I_2) + Py = 0 \tag{1.90}$$

Finally, by introducing the notation

$$E_r = \frac{EI_1 + E_t I_2}{I} \tag{1.91}$$

one obtains

$$E_r I y'' + P y = 0 \tag{1.92}$$

Equation (1.92) is the differential equation for the bending of a column stressed into the inelastic range of the material. Comparison of this equation with Eq. (1.1) for the elastic column indicates that the two are identical except that E has been replaced by E_r, the *reduced modulus*. It is evident from Eq. (1.91) that the value of E_r depends on the stress–strain characteristics of the material and on the shape of the cross section, and that E_r is always smaller than E.

Along a given column, E_r is constant; that is, it is not a function of the independent variable x. Equation (1.92) is therefore a linear equation with constant coefficients, and its solution is identical to that of Eq. (1.1) for the elastic column, except that the elastic modulus E is replaced by the reduced modulus E_r. The critical load of an initially straight column whose axial stress exceeds the proportional limit prior to buckling is therefore equal to

$$P_r = \frac{\pi^2 E_r I}{l^2} \tag{1.93}$$

The load given by Eq. (1.93) is commonly referred to as the reduced modulus load. Since $E_r < E$, the reduced modulus load, P_r, is always smaller than the Euler load.

For design purposes, Eq. (1.93) is usually rewritten in the form

$$(\sigma_r)_{cr} = \frac{\pi^2 E_r}{(l/r)^2} \tag{1.94}$$

where $(\sigma_r)_{cr}$ is the critical stress corresponding to the reduced modulus load. To obtain the critical stress for a given member, it is necessary to evaluate E_r. This is accomplished as follows. For a rectangular section, Eq. (1.86) reduces to

$$E c_1^2 = E_t c_2^2$$

where c_1 and c_2 are the distances from the neutral axis to the extreme fibers in tension and compression, respectively. Noting that h, the total depth of the cross section, is given by

$$h = c_1 + c_2$$

one obtains

$$c_1 = \frac{h\sqrt{E_t}}{\sqrt{E} + \sqrt{E_t}}, \qquad c_2 = \frac{h\sqrt{E}}{\sqrt{E} + \sqrt{E_t}}$$

Using these relations, the expression for the reduced modulus given by Eq. (1.91) can be simplified to

$$E_r = \frac{4EE_t}{(\sqrt{E} + \sqrt{E_t})^2} \tag{1.95}$$

In a similar manner, the reduced modulus of an idealized I section, that is, two flanges of equal area connected by a web of negligible thickness, is found to be

$$E_r = \frac{2EE_t}{E + E_t} \tag{1.96}$$

Since E_r depends on the tangent modulus at the critical stress, Eq. (1.94) connot be used directly to solve for $(\sigma_r)_{cr}$. Instead, the variation of E_t with $(\sigma_r)_{cr}$ is obtained from the stress–strain curve of the material and a column design curve, similar to the curve in Fig. 1-10, is constructed. The critical stress corresponding to any value of l/r can then be obtained directly from the design curve.

1.15 TANGENT MODULUS THEORY

The tangent modulus theory of inelastic column buckling will now be considered. In determining the critical load by this theory, the five assumptions made in the double modulus theory, listed on page 37, are retained. However, one assumption made previously, that the axial load remains constant as the column passes from the straight to a slightly bent position of equilibrium, no longer applies. Instead, the tangent modulus theory assumes that the axial load increases during the transition from the straight to the slightly bent position. It also assumes that the increase in the average axial stress is greater than the decrease in stress due to bending at the extreme fiber on the convex side of the member. Hence no strain reversal takes place on the convex side. The compressive stress increases at all points, and the tangent modulus governs the relation of stress to strain for the entire cross section.

The difference between the tangent modulus theory and double modulus theory can be summarized as follows: The double modulus theory assumes that the axial load remains constant as the column moves from the straight to a slightly bent position, at the critical load. Hence the compressive stress increases according to E_t on the concave side of the member and decreases according to E on the convex side. In the tangent modulus theory, the axial load is assumed to increase during the transition to the bent form. There is no strain reversal anywhere in the member, and the increase in stress is governed by E_t at all points in the cross section.

In the problems considered heretofore, the critical load was defined as the load at which equilibrium in the straight configuration ceases to be stable. However, in the present case the axial load is assumed to increase as the member bends subsequent to reaching the critical load. Hence the member is now stable at loads above the critical load, and the old definition of the critical load is no longer valid. A definition of the critical load, more suitable to the problem at hand, is the lowest load at which a bifurcation of equilibrium can take place, that is, the smallest load at which the deformation pattern of the member suddenly changes. The critical load satisfying this definition will now be determined.

Consider a column that is initially straight and remains straight until the axial load P equals the critical load. The column then moves from the straight position to a slightly bent configuration, and the axial load increases from P to $P + \Delta P$ (Fig. 1-22). It is assumed that ΔP is large enough, relative to the bending moment at any section, so that the stress at all points in the member

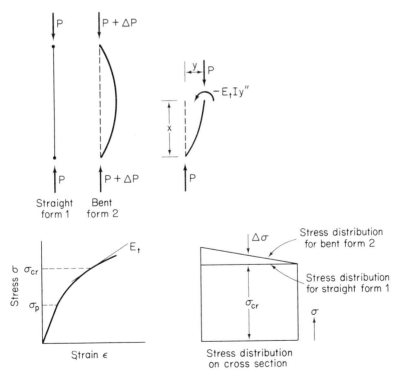

Fig. 1-22   Tangent modulus theory.

increases as bending takes place. Since deformations beyond the critical load are assumed to be infinitesimally small, the increase in stress $\Delta\sigma$ that occurs during bending is very small compared to the critical stress σ_{cr}, and E_t corresponding to σ_{cr} can be assumed to govern the increase in stress at all points in the member.

Since the same modulus governs bending deformations at all points in the member, the neutral axis coincides with the centroidal axis, and bending stresses vary linearly across the section as in elastic behavior. The only difference between this case and elastic bending is that increases in stress are related to increases in strain by E_t instead of E. For the bent form shown in Fig. 1-22, the internal bending moment at any section is

$$M_{\text{int}} = -E_t I y''$$

Taking into account that ΔP is negligible compared to P, the external moment is Py. Hence moment equilibrium at any section leads to

$$E_t I y'' + Py = 0 \tag{1.97}$$

Equation (1.97) is identical to Eq. (1.1), the differential equation of elastic buckling, except that E is replaced by E_t. The critical load obtained from the solution of Eq. (1.97) is therefore

$$P_{cr} = \frac{\pi^2 E_t I}{l^2} \tag{1.98}$$

This expression is generally referred to as the tangent modulus load. Comparison between Eq. (1.98) and Eqs. (1.91) and (1.93) indicates that the tangent modulus load is always smaller than the reduced modulus load and that the former, unlike the latter, is independent of the cross-sectional shape.

1.16 SHANLEY'S THEORY OF INELASTIC COLUMN BEHAVIOR

The analysis presented in this article concerns itself with the behavior of inelastic columns beyond the critical load. To carry out such an investigation, it is necessary to consider finite deformations. As long as an analysis of inelastic columns is limited to infinitesimally small bending deformations, the tangent modulus can be assumed to be constant over the entire part of the member where the compressive stress is increasing. This idealization was made in both the reduced modulus and the tangent modulus theory presented previously. However, for finite bending deformations, the actual complex variation of the tangent modulus in the plane of any cross section as well as along any longitudinal fiber must be considered. Since it is impossible to express this variation analytically, the differential equation of inelastic column buckling for finite deformations can only be solved by numerical procedures.

By using a simple column model, Shanley (Ref. 1.11) has shown that the numerical complexities that arise from considering the variation of the tangent modulus can be avoided and an approximate closed-form solution is obtainable. As shown in Fig. 1-23, the model consists of two infinitely rigid legs

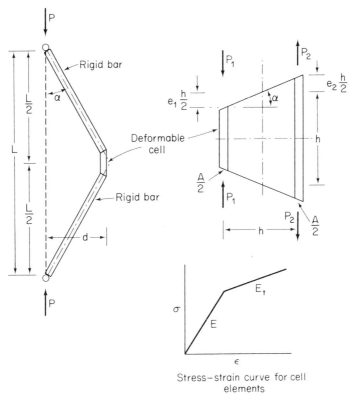

Fig. 1-23 Shanley model (Adapted from Ref. 1.11).

connected to each other at the center of the column by a deformable cell. The cell is made up of two axial elements a distance h apart. Each element has an area $A/2$ and a length h and behaves according to the bilinear stress–strain curve in Fig. 1-23. Concentration of all the deformable material, in two elements, at the center of the model obviates the need for considering the complex variation of material properties both along the length and throughout the cross section exhibited by a real column.

The model is assumed to remain straight until the critical load is reached. It is then deflected laterally a finite distance d. The resulting axial strains of the cell elements are e_1 and e_2. These strains are due to bending and any change that occurs in the axial load during bending. They do not include the axial strain present before bending begins. If the lateral deflection d remains fairly small, it is related to the slope of the legs, α, by

$$d = \frac{\alpha l}{2} \tag{1.99}$$

Since

$$\alpha = \frac{e_1 + e_2}{2}$$

Eq. (1.99) can be rewritten in the form

$$d = \frac{l}{4}(e_1 + e_2) \tag{1.100}$$

Since the model is in equilibrium in the deflected configuration, the external moment at midheight is equal to the internal moment at that point. The external moment is

$$M_e = Pd = \frac{Pl}{4}(e_1 + e_2) \tag{1.101}$$

Corresponding to the strains e_1 and e_2, there are axial loads P_1 and P_2 in the cell elements. Like the strains, these loads are not the total loads. They represent only the change in load that takes place in each element as the column passes from the straight to the bent form. If the effective modulii in the two elements are designated by E_1 and E_2, then

$$P_1 = e_1 E_1 \frac{A}{2}, \qquad P_2 = e_2 E_2 \frac{A}{2} \tag{1.102}$$

and the internal moment at the cell is equal to

$$M_i = (P_1 + P_2)\frac{h}{2} = \frac{hA}{4}(E_1 e_1 + E_2 e_2) \tag{1.103}$$

Equating external and internal moment gives

$$\frac{Pl}{4}(e_1 + e_2) = \frac{hA}{4}(E_1 e_1 + E_2 e_2)$$

from which

$$P = \frac{hA}{l}\frac{E_1 e_1 + E_2 e_2}{e_1 + e_2} \tag{1.104}$$

It is assumed that the loads, P_1 and P_2, are taken as positive if in the direction indicated in Fig. 1-23.

At this point, it is useful to obtain an expression for the *tangent modulus load* of the model. The tangent modulus theory assumes that there is no strain reversal at any point in the cross section at the instant that bending begins. Hence $E_1 = E_2 = E_t$, and Eq. (1.104) leads to

$$P_t = \frac{E_t A h}{l} \qquad (1.105)$$

To study the behavior of the model at finite deformations, a relation between the applied load and the lateral deflection will now be obtained. It is assumed that the applied load P increases as the column bends subsequent to reaching the critical load. Hence

$$E_1 = E_t \qquad (1.106)$$

and E_2 is either equal to E or E_t depending on whether or not strain reversal takes place on the convex side of the model after bending has started. Using the notation

$$\tau = \frac{E_2}{E_t} \qquad (1.107)$$

and substituting Eqs. (1.106) and (1.107) into Eq. (1.104), one obtains

$$P = \frac{A h E_t}{l} \frac{e_1 + \tau e_2}{e_1 + e_2} \qquad (1.108)$$

From Eq. (1.100)

$$e_1 + e_2 = \frac{4d}{l}$$

and

$$e_1 = \frac{4d}{l} - e_2$$

Substitution of these relationships into Eq. (1.108) leads to

$$P = \frac{A h E_t}{l}\left[1 + \frac{l}{4d}(\tau - 1)e_2\right]$$

or

$$P = P_t\left[1 + \frac{l}{4d}(\tau - 1)e_2\right] \qquad (1.109)$$

To express e_2 in terms of d, and thus put Eq. (1.109) into a more useful form, a second expression for P will now be obtained. It has already been assumed that the applied load P increases as the column bends. If it is now also assumed that bending starts at the tangent modulus load P_t, then

$$P = P_t + \Delta P \tag{1.110}$$

The increase in load ΔP that occurs during bending is given by

$$\Delta P = P_1 - P_2 = \frac{e_1 E_1 A}{2} - \frac{e_2 E_2 A}{2} \tag{1.111}$$

Employing Eqs. (1.106), (1.107), and (1.100), it can be shown that

$$\Delta P = \frac{AE_t}{2}\left[\frac{4d}{l} - (\tau + 1)e_2\right] \tag{1.112}$$

Hence

$$P = P_t + \frac{AE_t}{2}\left[\frac{4d}{l} - (\tau + 1)e_2\right]$$

or

$$P = P_t\left[1 + \frac{2d}{h} - \frac{l}{2h}(1 + \tau)e_2\right] \tag{1.113}$$

Equating the expressions for P given by Eqs. (1.109) and (1.113) leads to

$$e_2 = \frac{4d}{l(\tau - 1)} \frac{1}{\dfrac{h}{2d} + \dfrac{\tau + 1}{\tau - 1}} \tag{1.114}$$

Finally, substitution of this expression into Eq. (1.109) gives the desired load–deflection relation:

$$P = P_t\left(1 + \frac{1}{\dfrac{h}{2d} + \dfrac{\tau + 1}{\tau - 1}}\right) \tag{1.115}$$

Using this relation between the applied load P and the lateral deflection d, the postbuckling behavior of the model can be studied.

As assumed, the model begins to bend at the tangent modulus load; that is, $P = P_t$ when $d = 0$. As d increases, the variation of P with d depends on the value of $\tau = E_2/E_t$. This ratio is either equal to unity or E/E_t, depending on whether or not strain reversal takes place on the convex side of the model. If there is no strain reversal, $\tau = 1$, and P remains constant at P_t as the model bends. However, bending at constant load produces strain reversal. The assumption of no strain reversal thus leads to inconsistent results and must be discarded. Assuming that strain reversal does take place, $\tau = E/E_t$, and Eq. (1.115) indicates that P increases with increasing deflection.

It will now be shown that P increases and approaches P_r, the reduced modulus load, as the deflection d becomes large compared to h. The reduced modulus theory assumes that bending takes place at constant load. Hence $P_1 = P_2$, and $E_1 e_1 = E_2 e_2$, from which

$$e_2 = \frac{e_1 E_1}{E_2} = \frac{e_1 E_t}{E} = \frac{e_1}{\tau}$$

In view of Eq. (1.100)

$$e_2 = \frac{4d}{l} \frac{1}{1 + \tau}$$

Substitution of this relation into Eq. (1.109) leads to

$$P_r = \frac{AhE_t}{l}\left(1 + \frac{\tau - 1}{\tau + 1}\right) \tag{1.116}$$

the reduced modulus load. The load supported by the model [Eq. (1.115)] thus approaches the reduced modulus load [Eq. (1.116)] as the deflection becomes very large.

The behavior of the model obtained from Eq. (1.115) is summarized by the solid curve in Fig. 1-24. Bending begins at the tangent modulus load and

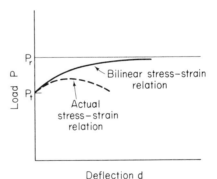

Fig. 1-24 Load–deflection curve of Shanley model.

progresses with increasing axial load. As the lateral deflection becomes large, the axial load approaches the reduced modulus load.

The most important difference between an actual column and the model is that E_t decreases with increasing compressive strain in an actual column, whereas it was assumed to remain constant in the model. A better approximation of the postbuckling curve than that given by the solid line in Fig. 1-24 is obtained if the decrease in E_t is taken into account. As shown by the dashed curve in the figure, the model then has a maximum load whose value lies somewhere between P_t and P_r.

Although the model represents an extreme simplification of the actual column, it does lead to the following valid conclusions regarding inelastic column buckling.

1. An initially straight column will begin to bend as soon as the tangent modulus load is exceeded.
2. Subsequent to the onset of bending, the axial load increases and reaches a maximum value that lies somewhere between the tangent modulus load and the reduced modulus load.
3. Although there is no strain reversal at the instant that bending begins, strain reversal does occur as soon as the bending deformations are finite.

Of these three findings, probably the most significant is that the maximum load of the column lies somewhere between the tangent modulus load and the reduced modulus load.

A more precise study than that conducted by Shanley involving real columns made of real materials indicates that P_{max} is usually closer to P_t than to P_r and that the ratio $P_t/P_{max} \cong 1.02$ to 1.10 (Ref. 1.13). It can thus be concluded that the tangent modulus load is very close to the maximum load that an inelastic column can support.

1.17 ECCENTRICALLY LOADED INELASTIC COLUMNS

In this article the behavior of an eccentrically loaded column, stressed beyond the proportional limit, will be considered. As pointed out previously, the relation of stress to strain in a column being bent inelastically varies in a complex manner from point to point in the member. It is therefore not possible to obtain an exact closed-form solution to the problem of inelastic bending of an eccentrically loaded column. Instead, the problem must be solved by means of a numerical procedure. Such a method has been devised by von Kármán (Ref. 1.12). However, it involves laborious calculations, and its use is therefore justified only if a very accurate solution is required. In most instances, an approximate solution suffices, and this can be obtained without unduly lengthy calculations if one or more simplifying assumptions are made. An approximate analysis of this type is presented here.* It is based on two assumptions:

1. The column axis deflects in a half-sinewave.

*This method of analyzing an eccentrically loaded inelastic column was suggested to the author by Warner Lansing of the Grumman Aircraft Engineering Corporation.

2. The stress varies linearly across the section. The actual stress–strain curve of the material is used to obtain the extreme fiber stresses, and a linear variation is then assumed to exist between these stresses. For an idealized I section consisting of two flanges connected by a web of negligible area, the linear approximation coincides with the exact stress distribution.

In addition to these two approximations, the usual assumptions, of plane sections remaining plane during bending and of deformations being small so that the curvature can be approximated by the second derivative, are made.

Consider a column that is loaded eccentrically, as shown in Fig. 1-25a. The stresses at any section consist of an average axial stress, $\sigma_0 = P/A$, and a bending stress, σ_b. As indicated in Fig. 1-25b, the extreme fiber stresses are designated by σ_1 and σ_2. Between these stresses a linear stress distribution, indicated by the solid line in the figure, is assumed in place of the actual stress variation, shown by a dashed line. The deformations of a typical element are shown in Fig. 1-25c. Using similar triangles, it is easily demonstrated that the curvature $1/r$ is given by

$$\frac{1}{r} = \frac{\epsilon_1 - \epsilon_2}{h}$$

in which ϵ_1 and ϵ_2 are the extreme fiber strains corresponding to the stresses σ_1 and σ_2 and h is the depth of the cross section. If the curvature is replaced by y'', one obtains

$$y'' = \frac{\epsilon_1 - \epsilon_2}{h} \tag{1.117}$$

It is convenient to designate the slope of the straight line joining the extreme fiber stresses on the stress–strain curve as the *chordal modulus*, E_{CH} (see Fig. 1-25d). Hence

$$E_{CH} = \frac{\sigma_2 - \sigma_1}{\epsilon_2 - \epsilon_1} \tag{1.118}$$

Substitution of this relation into Eq. (1.117) leads to

$$y'' = \frac{\sigma_1 - \sigma_2}{E_{CH} h} \tag{1.119}$$

Making use of the expressions

$$\sigma_1 = \frac{P}{A} - \frac{Mh}{2I}$$

$$\sigma_2 = \frac{P}{A} + \frac{Mh}{2I} \tag{1.120}$$

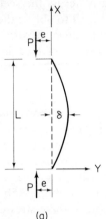

(a)

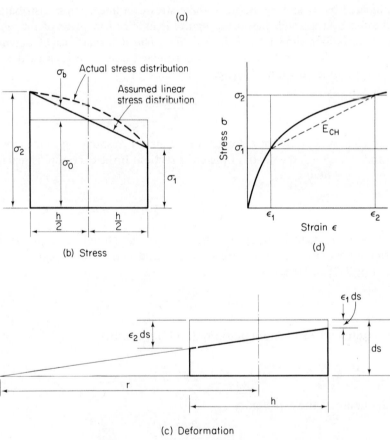

(b) Stress

(d)

(c) Deformation

Fig. 1-25 Eccentrically loaded inelastic column.

Eq. (1.119) can be rewritten in the form

$$y'' = -\frac{M}{E_{CH}I} \qquad (1.121)$$

in which the bending moment M, at any section, is equal to $P(e + y)$.

Equation (1.121) is the inelastic bending equation that results from assuming a linear stress variation between the extreme fiber stresses of the member. It is similar to the elastic moment–curvature relation except that the constant modulus, E, in the latter has been replaced by a variable chordal modulus, E_{CH}.

Assuming that the deformed shape of the column is given by

$$y = \delta \sin \frac{\pi x}{l} \qquad (1.122)$$

in which δ is the deflection at midheight, Eq. (1.121) becomes

$$\frac{\delta \pi^2}{l^2} \sin \frac{\pi x}{l} = \frac{M}{E_{CH}I} \qquad (1.123)$$

Substitution of $x = l/2$ and $M = P(e + \delta)$ into Eq. (1.123) gives

$$\delta = \frac{l^2}{\pi^2} \frac{P(e + \delta)}{E_{CH}I}$$

and because $I = Ar^2$,

$$\delta = \frac{e}{\dfrac{\pi^2 E_{CH}}{(L/r)^2 \sigma_0} - 1} \qquad (1.124)$$

Equation (1.124) gives the midheight deflection δ as a function of the average compression stress σ_0. However, a solution for δ can be obtained only if E_{CH} corresponding to a given value of σ_0 is known.

The maximum stress at midheight is given by

$$\sigma_2 = \frac{P}{A} + \frac{P(e + \delta)h}{2I}$$

or

$$\sigma_2 = \sigma_0 \left[1 + \frac{eh}{2r^2} \left(1 + \frac{\delta}{e} \right) \right] \qquad (1.125)$$

Substitution for δ/e from Eq. (1.124) into this expression leads to

$$\sigma_2 = \sigma_0 \left[1 + \frac{ec}{r^2} \frac{1}{1 - \dfrac{\sigma_0(L/r)^2}{\pi^2 E_{CH}}} \right] \qquad (1.126)$$

Equation (1.126) allows one to obtain E_{CH} corresponding to a given value of σ_0, and thus makes possible the evaluation of δ in Eq. (1.124). Due to the presence of σ_2, it is not possible to solve Eq. (1.126) directly. Instead, the equation must be solved by iteration. One assumes a value for E_{CH}, solves for σ_2 in Eq. (1.126), and then using this result one obtains a new estimate of E_{CH} from Eq. (1.118). It is assumed that the cross section of the member is doubly symmetric and that the minimum stress σ_1, in Eq. (1.118), is given by

$$\sigma_1 = \sigma_0 - (\sigma_2 - \sigma_0) \tag{1.127}$$

The use of Eqs. (1.124) and (1.126) in combination with Eq. (1.118) makes it possible to obtain the load–deflection curve of an eccentrically loaded column. The complex nature of inelastic bending becomes apparent when one considers the amount of numerical work required to obtain a solution, in spite of the fact that two very sweeping assumptions have been made.

Using the above procedure, the behavior of eccentrically loaded columns will now be examined. Consider a column whose cross section consists of two flanges connected by a web of negligible area (Fig. 1-26a). Each flange has an area $A = 20$ in.^{2} and the flanges are 10 in. apart. The slenderness ratio of the column is 30.4 and the member is constructed of an aluminum alloy having the stress–strain characteristics depicted in Fig. 1-26b. Load–deflection curves will be obtained for eccentricities of 1.0, 0.5, and 0.1 in. To illustrate the procedure used to construct the curves, a set of sample calculations is given.

Let it be required to obtain the deflection, δ, corresponding to $\sigma_0 = 38$ ksi and $e = 1.0$ in. The first step in the calculations is the determination of a set of values for σ_2 and E_{CH} that satisfies Eq. (1.126). Substitution of $\sigma_0 = 38$, $ec/r^2 = 0.2$, and $l/r = 30.4$ into Eq. (1.126) reduces it to the form

$$\sigma_2 = 38 + 7.6 \frac{1}{1 - (3560/E_{CH})} \tag{1.128}$$

As a first approximation, assume $\sigma_2 = 48$ ksi and $\sigma_1 = 28$ ksi.
From Fig. 1-26b, $\epsilon_2 = 0.00473$ and $\epsilon_1 - 0.00267$.
Using Eq. (1.118) gives $E_{CH} = 9.7 \times 10^3$ ksi.
From Eq. (1.128) one obtains $\sigma_2 = 50.0$ ksi.

As a second approximation, assume $\sigma_2 = 50.0$ ksi and $\sigma_1 = 26.0$ ksi.
From Fig. 1-26b, $\epsilon_2 = 0.00500$ and $\epsilon_1 = 0.00247$.
Using Eq. (1.118) gives $E_{CH} = 9.5 \times 10^3$ ksi.
From Eq. (1.128) one obtains $\sigma_2 = 50.2$ ksi.

As a third approximation, assume $\sigma_2 = 50.2$ ksi and $\sigma_1 = 25.8$ ksi.
From Fig. 1-26b, $\epsilon_2 = 0.00502$ and $\epsilon_1 = 0.00245$.
Using Eq. (1.118) gives $E_{CH} = 9.45 \times 10^3$ ksi.
From Eq. (1.128) one obtains $\sigma_2 = 50.2$ ksi.

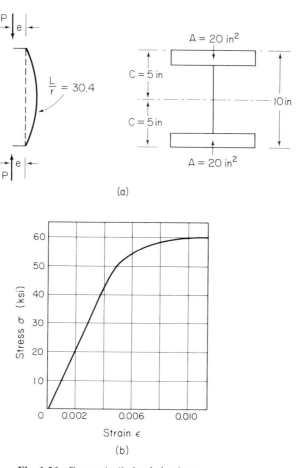

Fig. 1-26 Eccentrically loaded column—example.

Thus $\sigma_2 = 50.2$ ksi and $E_{CH} = 9.45 \times 10^3$ ksi satisfy Eq. (1.128), and the correct value of E_{CH} corresponding to $\sigma_0 = 38$ ksi is 9.45×10^3 ksi.

Having obtained E_{CH}, it is now possible to solve for the deflection δ using Eq. (1.124). Thus

$$\delta = \frac{1}{\dfrac{9.45}{3.56} - 1} = 0.61 \text{ in.}$$

In carrying out these calculations, it soon becomes apparent that there exist two solutions corresponding to every value of σ_0. Thus for $\sigma_0 = 38$ ksi there is another set of values for σ_2 and E_{CH}, aside from those just determined, that satisfies Eq. (1.128). By a trial-and-error procedure, similar to the one used in the preceding paragraph, it is found that $\sigma_2 = 59.7$ ksi and $E_{CH} =$

5.5×10^3 ksi is the second solution to Eq. (1.128). The deflection corresponding to $E_{CH} = 5.5 \times 10^3$ ksi is

$$\delta = \frac{1}{\dfrac{5.5}{3.56} - 1} = 1.85 \text{ in.}$$

Proceeding in a similar manner, sufficient data have been obtained to plot the load–deflection curves presented in Fig. 1-27. Curves giving the relation-

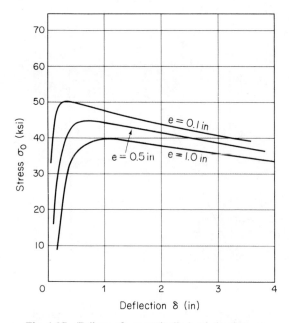

Fig. 1-27 Failure of eccentrically loaded columns.

ship between the average stress σ_0 and the midheight deflection δ are given for three different eccentricities of loading. The data used to plot these curves are listed in Table 1-2.

For each curve shown in the figure, the load increases with increasing deflection until a maximum load is reached. Beyond that, the load drops as the deflection continues to grow. Configurations on the ascending branch of the curve are stable, because an increase in load is required to produce an increase in deflection. By comparison, the descending branch of the curve represents unstable configurations, since increases in deflection involve decreases in load. The maximum point on the curve thus represents a transition from stable to unstable equilibrium. When the load corresponding to this point is reached, the column collapses.

Table 1-2 Load–deflection data for eccentrically loaded columns—inelastic theory

e = 1.0 in.		e = 0.5 in.		e = 0.1 in.	
σ_0 (ksi)	δ (in.)	σ_0	δ	σ_0	δ
20	0.21	20	0.11	20	0.02
25	0.28	25	0.14	30	0.03
30	0.35	30	0.18	40	0.06
32	0.38	35	0.25	45	0.09
34	0.44	40	0.29	48	0.16
36	0.49	42	0.36	50	0.26
38	0.57	44	0.42	50	0.32
40	0.72	45	0.55	48	0.77
40	1.22	45	0.64	45	1.08
38	1.71	44	1.01		
36	2.20	42	1.41		

The load–deflection curves in Fig. 1-27 are for a column whose slenderness ratio is 30.4. The tangent modulus load of this column is 52.5 ksi (Fig. 1-29). It is evident from Fig. 1-27 that the maximum load which the column can support approaches the tangent modulus load as the eccentricity approaches zero. This result substantiates the conclusion reached in Article 1.16; that is, the tangent modulus load is very close to the maximum load that a short concentrically loaded column can safely support. The curves in Fig. 1-27 also indicate that the maximum load drops sharply with increasing values of the eccentricity. The load-carrying capacity of short columns is thus seen to be very sensitive to eccentricities of loading.

The collapse mechanism illustrated by the curves in Fig. 1-27 is typical of what occurs in all column, regardless of whether they are long and buckle elastically or if they are short and buckle inelastically. The main difference between the behavior of long and short columns is that the onset of buckling and collapse occur almost simultaneously in short columns, whereas there exists a considerable delay between the start of buckling and collapse in very long columns. However, in both cases the final collapse of the member is brought about by inelastic behavior of the material.

Equilibrium of a bent column is achieved by maintaining a balance between the externally applied moment and the internal resisting moment at any section. Both moments are functions of the lateral deformation of the member. As soon as the stresses exceed the proportional limit, the stiffness of the material decreases, and the increase that occurs in the internal resisting moment for a given increase in deformation begins to grow smaller and smaller. At first, a corresponding decrease in the rate of increase of the applied load for a given increase in deflection is sufficient to maintain balance between the internal and external moments. Eventually, however, the increase in the internal moment, with growing deflections, becomes so small that equilibrium between it and the external moment can be maintained only by a decrease in the applied load. As a consequence, the load drops and the member collapses.

1.18 BUCKLING LOAD OF SHORT COLUMNS

In the preceding articles, various studies of inelastic buckling have been presented. It is now necessary to evaluate the results of these investigations and to decide upon a suitable design criterion for short columns. In other words, it is necessary to answer the question, "What is the inelastic buckling load that corresponds to the Euler load in the elastic range?"

The classical theory of stability defines the critical load as the load at which a perfect column can be in equilibrium both in the straight position and in an adjacent slightly bent form. For slender columns that buckle at stresses below the proportional limit, the classical theory leads to the Euler load. The analysis of an imperfect column also indicates that the Euler load is the buckling load of a slender column with small initial imperfections. If a slender column is carefully made and reasonable care is exercised in obtaining concentric loading in the testing machine, the column remains fairly straight until the Euler load is reached and then buckles laterally at constant load. Hence the classical concept of neutral equilibrium, an analysis of a slightly imperfect member, and test results all lead to the same conclusion—the Euler load is the buckling load of a slender column.

As indicated by Hoff (Ref. 1.5), the situation is unfortunately not as simple and straightforward when short columns, whose buckling stress is above the proportional limit, are considered. The classical concept of neutral equilibrium leads to the reduced modulus load. If the critical load is redefined as the lowest load at which a bifurcation of equilibrium is possible, regardless of what happens to the axial load during the transition to the bent form, then the tangent modulus load is the critical load. The tangent modulus load is also very close to the analytically obtained maximum load that an initially imperfect column can support, as the initial imperfection approaches zero. The results of carefully conducted tests indicate that the maximum load lies between the tangent modulus load and the reduced modulus load, usually very close to the former. It is thus apparent that the selection of a design criterion for inelastic buckling is not quite as clear cut as it was for elastic buckling. On the one hand, a choice must be made between the reduced modulus and tangent modulus theory, and on the other hand it must be recognized that what is usually simply referred to as inelastic buckling actually consists of two distinct phenomena. There is the load at which bending deflections suddenly begin to develop in what was previously a straight member, and there is the maximum load that the member can support. Fortunately, the difference between the failure load and the load at which bending begins is very small for inelastic columns. It is therefore unnecessary to differentiate between the two, at least as far as design considerations are concerned. Regarding the choice between the reduced modulus load and the tangent modulus load, a resolution of the problem is best arrived at by considering the merits of each individually.

1. The reduced modulus load has the dubious advantage of satisfying the classical criterion of stability. However, it has the disadvantage of being larger than the maximum load that an inelastic column can support.
2. The tangent modulus load agrees well with test results and is somewhat conservative. It is independent of the cross-sectional shape and is therefore easier to compute than the reduced modulus load. It does not satisfy the classical criterion of stability. It does, however, have the theoretical justification of being the lowest axial load at which a column can begin to bend. Based on these considerations, the tangent modulus load is usually preferred to the reduced modulus load.

In conclusion, it can be stated that, for design purposes, the tangent modulus load is the proper inelastic generalization of the Euler load.

1.19 BUCKLING STRENGTH OF ALUMINUM COLUMNS

The tangent modulus theory can be used to design a column only if its physical properties are constant throughout the member. This is usually the case for an aluminum-alloy column, and its buckling load is accordingly given by

$$P_{cr} = \frac{\pi^2 E_t I}{\lambda^2}$$

where λ is the effective length of the member. Substitution of $I = Ar^2$ and division by A gives the more useful buckling strength relation

$$\sigma_{cr} = \frac{\pi^2 E_t}{(\lambda/r)^2} \tag{1.129}$$

Since E_t is the slope of the stress–strain curve at the critical stress, Eq. (1.129) cannot be solved directly for the critical stress. However, the critical stress of a given member can be obtained directly from a graphical representation of Eq. (1.129). A curve of this type, which gives σ_{cr} as a function of λ/r and is known as a column strength curve, will now be obtained for a typical aluminum alloy. The stress–strain curve of the material is given in Fig. 1-28.

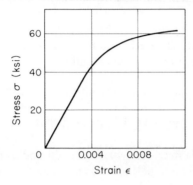

Fig. 1-28 Stress–strain curve for aluminum alloy.

Equation (1.129) can be rewritten in the form

$$\frac{\lambda}{r} = \pi \sqrt{\frac{E_t}{\sigma_{cr}}} \tag{1.130}$$

To plot the variation of σ_{cr} with λ/r given by Eq. (1.130), it is necessary to have corresponding values of E_t and σ_{cr}. These have been obtained from the stress–strain curve and are listed in Table 1-3. The values of λ/r obtained by

Table 1-3   Data for column strength curve for aluminum alloy

σ_{cr} (ksi)	E_t (ksi)	λ/r
42	10.5 $\times 10^3$	49.6
44	9.57	46.3
46	8.09	41.6
48	7.22	38.5
50	6.00	34.4
52	4.72	29.9
54	4.22	27.7
56	2.86	22.4
58	1.64	16.7
60	0.74	11.0

solving Eq. (1.130) are also listed in the table. Using these data, the column strength curve in Fig. 1-29 has been plotted. This is a design curve that can be used to determine the inelastic critical stress of any column made of the given material.

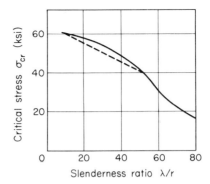

Fig. 1-29 Column curve for alumi
num alloy.

1.20 BUCKLING STRENGTH OF HOT-ROLLED WIDE-FLANGE STEEL COLUMNS

The simple and straightforward procedure used to obtain the column strength curve for an aluminum alloy in article 1.19, unfortunately, cannot be applied to structural steel. In an aluminum column all fibers exhibit the same stress–strain characteristics. This is, however, not the case for structural-steel columns. Residual stresses, stemming from the manufacturing process of the member, cause the stress–strain characteristics to vary from fiber to fiber, and a direct application of the tangent modulus theory is not possible.

If a compression test is run using a coupon of material taken parallel to the axis of a structural-steel member, a stress–strain curve similar to that shown in Fig. 1-30a is obtained. The material behaves in a linear manner up to the yield stress and then deforms a considerable amount at constant stress.

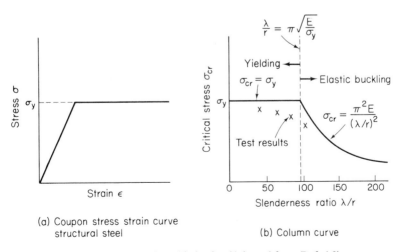

(a) Coupon stress strain curve structural steel

(b) Column curve

Fig. 1-30 Structural-steel behavior (Adapted from Ref. 4.8).

Using the stress–strain curve in Fig. 1-30a, the tangent modulus theory leads to the column strength curve shown in Fig. 1-30b. According to this curve, a member will fail as a result of elastic buckling if $\lambda/r > \pi\sqrt{E/\sigma_y}$ and by yielding if $\lambda/r < \pi\sqrt{E/\sigma_y}$. However, a large number of tests have shown that columns of intermediate slenderness ratio tend to buckle at loads significantly below those given by the curve in Fig. 1-30b. At one time, this discrepancy was attributed entirely to unavoidable eccentricities of loading and initial inperfections in the member. However, during the 1950s, a series of extensive investigations at Lehigh University demonstrated conclusively that residual stresses account for a large portion of the discrepancy between the theoretical curve and the test results in Fig. 1-30b. An excellent summary of these findings is given in a paper by Beedle and Tall (Ref. 1.14).

Residual Stresses in Hot-Rolled Steel Members

Hot-rolled structural-steel members develop residual stresses as a result of uneven cooling during the manufacturing process. In wide-flange shapes, the tips of the flanges cool more rapidly than the area at the intersection of the web and the flange, where a relatively large mass of material is situated. While the flange tips cool and contract, the flange center is still warm and soft. Hence it can follow the deformation of the tips without causing stresses to be induced in the member. Later, however, when the flange center cools and tries to shrink, the deformation is resisted by the already cold and rigid flange tips. As a result, equilibrium is finally achieved with the flange center in tension and the flange tips in compression (Fig. 1-31). The central part of

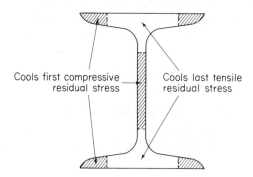

Cools first compressive residual stress

Cools last tensile residual stress

Fig. 1-31   Uneven cooling of hot-rolled wide-flange shape.

the web also cools more rapidly than the web–flange junction, and compressive residual stresses consequently also develop in the web. Because of their proximity to the neutral axis, these residual stresses are, however, much less important than those in the flanges.

The presence of residual stresses in structural-steel columns has been confirmed experimentally both by the method of sectioning and by obtaining average stress–strain curves from stub column tests, that is, compression tests of very short columns. In the method of sectioning, the member is cut into a large number of longitudinal strips, which relieves the residual stresses present prior to cutting. If the length of each strip is measured before and after cutting, the changes in length are indicative of the residual stresses present in the original member. Based on a large number of investigations (Ref. 1.14), it has been concluded that the average value of the maximum compressive residual stress in hot-rooled wide-flange shapes of moderate-strength steels at the tip of the flange is approximately equal to 0.3 of the yield strength. A simple idealization of the residual stress pattern in a flange is shown in Fig. 1-32. It assumes a linear stress variation from a maximum

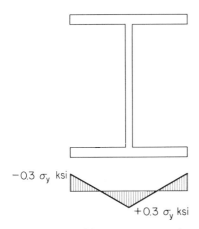

Fig. 1-32   Residual stress pattern in flange.

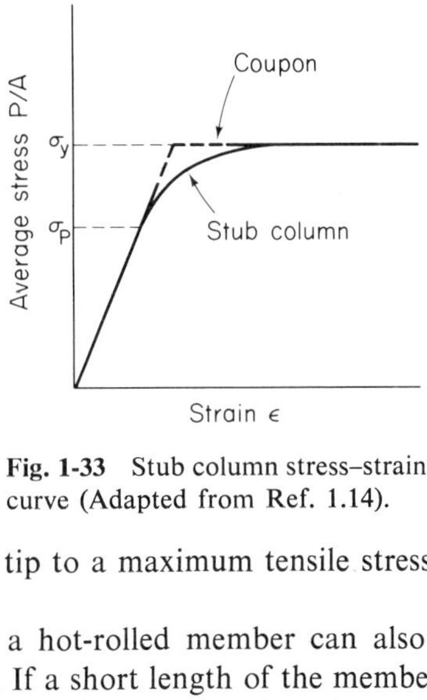

Fig. 1-33   Stub column stress–strain curve (Adapted from Ref. 1.14).

compressive stress of $0.3\sigma_y$ at the flange tip to a maximum tensile stress of $0.3\sigma_y$ at the flange–web juncture.

The presence of residual stresses in a hot-rolled member can also be detected by means of a stub-column test. If a short length of the member is compressed in a testing machine and the strain is plotted against the average stress, P/A, an average stress–strain curve for the entire cross section, as shown in Fig. 1-33, is obtained. The dashed curve, which gives the stress–strain relationship of a coupon, is included for comparison. Since the coupon is free of residual stresses, all its fibers remain elastic until the applied stress reaches the yield strength of the material. Subsequently, each deforms freely at constant stress. By comparison, residual stresses are present in the stub column, causing those fibers with an initial compressive stress to yield before the applied stress reaches the yield strength of the material. Yielding then spreads progressively, as the load is increased, from the fibers initially in compression to those with no initial stress, and finally to those with an initial tensile stress. The stub-column stress–strain relation thus exhibits a gradual yielding curve between the proportional limit and the yield strength, due to the presence of residual stresses.

By depicting the internal stress distribution at various load levels, Beedle and Tall (Ref. 1.14) demonstrate precisely how residual stresses affect the behavior of a compression member. In their illustration they make use of an I section with a linear residual stress distribution, as shown in Fig. 1-34a.

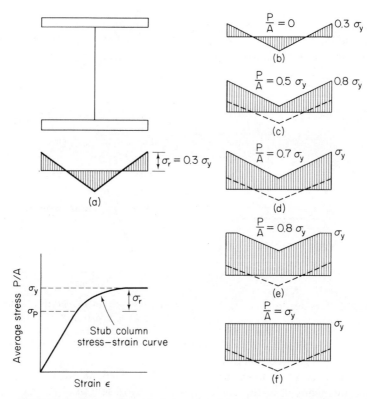

Fig. 1-34 Influence of residual stress on stub column stress–strain curve (Adapted from Ref. 1.14).

Prior to the application of an external load, only the residual stresses are present (Fig. 1-34b). With an external load acting, the stresses consist of the sum of the original residual stresses and the additional stress required to balance the applied load (Fig. 1-34c). Yielding commences, at the flange tips, when the average applied stress P/A plus the residual stress σ_r at these points is equal to the yield strength σ_y of the material (Fig. 1-34d). Thus σ_p, the proportional limit of the stub-column stress–strain curve, is

$$\sigma_p = \sigma_y - \sigma_r$$

For the case being considered, $\sigma_p = 0.7\sigma_y$. As the applied stress, P/A, increases beyond $0.7\sigma_y$, yielding spreads inward from the flange tips toward the flange center (Fig. 1-34e). At $P/A = \sigma_y$, the entire cross section has started to yield (Fig. 1-34f). The decrease in stiffness exhibited by the stub column above the proportional limit is thus due to a gradual reduction of the effective load-resisting area. By comparison, an aluminum stub column exhibits a gradually yielding stress–strain relation because each of its fibers has a gradually yielding stress–strain curve.

Column Strength Curves for Hot-Rolled Structural-Steel Members

The presence of residual stresses in structural-steel columns makes it impossible to determine the critical load directly from the tangent modulus theory. However, the basic concept underlying Shanley's theory of inelastic column buckling does apply. According to this concept, axial load and bending increase simultaneously after the critical load has been reached, and no strain reversal occurs as the member begins to buckle. For a steel column, the absence of strain reversal at buckling means that only the elastic part of the cross section contributes to the internal resisting moment of the deformed member. This important observation was first made by Yang, Beedle, and Johnston (Ref. 1.15). Based on it, one can conclude that the critical load in the inelastic range is given by the Euler load with the moment of inertia of the entire cross section, I, replaced by I_e, the moment of inertia of the elastic part of the cross section. Thus

$$P_{\mathrm{cr}} = \frac{\pi^2 E I_e}{\lambda^2}$$

or

$$\sigma_{\mathrm{cr}} = \frac{\pi^2 E}{(\lambda/r)^2} \frac{I_e}{I} \tag{1.131}$$

Equation (1.131) indicates that the critical stress of a steel column is equal to the Euler stress multiplied by the reduction factor I_e/I.

The ratio I_e/I depends on the residual stress distribution, on the shape of the member, and on the axis about which the column bends. Consider the idealized I section shown in Fig. 1-35. In addition to neglecting the bending resistance of the web, it is justified to neglect the moment of inertia of the flanges about their own centroidal axis for such sections. If the flanges are partially yielded (shaded area), and the section bends about its strong axis, the x-x axis, I_e/I is given by

$$\frac{I_e}{I} = \frac{2b_e t h^2/4}{2b t h^2/4} = \frac{A_e}{A} \tag{1.132}$$

in which b and A are the width and area of the flange, and b_e and A_e the

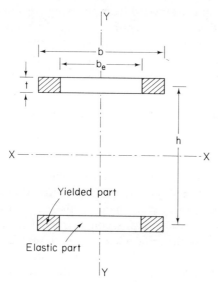

Fig. 1-35   Partially yielded section.

elastic parts of these quantities. If, on the other hand, bending takes place about the weak axis, the y-y axis, I_e/I is given by

$$\frac{I_e}{I} = \frac{2b_e^3 t/12}{2b^3 t/12} = \left(\frac{A_e}{A}\right)^3 \tag{1.133}$$

Letting $\tau = A_e/A$, Eq. (1.131) can be written in the form

$$\sigma_{cr} = \frac{\pi^2 E}{(\lambda/r)^2}\tau \tag{1.134}$$

for strong-axis bending, and

$$\sigma_{cr} = \frac{\pi^2 E}{(\lambda/r)^2}\tau^3 \tag{1.135}$$

for weak-axis bending. Comparison of Eqs. (1.134) and (1.135) indicates that the reduction factor is much larger for weak-axis bending than for strong-axis bending and that each case will therefore have a different column-strength curve.

To plot the column curves corresponding to Eqs. (1.134) and (1.135), it is necessary to know how τ varies with the average axial stress, P/A. This relation can be determined either experimentally, by obtaining a stub-column stress–strain curve, or analytically, if the residual stress distribution is known. The stub-column stress–strain curve is a plot of strain versus average stress. Its slope is given by

$$E_t = \frac{d\sigma_A}{d\epsilon} = \frac{dP/A}{dP/A_e E} = \frac{EA_e}{A} \tag{1.136}$$

from which

$$\tau = \frac{A_e}{A} = \frac{E_t}{E} \tag{1.137}$$

The factor τ is thus equal to the ratio of the tangent modulus of the stub-column stress–strain curve to the elastic modulus.

Alternatively, τ can be determined analytically using the idealized I section and the linear residual stress distribution shown in Fig. 1-36a. When

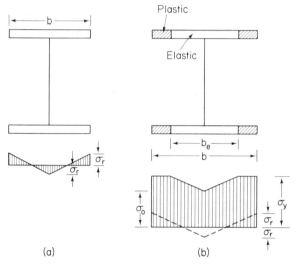

Fig. 1-36   Residual stress in idealized I section.

the average applied stress $\sigma_A = P/A$ is above the proportional limit of the stub column, the cross section is partially plastic and partially elastic, as shown in Fig. 1-36b. The dashed lines represent the initial residual stresses. The total load P acting on the member is given by

$$P = 2\sigma_y(A - A_e) + 2\frac{\sigma_0 + \sigma_y}{2}A_e \tag{1.138}$$

in which σ_0 is the stress at the center of the flange. From the geometry of the figure, it can be shown that

$$\sigma_0 = \sigma_y - 2\sigma_r\frac{b_e}{b}$$

or

$$\sigma_0 = \sigma_y - 2\sigma_r\frac{A_e}{A}$$

Substitution of this relation into Eq. (1.138) leads to

$$P = 2\sigma_y A - 2\sigma_r\frac{A_e^2}{A}$$

Dividing through by the cross-sectional area, $2A$, gives

$$\sigma_A = \sigma_y - \sigma_r \left(\frac{A_e}{A}\right)^2$$

and replacing A_e/A with τ one obtains

$$\tau = \sqrt{[1 - (\sigma_A/\sigma_y)](\sigma_y/\sigma_r)} \qquad (1.139)$$

Equation (1.139) gives the desired variation of τ with the average axial stress σ_A. Using this relation in Eqs. (1.134) and (1.135), two column-strength curves, one for strong-axis bending and one for weak-axis bending, have been obtained. The curves are shown in Fig. 1-37 as solid lines. The upper curve is

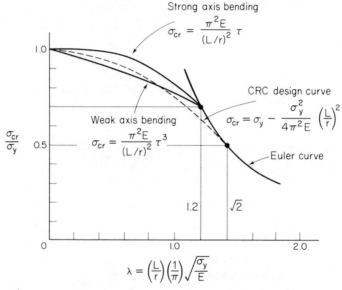

Fig. 1-37   Column curves for wide-flange shapes with residual stresses (Adapted from Ref. 4.8).

for strong-axis bending and the lower curve for weak-axis bending. These curves are for an idealized I section with the linear residual stress distribution depicted in Fig. 1-36a. A similar set of curves can be developed for any other cross-sectional shape and residual stress distribution. An extensive investigation of residual stress patterns in wide-flange shapes (Ref. 1.14) has indicated that the actual stress distribution falls somewhere between the linear one assumed here and a parabolic one with the same maximum residual compression stress; that is, $\sigma_{r(\max)} = 0.3\sigma_y$. The curves in Fig. 1-37 therefore give a reasonable estimate of the strength of hot-rolled wide-flange structural-steel shapes.

The dashed line in the figure, which provides a compromise between strong- and weak-axis bending, was recommended by the Column Research Council in the second edition of its guide (Ref. 1.16). It is a parabola of the form

$$\sigma_{\text{cr}} = A - B\left(\frac{\lambda}{r}\right)^2$$

and was first proposed by Bleich (Ref. 1.12). The constants A and B are evaluated from the conditions that $\sigma_{\text{cr}} = \sigma_y$ at $\lambda/r = 0$ and that the parabola intersect the Euler curve at the proportional limit $\sigma_y - \sigma_r$. These conditions lead to

$$\sigma_{\text{cr}} = \sigma_y - \frac{\sigma_r(\sigma_y - \sigma_r)}{\pi^2 E}\left(\frac{\lambda}{r}\right)^2$$

Although the maximum compressive residual stress in the flange of structural-steel members is approximately $0.3\sigma_y$, a curve better suited to both weak- and strong-axis bending is obtained by letting $\sigma_r = 0.5\sigma_y$. Thus

$$\sigma_{\text{cr}} = \sigma_y - \frac{\sigma_y^2}{4\pi^2 E}\left(\frac{l}{r}\right)^2 \tag{1.140}$$

Equation (1.140) corresponds to the dashed curve in Fig. 1-37.

1.21 DESIGN OF STEEL COLUMNS

The Euler equation accurately predicts the strength of steel columns that buckle elastically. It is therefore customary to base the design of slender steel columns on the Euler load. For example, in the 1969 AISC design specifications, the allowable stress in compression for elastic buckling is given by

$$\sigma_{\text{all}} = \frac{12\pi^2 E}{23(\lambda/r)^2} \tag{1.141}$$

where λ is the effective length of the member (Ref. 1.17). In this formula the allowable stress is taken equal to the Euler stress divided by a safety factor of 23/12. The safety factor accounts for reductions in strength resulting from initial eccentricities and other deviations from the ideal conditions assumed in the Euler theory.

Theoretically, the inelastic buckling load of a steel column should be given by the tangent modulus load. However, due to the presence of residual stresses in most steel members, a straightforward application of the tangent modulus theory does not give a satisfactory estimate of the strength of short columns. During the first half of the twentieth century the significance of residual stresses, although suspected, was not sufficiently appreciated. As a consequence, no rational theory for inelastic buckling was developed. Instead, design formulas were simply obtained by fitting a curve to experimentally obtained buckling loads. Two of the most commonly used relationships were the straight-line formula

$$\sigma_{all} = \frac{A - B(l/r)}{S.F.}$$

and the Johnson parabola

$$\sigma_{all} = \frac{A - B(l/r)^2}{S.F.}$$

In both of these expressions A and B are empirically determined constants and S.F. is a safety factor. An example of the latter formula can be found in the 1949 AISC design specifications (Ref. 1.18), where the allowable stress for inelastic buckling is given by

$$\sigma_{all} = 17,000 - 0.485\left(\frac{l}{r}\right)^2 \tag{1.142}$$

The first theoretically based formula for short steel columns was not developed until after an extensive investigation at Lehigh University in the 1950s proved conclusively that residual stresses are responsible for the difference in strength between the results of the tangent modulus theory and actual test observations. This study, which is summarized in Article 1.20, led to the CRC column-strength curve given by Eq. (1.140). Shortly thereafter the AISC adopted the CRC curve as its design criterion, and the allowable stress in the 1969 specifications (Ref. 1.17) is accordingly given by

$$\sigma_{all} = \frac{\sigma_y\left[1 - \dfrac{\sigma_y(\lambda/r)^2}{4\pi^2 E}\right]}{S.F.} \tag{1.143}$$

To account for the fact that the sensitivity of a column to eccentricities and variations in the support conditions increases with λ/r, the safety factor in Eq. (1.143) is a function of λ/r.

The early research on the strength of short steel columns was largely confined to hot-rolled wide-flange shapes with a yield stress of 33 or 36 ksi. However, since that time numerous additional investigations have been conducted involving a variety of different shapes, steel grades, and fabrication procedures (Refs. 1.19 and 1.20). It is now evident from the results of these studies that the strengths of different types of steel columns vary considerably and that more than a single design curve may therefore be desirable.

To this end, the Column Research Council in the third edition of its guide is recommending the use of three column-strength curves in place of the former one, each of these curves being representative of the strength of a related category of columns. Included in the three groups of columns covered by these curves are hot-rolled and cold-straightened members, wide-flange and box shapes, and round bars and members composed of welded plates.

In addition to revealing the need for multiple column-strength curves, recent studies have also demonstrated the desirability of including the effect of initial imperfections in the theory instead of in the safety factor (Ref. 1.21). Thus the new column curves give the maximum strengths of initially bent columns, whereas Eq. (1.140) gives the critical load of an initially straight column. An initial out of straightness of $l/1000$ is used in the multiple column-strength curves.

References

1.1 M. SALVADORI and R. HELLER, *Structure in Architecture* (Englewood Cliffs, N.J.: Prentice-Hall, Inc., 1963).

1.2 S. P. TIMOSHENKO and J. M. GERE, *Theory of Elastic Stability*, 2nd ed. (New York: McGraw-Hill Book Company, 1961).

1.3 N. J. HOFF, *The Analysis of Structures* (New York: John Wiley & Sons, Inc., 1956).

1.4 L. EULER, "Sur la force de colonnes," *Mémoires de l'Académie de Berlin*, 1759.

1.5 N. J. HOFF, "Buckling and Stability," *Journal of the Royal Aeronautical Society*, Vol. 58, Jan. 1954.

1.6 C. T. WANG, *Applied Elasticity* (New York: McGraw-Hill Book Company, 1953).

1.7 A. CONSIDÈRE, "Résistance des pièces comprimées," *Congrès International des Procédés de Construction, Paris*, Vol. 3, 1891.

1.8 F. ENGESSER, "Ueber die Knickfestigkeit gerader Stäbe," *Zeitschrift für Architektur und Ingenieurwesen*, Vol. 35, 1889.

1.9 F. ENGESSER, "Knickfragen," *Schweizerische Bauzeitung*, Vol. 26, 1895.

1.10 T. VON KÁRMÁN, "Untersuchungen über knickfestigkeit," *Mitteilungen über Forschungsarbeiten auf dem Gebiete des Ingenieurwesens, Berlin*, No. 81, 1910.

1.11 F. R. SHANLEY, "Inelastic Column Theory " *Journal of the Aeronautical Sciences*, Vol. 14, No. 5, 1947.

1.12 F. BLEICH, *Buckling Strength of Metal Structures* (New York: McGraw-Hill Book Company, 1952).

1.13 J. E. DUBERG and T. W. WILDER, "Column Behavior in the Plastic Stress Range," *Journal of the Aeronautical Sciences*, Vol. 17, No. 6, 1950.

1.14 L. S. BEEDLE and L. TALL, "Basic Column Strength," *Journal of the Structural Division, ASCE*, Vol. 86, No. ST7, 1960.

1.15   C. H. Yang, L. S. Beedle, and B. G. Johnston, "Residual Stress and the Yield Strength of Steel Beams," *Welding Journal*, Vol. 31, No. 4, 1952.

1.16   B. G. Johnston, *Guide to Design Criteria for Metal Compression Members*, 2nd ed. (New York: John Wiley & Sons, Inc., 1966).

1.17   *AISC, Steel Construction Manual*, 7th ed. (New York: American Institute of Steel Construction, 1970).

1.18   *AISC, Steel Construction Manual*, 5th ed. (New York: American Institute of Steel Construction, 1947).

1.19   R. Bjorhovde and L. Tall, "Maximum Column Strength and the Multiple Column Curve Concept," *Fritz Laboratory Report No. 337.29*, Lehigh University, Oct. 1971.

1.20   B. G. Johnston, *Guide to Design Criteria for Metal Compression Members*, 3rd ed. (New York: John Wiley & Sons, Inc., 1973).

1.21   R. H. Batterman and B. G. Johnston, "Behavior and Maximum Strength of Metal Columns," *Journal of the Structural Division, ASCE*, Vol. 93, No. ST2, 1967.

Problems

1.1   Determine the magnitude of the critical load for the axially loaded column shown in Fig. P1-1. The column is hinged at both ends and prevented from

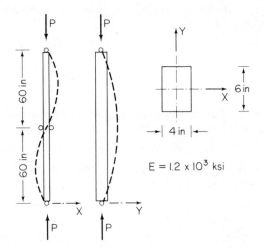

Fig. P1-1

moving in the x direction at its midpoint. The column is, however, free to move in the y direction at midspan. Assume that the column buckles elastically.

1.2   Write the second-order differential equation for the bending of the column shown in Fig. P1-2 and use it to determine the critical load of the column.

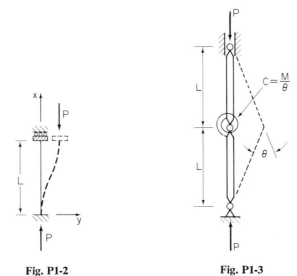

Fig. P1-2   Fig. P1-3

At its lower end the column is completely fixed. At the upper end the column is prevented from rotating, but free to translate laterally. ($P_{cr} = \pi^2 EI/L^2$)

1.3 Find the critical load of the one-degree-of-freedom model of a column shown in Fig. P1-3. The model consists of two rigid bars pin connected to each other and to the supports. A linear rotational spring of stiffness $C = M/\theta$, where M is the moment at the spring and θ is the angle between the two bars, also connects the two bars to each other. ($P_{cr} = 2C/L$)

1.4 Using the model in Fig. P1-3, obtain and plot relationships for load versus lateral deflection when
(a) the lateral deflections are large,
(b) the load is applied eccentrically,
(c) the model has an initial lateral deflection d_0.
Which fundamental characteristics of an actual column are demonstrated by these models?

1.5 Determine the critical load of the column on three supports shown in Fig. P1-4.

Fig. P1-4

(Hint: Write separate equations for each span and make use of the conditions of continuity at the center support.)

1.6 Using the tabulated stainless-steel stress-strain data, construct a column design curve, that is, a curve of tangent-modulus stress versus slenderness ratio.

σ (ksi)	ϵ (in./in.)	σ (ksi)	ϵ (in./in.)
10.0	0.00004	32.5	0.00018
20.0	0.00008	35.0	0.00026
25.0	0.00010	37.5	0.00050
27.5	0.000115	38.0	0.00080
30.0	0.00014		

1.7 Using the procedure outlined in Article 1.17 and the stress–strain data of Problem 1.6, determine the maximum load that the eccentrically loaded column with the idealized I section shown in Fig. P1-5 can support. (Assume the same stress–strain properties for tension and compression.)

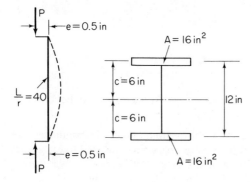

Fig. P1-5

2
APPROXIMATE
METHODS
OF ANALYSIS

2.1 INTRODUCTION

In Chapter 1, the behavior of axially loaded bars was investigated by formulating the governing differential equation and obtaining the exact solution. However, in many instances exact solutions are either difficult or impossible to obtain, and approximate methods of analysis must be employed. The approximate methods presented in this chapter include the energy method, the method of finite differences, and the stiffness matrix method. The latter two involve a considerable amount of numerical work and are therefore especially suitable for use when a high-speed electronic computer is available.

In one way or another, each of the methods considered in this chapter replaces the actual continuous system with a finite-degree-of-freedom system. The behavior of a continuous system with an infinite number of degrees of freedom is described by one or more differential equations. On the other hand, the behavior of a finite-degree-of-freedom system is described by one or more algebraic equations. In essence, the approximate method thus substitutes algebraic equations, which are usually relatively easy to solve, for differential equations, whose solution may be very difficult to obtain.

2.2 CONSERVATION OF ENERGY PRINCIPLE

By means of the concept of neutral equilibrium, the problem of determining
the critical load is reduced to establishing equilibrium in a slightly bent form.
In Chapter 1, equilibrium of a column was established by requiring the sum
of the moments acting on the column to vanish. In this article equilibrium will
be established by satisfying the law of conservation of energy. This principle
can be stated in the following form:

> A conservative system is in equilibrium if the strain energy
> stored is equal to the work performed by the external loads.

A conservative system is one in which the work performed by both internal
and external forces is independent of the path traveled by these forces and
depends only on the initial and final positions. The presence of internal
friction due to inelastic behavior or external friction would thus result in a
nonconservative system.

It will now be shown how the principle of conservation of energy can be
used to solve for the critical load of a column.* For an axially loaded bar
(Fig. 2-1a), as long as it remains perfectly straight, the external work is given
by

$$W = \tfrac{1}{2}P\Delta_a$$

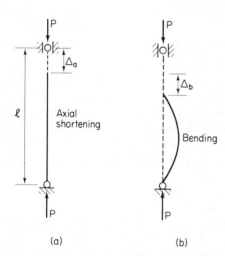

(a)   (b)

Fig. 2-1 Column shortening due to
axial compression and bending.

where Δ_a is the axial shortening of the bar. The strain energy stored in the
member is

$$U = \frac{P^2 l}{2AE}$$

*A solution of this sort was given by Timoshenko in 1910 (Ref. 2.1).

Substituting

$$\Delta_a = \frac{Pl}{AE}$$

in the expression for the external work, W, and equating the resulting relation to the strain energy, U, leads to the identity

$$\frac{P^2 l}{2AE} \equiv \frac{P^2 l}{2AE}$$

The unbent form is thus shown to be an equilibrium configuration for all values of the load P.

If the axially compressed bar is given a small lateral displacement (Fig. 2-1b), the strain energy will be increased an amount ΔU due to the bending of the member, and the external work will increase an amount ΔW due to the downward motion Δ_b of the applied load P. At the critical load the member is in equilibrium not only in the straight configuration but also in the slightly bent form. Hence the change in external work ΔW and the increase in the strain energy ΔU that occur during the transition from the straight to the bent position must be equal to one another at the critical load. The energy criterion for determining the critical load is therefore given by

$$\Delta W = \Delta U \tag{2.1}$$

where ΔW and ΔU refer to changes in work and energy that occur during bending at constant axial load.

To evaluate the quantity ΔW, it is necessary to obtain an expression for Δ_b, the distance by which the ends of the member approach one another as a result of transverse bending. From Fig. 2-2, Δ_b is seen to be equal to the difference between the arc length S and its chord L.

$$\Delta_b = S - L$$

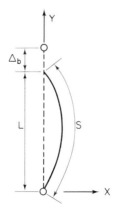

Fig. 2-2 Difference in length between arc and chord.

From the Pythagorean theorem, the length of a differential element of arc, ds, is

$$ds = (dx^2 + dy^2)^{1/2} = \left[1 + \left(\frac{dy}{dx}\right)^2\right]^{1/2} dx$$

Integrating the left side of the equation from 0 to S and the right side from 0 to L, one obtains

$$S = \int_0^L \left[1 + \left(\frac{dy}{dx}\right)^2\right]^{1/2} dx$$

This integral can be evaluated if the integrand is expanded by means of the binomial theorem. The theorem states that

$$(a + b)^n = a^n + na^{n-1}b + \frac{n(n-1)}{2!}a^{n-2}b^2 + \cdots$$

If deformations are assumed to be small, the higher powers of $(dy/dx)^2$ can be neglected, and the expression for the arc length reduces to

$$S = \int_0^L \left[1 + \frac{1}{2}\left(\frac{dy}{dx}\right)^2\right] dx$$

from which

$$S - L = \int_0^L \frac{1}{2}\left(\frac{dy}{dx}\right)^2 dx$$

Since $\Delta_b = S - L$, the axial shortening due to bending is given by

$$\Delta_b = \frac{1}{2}\int_0^L \left(\frac{dy}{dx}\right)^2 dx \tag{2.2}$$

Using Eq. (2.2), one is able to calculate the change in external work, which is

$$\Delta W = P\Delta_b \tag{2.3}$$

No factor of $\frac{1}{2}$ is present in ΔW because P remains constant during the displacement Δ_b. Substitution of Eq. (2.2) into Eq. (2.3) yields

$$\Delta W = \frac{P}{2}\int_0^L \left(\frac{dy}{dx}\right)^2 dx \tag{2.4}$$

The increase in strain energy due to bending, which corresponds to the above increment of external work, is

$$\Delta U = \frac{EI}{2} \int_0^L \left(\frac{d^2y}{dx^2}\right)^2 dx \qquad (2.5)$$

To evaluate the integrals in Eqs. (2.4) and (2.5), it is necessary to assume a suitable function for the deflection, y. Letting

$$y = A \sin \frac{\pi x}{l}$$

one obtains

$$\Delta U = \frac{A^2 EI\pi^4}{2L^4} \int_0^L \sin^2 \frac{\pi x}{L} \, dx \qquad (2.6)$$

and

$$\Delta W = \frac{A^2 P\pi^2}{2L^2} \int_0^L \cos^2 \frac{\pi x}{L} \, dx \qquad (2.7)$$

Since

$$\int_0^L \sin^2 \frac{\pi x}{L} \, dx = \frac{L}{2}$$

$$\int_0^L \cos^2 \frac{\pi x}{L} \, dx = \frac{L}{2}$$

Eqs. (2.6) and (2.7) become

$$\Delta U = \frac{A^2 EI\pi^4}{4L^3}$$

$$\Delta W = \frac{A^2 P\pi^2}{4L}$$

The principle of conservation of energy requires that $\Delta U = \Delta W$. Hence

$$\frac{A^2 EI\pi^4}{4L^3} = \frac{A^2 P\pi^2}{4L}$$

from which

$$P_{cr} = \frac{\pi^2 EI}{L^2}$$

In this case, the exact value of the critical load was obtained because the exact deflection curve was used in the energy expressions. However, the energy method is usually employed when the solution to the differential equation, which is the deflection curve, is not known. In that case, a reasonably accurate shape is assumed and an approximation of the critical load is obtained.

From a mathematical point of view, assuming a deflection curve reduces the number of degrees of freedom in the system. Degrees of freedom are defined as the number of coordinates required to fix the position of the system. A continuous member, such as the column considered here, requires an infinite number of coordinates to fix the position of its deflected shape completely. However, if the deflected shape is assumed to be a sine curve, then a single coordinate, such as the amplitude at the center, suffices to locate the entire deflection curve. The assumption of a sine curve for the deflection, y, in the preceding problem thus reduced the system from one with an infinite number of degrees of freedom to one with a single degree of freedom, and the critical load was obtained by solving a single algebraic equation instead of a differential equation.

2.3 CALCULATION OF THE CRITICAL LOAD USING AN APPROXIMATE DEFLECTION CURVE

The energy method leads to good approximations of the critical load, provided the assumed shape is reasonably close to the actual deflection curve. Two characteristics of the deflection curve require special attention, if decent results are to be obtained. First, it is important that the assumed shape satisfy as many of the boundary conditions of the system as possible. If it is not possible to satisfy both the geometric boundary conditions (deflection and shape) and the natural boundary conditions (shear and bending moment), then at least the geometric boundary conditions should be satisfied. Second, it is necessary to choose a shape that is at least reasonably accurate. For example, almost any single half-wave can be used to approximate the deflected shape of a hinged-hinged column with reasonable accuracy. However, any two-wave curve would lead to a completely erroneous solution. In simple problems such as the buckling of a column, the general shape of the deflection is fairly obvious, and there is consequently little likelihood of assuming a completely unsatisfactory function. However, in more complicated problems, such as the buckling of plates and shells, there exists a great deal of uncertainty about the shape of the buckling mode, and a great deal of discretion must therefore be excercised in choosing a deflection function.

In general, trigonometric functions and polynomials, because they are easy to integrate, are the most convenient functions for approximating deflection curves.

As an illustration, the critical load of the hinged-hinged column, obtained in Article 2.2 by using the exact deflection curve, will now be obtained using an approximate deflection curve. The deflection curve is assumed to be given by the polynomial

$$y = a + bx + cx^2$$

The first and second derivatives of this function are

$$y' = b + 2cx$$

and

$$y'' = 2c$$

The boundary condition $y = 0$ at $x = 0$ is satisfied if

$$a = 0$$

and the condition $y = 0$ at $x = l$ leads to

$$b = -cl$$

Hence

$$y = c(x^2 - xl) \tag{2.8}$$

Equation (2.8) satisfies the conditions of slope and deflection at each end of the member. However, it assumes a constant curvature and therefore does not satisfy the conditions of zero moment at each support. Substitution of Eq. (2.8) into the expressions for external work and strain energy given by Eqs. (2.4) and (2.5) leads to

$$\Delta W = \frac{Pc^2 l^3}{6} \tag{2.9}$$

and

$$\Delta U = 2EIc^2 l \tag{2.10}$$

Equating these expressions, one obtains

$$P_{cr} = \frac{12EI}{l^2}$$

Comparison of the exact answer, $9.87EI/l^2$, with this solution indicates that the latter is in error by about 21 %.

The foregoing solution was obtained using the expression

$$\Delta U = \int_0^l \frac{EI}{2} (y'')^2 \, dx \tag{2.11}$$

Alternatively, it is possible to express the change in strain energy by

$$\Delta U = \int_0^l \frac{M^2}{2EI} \, dx = \int_0^l \frac{(Py)^2 \, dx}{2EI} \tag{2.12}$$

Substitution of the assumed deflection given by Eq. (2.8) into Eq. (2.12) leads to

$$\Delta U = \frac{P^2 l^5 c^2}{60EI}$$

Equating this expression for the strain energy to the external work given by Eq. (2.9), one obtains

$$P_{cr} = \frac{10EI}{l^2}$$

In this case, the approximate solution is in error by only 1.3%.

The different results obtained using Eqs. (2.11) and (2.12) have led Timoshenko and Gere (Ref. 1.2) to reach the following conclusion. If the true deflection curve is used, both Eqs. (2.11) and (2.12) lead to the same answer, because both y and y'' are exact. However, if an approximate expression is used for the deflection curve, the error in y'' is considerably larger than the error in y. The expression for ΔU based on y therefore gives more accurate results than the expression based on y''.

As a rule, the energy method leads to values of the critical load that are higher than the exact solution. For the hinged-hinged column to be in equilibrium in a bent position without any external restraints except the axial loads, the deformed shape must be a sine curve. Equilibrium in any other configuration compatible with the boundary conditions can be maintained only by the addition of restraints to the member. These restraints will cause the system to be stiffer than the original one, and they will consequently cause it to have a higher buckling load than the actual system.

2.4 PRINCIPLE OF STATIONARY POTENTIAL ENERGY

In Articles 2.2 and 2.3 the principle of conservation of energy was used to obtain the critical load of a column. In this article, a somewhat different and more powerful energy criterion known as the principle of stationary potential energy will be considered. The development of the stationary energy theorem presented here follows the general outline of the derivation given by Hoff (Ref. 1.3). Since only the barest essentials of the derivation are presented here, the reader may wish to consult Ref. 1.3 for a more in-depth treatment of the subject.

Principle of Virtual Displacements

Consider a small particle, of mass Q, acted on by a set of n forces F_i, as shown in Fig. 2-3. Then imagine that the particle undergoes a small arbitrary displacement δr. The displacement has nothing whatsoever to do with any actual motion that may occur as a result of the forces acting on the particle. It is a fictitious displacement that is only imagined to take place. It is also assumed that neither the direction nor the magnitude of the forces acting on

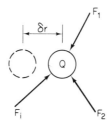

Fig. 2-3 Virtual displacement of
mass particle.

the particle will change during the displacement. This type of displacement is
called a *virtual displacement*.

During the virtual displacement, each of the forces acting on the particle
will do an amount of work equal to the product of the displacement and the
component of the force in the direction of the displacement. This work is
called *virtual work*. Letting the component of any force F_i in the direction of
the virtual displacement be given by F_{ir}, the total virtual work, δW, due to all
the forces acting on the particle is equal to

$$\delta W = F_{1r}\,\delta r + F_{2r}\,\delta r + \cdots + F_{nr}\,\delta r$$

or
$$\delta W = \left(\sum_{i=1}^{n} F_{ir}\right)\delta r \tag{2.13}$$

If the particle is in equilibrium, the resultant of all the forces acting on the
particle must vanish. The quantity $\sum F_{ir}$, which is the component of the
resultant in the direction of δr, must therefore be equal to zero. This leads to
the conclusion that the virtual work must be equal to zero for a particle in
equilibrium. Since a particle not in equilibrium can have a zero resultant in
one direction but not in every direction, equilibrium is rigorously established
only if $\delta W = 0$ for any and every virtual displacement. The principle of
virtual displacements embodied in the foregoing conclusions can be stated in
the following form:

> A particle of mass is in equilibrium if the total virtual work
> done by all the forces acting on the particle is equal to zero for
> any arbitrary virtual displacement.

Having established the principle of virtual displacements for a single mass
particle, we shall now consider the extension of the principle to an elastic
body of finite dimensions. As shown by Hoff (Ref. 1.3), one can do this by
using a model to represent the elastic body. The model shown in Fig. 2-4a
consists of several mass particles connected to one another by a series of
massless springs. If this system is in equilibrium under a set of external forces,
each particle is also in equilibrium under its own set of forces. The forces
acting on each particle may include forces that are external to the entire

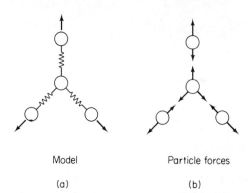

Model   Particle forces

(a)   (b)

Fig. 2-4 Spring–mass model of elastic body (Adapted from Ref. 1.5).

system and spring forces, which are internal forces when the body as a whole is considered (Fig. 2-4b).

The principle of virtual displacements for a mass particle can be applied to any one of these particles. Since the particle is in equilibrium, the virtual work due to the forces acting on the particle must vanish for any virtual displacement applied to the whole system. Thus the virtual work due to all the forces acting on all the particles is also equal to zero. It is desirable to consider this total virtual work to consist of two parts, one due to the external forces applied to the body as a whole, and the other due to the internal spring forces that act on the individual particles.

The principle of virtual displacements may now be restated, for elastic bodies of finite dimensions, as follows:

> An elastic body of finite size is in equilibrium if the virtual work done by the external forces plus the virtual work done by the internal forces is equal to zero for any arbitrary virtual displacement.

This can be expressed analytically by

$$\delta W_i + \delta W_e = 0 \qquad (2.14)$$

in which δW_i and δW_e are the increments of internal and external virtual work that result from a virtual displacement.

Principle of Stationary Potential Energy

We are now ready to develop the principle of stationary potential energy. For a structure subjected to a set of n loads, P_i, and a virtual displacement, δr, the external virtual work, δW_e, is given by

$$\delta W_e = \sum_{i=1}^{n} P_{ir}\, \delta r \qquad (2.15)$$

in which P_{ir} is the component of any force P_i in the direction of the virtual displacement. The internal virtual work could be determined by means of a similar equation if it were possible to isolate all the internal forces. However, for most structures this cannot be readily done, and one must therefore find an alternative way of calculating the internal work.

Let us apply to the spring–mass system in Fig. 2-5 a virtual displacement

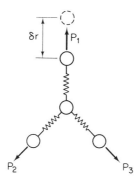

Fig. 2-5 Virtual displacement of particle in spring–mass model.

consisting of a vertical motion δr of the uppermost of the four particles, as indicated. The only internal force that moves as a result of this displacement is the one acting on the uppermost particle. Hence the internal virtual work for the system is equal to that force multiplied by its displacement. That is,

$$\delta W_i = -P_1 \delta_r \qquad (2.16)$$

The internal virtual work is negative, because the direction of P_1 is opposite to that of the displacement δ_r.

As a result of the virtual displacement, the strain energy in the spring attached to the uppermost particle changes by an amount δU, equal to

$$\delta U = P_1 \delta_r \qquad (2.17)$$

Comparison of this expression with the one in Eq. (2.16) indicates that

$$\delta W_i = -\delta U \qquad (2.18)$$

In other words, the internal virtual work δW_i is equal in magnitude and opposite in sign to the change in the strain energy δU. The total virtual work for an elastic body can thus be obtained by combining the external virtual work with the negative of the change in the strain energy, and Eq. (2.14) can be rewritten as

$$\delta W_e + \delta W_i = \sum_i P_{ir} \, \delta r - \delta U = 0 \qquad (2.19)$$

It is customary in theoretical mechanics to refer to the increment of external work δW_e due to a virtual displacement as a change in potential energy and to let $-\delta V$ represent this quantity. Thus

$$\delta V = -\sum_i P_{ir}\, \delta r \tag{2.20}$$

Accordingly, Eq. (2.19) can be written in the form

$$\delta U + \delta V = 0$$

or

$$\delta(U + V) = 0 \tag{2.21}$$

The quantity $U + V$ consisting of the strain energy and the potential energy of the external loads is referred to as the total potential energy of the system, and the symbol δ denotes the change in this quantity caused by a virtual displacement.

The principle expressed by Eq. (2.21) is known as the theorem of stationary potential energy. It can be stated in the following terms:

> An elastic structure is in equilibrium if no change occurs in the total potential energy of the system when its displacement is changed by a small arbitrary amount.

If the system has an infinite number of degrees of freedom, equilibrium is definitely established only when it has been shown that the total potential energy does not change for any of the infinitely many possible changes in the displacement of the system. As will be shown later, to do this requires the use of the calculus of variations. However, if the system has only a single degree of freedom, equilibrium is established simply by requiring that no change occur in one displacement parameter, and this can be accomplished using ordinary differential calculus. The significance of the principle of stationary potential energy is thus easiest to grasp if one considers a one-degree-of-freedom system. For such a system, if the single degree of freedom is represented by the coordinate x, the total potential energy will be a function of x, and its variation will be given by

$$\delta(U + V) = \frac{d(U + V)}{dx}\, \delta x$$

Since δx is arbitrary, the variation of the total potential energy can be made equal to zero only if

$$\frac{d(U + V)}{dx} = 0 \tag{2.22}$$

Equation (2.22) signifies that a curve of $U + V$ plotted against x will have a horizontal tangent at the value of x that corresponds to equilibrium. In other words, equilibrium corresponds to either a minimum or a maximum of the total potential energy of the system. Since an equilibrium position is stable if energy must be added to the system to deform it, and unstable if energy is released when it deforms, stable equilibrium corresponds to a minimum of the total potential energy and unstable equilibrium to a maximum. The character of the equilibrium state can be determined analytically from the sign of the second variation of the total potential energy. A positive sign indicates stable equilibrium, whereas a negative sign indicates unstable equilibrium.

A graphical illustration of these concepts can be obtained by considering the surface in Fig. 1-2. Assuming that the surface represents the total potential energy of a one-degree-of-freedom system, the deflection configurations corresponding to line ABC, along which the surface has horizontal tangents, are equilibrium configurations. Of these, those between A and B, where the stationary points are minimum points, are stable, and those between B and C, where the stationary points are maximum points, are unstable.

To illustrate the preceding principles somewhat further, let us consider the one-degree-of-freedom spring–mass system shown in Fig. 2-6a. If the

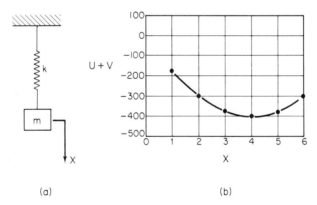

(a)   (b)

Fig. 2-6 Potential energy of one-degree-of-freedom system.

weight of the mass is 200 lb and if the stiffness of the spring is 50 lb/in., the system will come to rest with the spring stretched 4 in. Letting the elongation of the spring be given by x, the strain energy stored in the spring is

$$U = 25x^2$$

and the potential energy of the external loads, as defined by Eq. (2.20), is

$$V = -200x$$

Hence the total potential energy of the system is

$$U + V = 25x^2 - 200x$$

A plot of $U + V$ versus x, shown in Fig. 2-6b, indicates that the total potential energy has a horizontal tangent when $x = 4$. At the equilibrium configuration $x = 4$, the total potential energy of the system is thus shown to have a stationary value. In this instance the stationary value corresponds to a minimum point, signifying that the equilibrium configuration $x = 4$ is a stable one.

Evaluation of the Critical Load

In the preceding pages we have formed two conclusions: equilibrium is established if the first variation of the total potential energy vanishes, and the sign of the second variation determines whether the equilibrium is stable or not. It is possible to calculate the critical load of a system using either of these two results. Since the critical load is the load at which a system in equilibrium passes from stable to unstable equilibrium, the critical load can be determined by finding the load at which the second variation of the total potential energy of the system changes from positive to negative, that is, the load for which $\delta^2(U + V) = 0$. A second approach for finding the critical load is to determine the load at which neutral equilibrium is possible, that is, the load at which equilibrium in a deformed configuration is possible. In this case one need not check the stability of the system. Instead, one has only to establish the equilibrium of a deformed configuration, and this can be accomplished by requiring that $\delta(U + V) = 0$ for the deformed configuration. Since the latter approach replaces the somewhat complicated problem of investigating the stability of a system with the simpler problem of establishing equilibrium, it will be used in this book whenever we are looking for a critical load. The former approach must, however, be followed whenever it is necessary to establish the stability of a deformed configuration.

2.5 CALCULUS OF VARIATIONS

The calculus of variations is a generalization of the maximum or minimum problem of ordinary calculus. It seeks to determine a function $y = y(x)$ that extremizes (i.e., maximizes or minimizes) a definite integral

$$I = \int_{x_1}^{x_2} F(x, y, y', \dots, y^{(n)}) \, dx \tag{2.23}$$

whose integrant contains y and its derivatives. In structural mechanics this amounts to finding the deformed shape of a system that will cause the total potential energy of the system to have a stationary value. The deformation that satisfies this criterion corresponds to the equilibrium state of the system.

Although the calculus of variations is similar to the maximum–minimum problem of ordinary calculus, it does differ from the latter in one important aspect. In ordinary calculus one obtains the actual value of a variable for which a given function has an extremum point. However, in the calculus of variations one does not obtain the function that extremizes a given integral. Instead, one only obtains the differential equation that the function must satisfy. Thus the calculus of variations is not a computational tool for solving a problem. It is only a device for obtaining the governing equations of the problem.

As an illustration of the use of the calculus of variations, let us determine the conditions that must be satisfied by a perfect column if it is to be in equilibrium in a slightly deformed position. Consider the hinged-hinged column shown in Fig. 2-7. The strain energy of bending for the member is

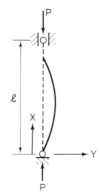

Fig. 2-7 Hinged-hinged column.

$$U = \int_0^l \frac{EI}{2}(y'')^2 \, dx \qquad (2.24)$$

According to Eq. (2.20), the potential energy of the external loads consists of the negative product of the axial load and the vertical distance that the load moves as the member bends. Hence

$$V = -\int_0^l \frac{P}{2}(y')^2 \, dx \qquad (2.25)$$

Combining U and V, one obtains for the total potential energy of the system

$$U + V = \int_0^l \left[\frac{EI}{2}(y'')^2 - \frac{P}{2}(y')^2 \right] dx \qquad (2.26)$$

It is now assumed that a deformed shape $y = y(x)$ exists for which the total potential energy of the system has a stationary value, that is, a function y for which $\delta(U + V) = 0$. This function $y(x)$ must be continuous, and it must satisfy the boundary conditions $y(0) = y(l) = 0$. To determine $y(x)$, it is necessary to form a family of nearby functions $\bar{y}(x)$ with which $y(x)$ can be compared. This family of curves is obtained by choosing an arbitrary function $\eta = \eta(x)$ and adding $\eta(x)$ multiplied by a small parameter ϵ to $y(x)$. Thus

$$\bar{y}(x) = y(x) + \epsilon\eta(x) \tag{2.27}$$

For any given function $\eta(x)$, each different value of ϵ represents a single member of the family of curves given by Eq. (2.27). In order that each of the comparison curves satisfies the boundary conditions, $\bar{y}(0) = \bar{y}(l) = 0$, the function $\eta(x)$ must vanish at the supports. Thus

$$\eta(0) = \eta(l) = 0 \tag{2.28}$$

A graphical representation of $\bar{y}(x)$ is given in Fig. 2-8.

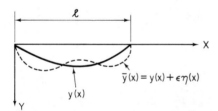

Fig. 2-8 Comparison of $y(x)$ with nearby function $\bar{y}(x)$.

It is now desirable to express the potential energy of the system in terms of the generalized displacement $\bar{y}(x)$. Replacing $y(x)$ with $\bar{y}(x)$ in Eq. (2.26) leads to

$$U + V = \int_0^l \left[\frac{EI}{2}(y'' + \epsilon\eta'')^2 - \frac{P}{2}(y' + \epsilon\eta')^2 \right] dx \tag{2.29}$$

For a given $\eta(x)$, the potential energy is a function of the parameter ϵ. Furthermore, for $\epsilon = 0$, $\bar{y}(x)$ becomes $y(x)$, which is the member of the family of curves that extremizes $U + V$. Accordingly, the potential energy has an extremum value with respect to ϵ, when $\epsilon = 0$. That is,

$$\left| \frac{d(U + V)}{d\epsilon} \right|_{\epsilon=0} = 0 \tag{2.30}$$

A problem of variational calculus has thus been reduced to an ordinary minimum problem of differential calculus.

Differentiation of Eq. (2.29) under the integral sign leads to

$$\frac{d(U + V)}{d\epsilon} = \int_0^l [EI(y'' + \epsilon\eta'')\eta'' - P(y' + \epsilon\eta')\eta'] \, dx$$

This expression must vanish for $\epsilon = 0$. Hence

$$\int_0^l (EIy''\eta'' - Py'\eta') \, dx = 0 \qquad (2.31)$$

Before continuing, it is worthwhile to consider a derivation of Eq. (2.31) introduced by Hoff (Ref. 1.3), which differs somewhat from the preceding analysis. Equation (2.26) gives the total potential energy as a function of the displacement $y(x)$. If $y(x)$ is increased by a small amount $\Delta y(x)$, where

$$\Delta y(x) = \epsilon\eta(x)$$

the total displacement becomes

$$y(x) + \Delta y(x) = y(x) + \epsilon\eta(x)$$

and the corresponding potential energy is

$$(U + V) + \Delta(U + V) = \int_0^l \left[\frac{EI}{2}(y'' + \epsilon\eta'')^2 - \frac{P}{2}(y' + \epsilon\eta')^2 \right] dx \qquad (2.32)$$

The change in the potential energy due to the increase in deflection Δy can be obtained by subtracting the expression given in (2.26) from the energy given in (2.32). Thus

$$\Delta(U + V) = \int_0^l \left[EI\left(\epsilon\eta''y'' + \frac{\epsilon^2\eta''^2}{2}\right) - P\left(\epsilon\eta'y' + \frac{\epsilon^2\eta'^2}{2}\right) \right] dx \qquad (2.33)$$

If the change in y had been a virtual displacement, instead of a real displacement, the terms containing the square of $\epsilon\eta(x)$ or the square of its derivatives would not be present in Eq. (2.33). These higher-order terms are caused by changes in the forces that accompany an actual displacement. They are absent for a virtual displacement, during which the forces are assumed to remain constant. Hence the variation in the potential energy corresponding to a virtual displacement δy can be obtained from Eq. (2.33) by dropping the higher-order terms; that is,

$$\delta(U + V) = \epsilon \int_0^l [EI(\eta''y'') - P(\eta'y')] \, dx$$

Finally, the requirement that this expression vanish when the system is in equilibrium leads to

$$\int_0^l (EI\eta''y'' - P\eta'y') \, dx = 0$$

which is identical to Eq. (2.31).

To simplify Eq. (2.31), the derivatives of $\eta(x)$ inside the integral sign must be eliminated through integration by parts. The second term on the right-hand side of Eq. (2.31) is considered first. Making the substitutions

$$u = y', \qquad dv = \eta' \, dx$$

and integrating by parts according to

$$\int_0^l u \, dv = uv \Big|_0^l - \int_0^l v \, du$$

one obtains

$$\int_0^l y'\eta' \, dx = y'\eta \Big|_0^l - \int_0^l \eta y'' \, dx \tag{2.34}$$

In view of Eq. (2.28), η vanishes at the supports, and Eq. (2.34) reduces to

$$\int_0^l y'\eta' \, dx = -\int_0^l \eta y'' \, dx \tag{2.35}$$

In a similar manner, the first term on the right-hand side of Eq. (2.31) can be reduced by two integrations by parts. Making the substitution

$$u = y'', \qquad dv = \eta'' \, dx$$

and integrating by parts, one obtains

$$\int_0^l y''\eta'' \, dx = y''\eta' \Big|_0^l - \int_0^l \eta' y''' \, dx$$

This expression is further reduced by making the substitutions

$$u = y''', \qquad dv = \eta' \, dx$$

in the second term on the right-hand side. This leads to

$$\int_0^l y'''\eta' \, dx = y'''\eta \Big|_0^l - \int_0^l y^{IV}\eta \, dx$$

from which

$$\int_0^l y'''\eta' \, dx = -\int_0^l y^{IV}\eta \, dx$$

Thus
$$\int_0^l y''\eta'' \, dx = y''\eta'\Big|_0^l + \int_0^l y^{IV}\eta \, dx \qquad (2.36)$$

Substitution of the results obtained in Eqs. (2.35) and (2.36) into Eq. (2.31) leads to

$$\int_0^l (EIy^{IV} + Py'')\eta \, dx + (EIy''\eta')_0^l = 0 \qquad (2.37)$$

Except for the conditions $\eta(0) = \eta(L) = 0$, the function $\eta(x)$ is completely arbitrary. It can therefore be shown that Eq. (2.37) is satisfied only if each of its two parts is equal to zero; that is,

$$\int_0^l (EIy^{IV} + Py'')\eta \, dx = 0$$

$$[EIy''\eta']_0^l = 0$$

Since $\eta'(0)$, $\eta'(L)$, and $\eta(x)$ are not zero, and since $\eta'(0)$ is independent of $\eta'(L)$, it follows that $y(x)$ must satisfy the relations

$$EIy^{IV} + Py'' = 0 \qquad (2.38)$$
$$EIy''\big|_{x=0} = 0 \qquad (2.39)$$
$$EIy''\big|_{x=l} = 0 \qquad (2.40)$$

These three relations must be satisfied in order that the potential energy have a stationary value and in order that $y(x)$ be the equilibrium configuration of the slightly deformed column. Equation (2.38) is of course the Eulerian differential equation of an axially loaded member, obtained previously by considering the moment equilibrium of an element of the deformed member.

Equations (2.39) and (2.40), which indicate that the bending moment must vanish at the ends of the member, are known as natural boundary conditions. The other two boundary conditions, $y(0) = 0$ and $y(L) = 0$, which were stipulated at the outset, are called geometric boundary conditions. In general, the conditions of slope and deflection at the ends of the member are the geometric boundary conditions. These must be specified at the beginning of the problem. The conditions of moment and shear at the ends of the member are the natural boundary conditions, and these together with the differential equations are obtained by minimizing the potential energy.

The differential equation of a continuous system can be obtained either by considering the equilibrium of a deformed element of the system or by using the principle of stationary potential energy and the calculus of variations. For an axially loaded member there is no doubt that the equation can be established more easily by the former of these two methods. However, when considering more complex systems, such as cylindrical and spherical shells, it is often simpler to obtain the differential equations by extremizing the potential energy rather than by writing equations of equilibrium of forces and moments.

2.6 RAYLEIGH–RITZ METHOD

The rigorous application of the stationary energy theorem to continuous systems requires the use of the calculus of variations. This approach to the problem of finding the equilibrium configuration of a structure has two disadvantages. First, the variational calculus that must be used is far too complex for routine problem solving, and, second, only the differential equation and not its solution is obtained. Fortunately, there exists a method by which the principle of stationary potential energy can be applied approximately; known as the Rayleigh–Ritz method, having neither of the two aforementioned disadvantages. In this method, one assumes a suitable shape for the deformation of the system and thus reduces it from an infinite-degree-of-freedom system to a finite-degree-of-freedom system. The principle of stationary potential energy then leads directly to the equilibrium configuration, and only ordinary differential calculus has to be used in the process.

As an example, the critical load of a column fixed at one end and free at the other (Fig. 2-9) will be obtained. According to the concept of neutral

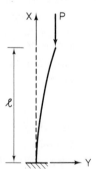

Fig. 2-9 Fixed-free column.

equilibrium, the critical load is the load at which a system can be in equilibrium in a slightly bent position. The problem of finding the critical load is thus equivalent to finding the deflected shape in which equilibrium is possible, and this latter problem can be solved by requiring the first variation of the total potential energy to vanish.

The deflection curve of the member is assumed to be given by the polynomial

$$y = a + bx + cx^2$$

Two of the constants in this expression can be evaluated from the boundary conditions at the base of the member. The condition

$$y = 0 \quad \text{at } x = 0$$

is satisfied if $a = 0$, and from the requirement that

$$y' = 0 \quad \text{at } x = 0$$

one obtains $b = 0$. Thus

$$y = cx^2$$

This relation satisfies the geometric boundary conditions of zero deflection and zero slope at the fixed end of the member, but not the natural boundary condition of zero moment at the free end.

The strain energy stored in the member due to bending is

$$U = \frac{EI}{2} \int_0^l (y'')^2 \, dx = \frac{EI}{2} \int_0^l 4C^2 \, dx = 2EIC^2l \tag{2.41}$$

According to Eq. (2.20), the potential energy of the external load consists of the negative product of the load and the distance that the load moves as the member bends. Thus

$$V = -\frac{P}{2} \int_0^l (y')^2 \, dx = -\frac{P}{2} \int_0^l 4C^2x^2 \, dx = -\frac{2}{3}PC^2l^3 \tag{2.42}$$

It is important to distinguish between the concept of work, as used in the principle of conservation of energy, and the concept of potential energy used here. The former refers to the total work performed during the entire deformation sequence. It is equal to the product of force and distance or one half that quantity, depending on whether the load remains constant or increases linearly from zero to its final value during the deformation process. By comparison, the potential energy is the energy of the full load. It is equal to the product of the total force and the distance, regardless of how the force varies during the interval in which the deformation takes place. The factor one half, sometimes present in the work term, therefore never appears in the potential energy terms.

Combining Eqs. (2.41) and (2.42), one obtains for the total potential energy

$$U + V = 2EIC^2l - \frac{2P}{3}C^2l^3 \tag{2.43}$$

The deflected shape of the system will be an equilibrium configuration if $U + V$ has a stationary value. For the continuous system considered in the previous section the total potential energy, as given by Eq. (2.26), was in terms of the function $y(x)$. To find the deflection $y(x)$ that corresponded to a stationary value of $U + V$, it was necessary to use variational calculus. As a consequence of having assumed a shape for the deflection of the column, in this problem, the total potential energy, as given by Eq. (2.43), is now a function of a single parameter C, and differential calculus suffices to find the value of C that extremizes $U + V$. Thus the expression

$$\delta(U + V) = 0$$

can be replaced by

$$\frac{d(U + V)}{dC} \delta C = 0$$

or simply by

$$\frac{d(U + V)}{dC} = 0 \tag{2.44}$$

since δC, the virtual displacement, is arbitrary.

Carrying out the differentiation indicated in Eq. (2.44), one obtains

$$4EICl - \tfrac{4}{3}PCl^3 = 0$$

from which

$$C\left(P - \frac{3EI}{l^2}\right) = 0 \tag{2.45}$$

Equation (2.45) gives the trivial solution of equilibrium at any load, provided the column remains straight, and the critical load

$$P_{cr} = \frac{3EI}{l^2} \tag{2.46}$$

Comparison of this solution with the exact buckling load $\pi^2 EI/4l^2$ indicates that the approximate answer is in error by about 21.6%.

The exact buckling load will be obtained if an infinite series is used for the assumed deflection. A better solution than that given by Eq. (2.46) should therefore result if the number of parameters in the assumed deflection function is increased from one to two. Letting

$$y = Cx^2 + Dx^3$$
$$y' = 2Cx + 3Dx^2$$
$$y'' = 2C + 6Dx$$

the strain energy due to bending is

$$U = \frac{EI}{2} \int_0^l (y'')^2 \, dx = \frac{EI}{2} \int_0^l (4C^2 + 24CDx + 36D^2x^2) \, dx \tag{2.47}$$
$$= 2EIl(C^2 + 3CDl + 3D^2l^2)$$

and the potential energy of the external load is

$$V = -\frac{P}{2} \int_0^l (y')^2 \, dx = -\frac{P}{2} \int_0^l (4C^2x^2 + 12CDx^3 + 9D^2x^4) \, dx \tag{2.48}$$
$$= -\frac{Pl^3}{30}(20C^2 + 45CDl + 27D^2l^2)$$

Adding Eqs. (2.47) and (2.48) gives

$$U + V = 2EIl(C^2 + 3DCl + 3D^2l^2) - \frac{Pl^3}{30}(20C^2 + 45CDl + 27D^2l^2) \tag{2.49}$$

The total potential energy given by (2.49) is a function of two variables C and D. The variation of $U + V$ therefore takes the form

$$\delta(U + V) = \frac{\partial(U + V)}{\partial C} \delta C + \frac{\partial(U + V)}{\partial D} \delta D \tag{2.50}$$

Since δC and δD are arbitrary, the expression in (2.50) will vanish if

$$\frac{\partial(U + V)}{\partial C} = 0, \qquad \frac{\partial(U + V)}{\partial D} = 0 \tag{2.51}$$

Carrying out these operations, one obtains

$$\frac{\partial(U + V)}{\partial C} = 2EIl(2C + 3Dl) - \frac{Pl^3}{30}(40C + 45Dl) = 0 \tag{2.52}$$

and $\quad \dfrac{\partial(U + V)}{\partial D} = 2EIl(3Cl + 6Dl^2) - \dfrac{Pl^3}{30}(45Cl + 54Dl^2) = 0 \tag{2.53}$

Introducing the notation

$$\alpha = \frac{Pl^2}{EI}$$

and rearranging terms, Eqs. (2.52) and (2.53) can be rewritten in the form

$$(24 - 8\alpha)C + l(36 - 9\alpha)D = 0$$
$$(20 - 5\alpha)C + l(40 - 6\alpha)D = 0$$

(2.54)

Because the right-hand side of each equation is zero, one refers to them as homogeneous equations. The solutions for C and D can be given as the quotients of two determinants. Thus

$$C = \frac{\begin{vmatrix} 0 & l(36 - 9\alpha) \\ 0 & l(40 - 6\alpha) \end{vmatrix}}{\begin{vmatrix} 24 - 8\alpha & l(36 - 9\alpha) \\ 20 - 5\alpha & l(40 - 6\alpha) \end{vmatrix}}$$

$$D = \frac{\begin{vmatrix} 24 - 8\alpha & 0 \\ 20 - 5\alpha & 0 \end{vmatrix}}{\begin{vmatrix} 24 - 8\alpha & l(36 - 9\alpha) \\ 20 - 5\alpha & l(40 - 6\alpha) \end{vmatrix}}$$

Since each of the numerator determinants is equal to zero, one obvious solution to Eq. (2.54) is $C = D = 0$. This is the trivial solution of equilibrium at all loads, provided the member remains straight. A nonzero value is possible for C and D only if the denominator determinant is also equal to zero. An eigenvalue problem for a finite-degree-of-freedom system, such as the buckling problem being considered, will always lead to a set of homogeneous equations. The nontrivial solutions of such a problem are therefore always obtained by setting the determinant of the governing equations equal to zero. For the case being studied, this means that

$$\begin{vmatrix} 24 - 8\alpha & l(36 - 9\alpha) \\ 20 - 5\alpha & l(40 - 6\alpha) \end{vmatrix} = 0$$

Expansion of the determinant leads to

$$3\alpha^2 - 104\alpha + 240 = 0$$

(2.55)

This equation is known as the characteristic equation. Its roots are the eigenvalues, that is, the loads at which nonzero deflections are possible. The nonzero deflections are called eigenvectors. The smallest eigenvalue is the critical load, and the corresponding eigenvector is the buckling mode shape. The smallest root of Eq. (2.55) is $\alpha = 2.49$, from which

$$P_{cr} = 2.49\frac{EI}{l^2}$$

This solution differs from the exact answer by slightly less than 1%. A marked increase in accuracy has thus been achieved by increasing the number of terms in the assumed deflection function. The rate at which the solution usually converges to the exact answer should not be expected to be as rapid as was the case here. In general, the more complicated the deflection shape is the more parameters are needed to obtain a very accurate result.

2.7 BUCKLING LOAD OF COLUMN WITH VARIABLE CROSS SECTION

The Rayleigh–Ritz method is especially useful when an exact solution of the differential equation is lengthy and complicated. A good example of such a case is the calculation of the critical load for a column with a variable cross section. The axially loaded member shown in Fig. 2-10 has a moment of

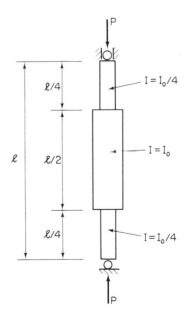

Fig. 2-10 Column with varying moment of inertia.

inertia, I_0, along the middle half of its length and a moment of inertia, $I_0/4$, along the end portions. The member is hinged at both ends, and it is therefore assumed that the buckled shape can be approximated by the relation

$$y = a \sin \frac{\pi x}{l}$$

This expression satisfies the geometric boundary conditions of zero deflection and nonzero slope at the ends of the member, and the natural boundary conditions of zero moment, that is, zero curvature, at the ends of the member.

Making use of symmetry, the strain energy of bending is

$$U = 2\left[\frac{EI_0}{8} \int_0^{l/4} (y'')^2 \, dx + \frac{EI_0}{2} \int_{1/4}^{l/2} (y'')^2 \, dx \right] \tag{2.56}$$

To evaluate this expression, the following integrals are needed:

$$\int_0^{l/4} (y'')^2 \, dx = \frac{a^2 \pi^4}{l^4} \int_0^{l/4} \sin^2 \frac{\pi x}{l} \, dx = \frac{0.045 a^2 \pi^4}{l^3}$$

$$\int_{1/4}^{l/2} (y'')^2 \, dx = \frac{a^2 \pi^4}{l^4} \int_{1/4}^{l/2} \sin^2 \frac{\pi x}{l} \, dx = \frac{0.205 a^2 \pi^4}{l^3}$$

Substitution of these relations in Eq. (2.56) leads to

$$U = 0.216 \frac{EI_0 a^2 \pi^4}{l^3} \tag{2.57}$$

The potential energy of the applied load is

$$V = -\frac{P}{2} \int_0^l (y')^2 \, dx = -\frac{Pa^2 \pi^2}{2l^2} \int_0^l \cos^2 \frac{\pi x}{l} \, dx = -\frac{Pa^2 \pi^2}{4l} \tag{2.58}$$

Combining Eqs. (2.57) and (2.58), one obtains for the total potential energy

$$U + V = 0.216 \frac{EI_0 a^2 \pi^4}{l^3} - \frac{Pa^2 \pi^2}{4l} \tag{2.59}$$

For the deflected shape to be an equilibrium configuration, it is necessary for the total potential energy to have a stationary value. Since the energy is a function of a, it will have a stationary value provided its derivative with respect to a vanishes. Thus

$$\frac{d(U + V)}{da} = 0.432 \frac{EI_0 a \pi^4}{l^3} - \frac{Pa \pi^2}{2l} = 0$$

from which

$$a\left(0.864\frac{EI_0\pi^2}{l^2} - P\right) = 0 \tag{2.60}$$

Equation (2.60) leads to the trivial solution of equilibrium at all loads provided $a = 0$, and the critical load

$$P_{cr} = \frac{0.864\pi^2 EI_0}{l^2}$$

The exact answer, obtained from the solution of the differential equation by Timoshenko and Gere (Ref. 1.2), is

$$P_{cr} = \frac{0.65\pi^2 EI_0}{l^2}$$

Comparison of the approximate solution with the exact buckling load indicates that the former is in error by about 33%.

The accuracy of the approximate solution can be improved by increasing the number of parameters in the assumed deflection function. The half-sine-wave used as a first approximation is the exact deflection curve for a column of uniform cross section. One would expect the deflection of a column that is stiffer at the center than near the supports to be similar to a half-sinewave, but somewhat flatter at the middle. Consequently, the deflection curve will be approximated by

$$y = a \sin\frac{\pi x}{l} + b \sin\frac{3\pi x}{l}$$

As before, the total potential energy is given by

$$U + V = 2\left[\frac{EI_0}{8}\int_0^{l/4} (y'')^2\, dx + \frac{EI_0}{2}\int_{l/4}^{l/2} (y'')^2\, dx\right] - \frac{P}{2}\int_0^l (y')^2\, dx \tag{2.61}$$

The derivatives of y and the squares of these quantities are

$$y' = \frac{a\pi}{l}\cos\frac{\pi x}{l} + \frac{3b\pi}{l}\cos\frac{3\pi x}{l}$$

$$(y')^2 = \frac{a^2\pi^2}{l^2}\cos^2\frac{\pi x}{l} + \frac{6ab\pi^2}{l^2}\cos\frac{\pi x}{l}\cos\frac{3\pi x}{l} + \frac{9b^2\pi^2}{l^2}\cos^2\frac{3\pi x}{l}$$

$$y'' = -\frac{a\pi^2}{l^2}\sin\frac{\pi x}{l} - \frac{9b\pi^2}{l^2}\sin\frac{3\pi x}{l}$$

$$(y'')^2 = \frac{a^2\pi^4}{l^4}\sin^2\frac{\pi x}{l} + \frac{18ab\pi^4}{l^4}\sin\frac{\pi x}{l}\sin\frac{3\pi x}{l} + \frac{81b^2\pi^4}{l^4}\sin^2\frac{3\pi x}{l}$$

The following definite integrals are needed for evaluating the total potential energy:

$$\int_0^{l/4} \sin^2 \frac{\pi x}{l} \, dx = 0.045l$$

$$\int_{1/4}^{l/2} \sin^2 \frac{\pi x}{l} \, dx = 0.205l$$

$$\int_0^{l/4} \sin^2 \frac{3\pi x}{l} \, dx = 0.152l$$

$$\int_{1/4}^{l/2} \sin^2 \frac{3\pi x}{l} \, dx = 0.098l$$

$$\int_0^{l/4} \sin \frac{\pi x}{l} \sin \frac{3\pi x}{l} \, dx = 0.080l \qquad (2.62)$$

$$\int_{1/4}^{l/2} \sin \frac{\pi x}{l} \sin \frac{3\pi x}{l} \, dx = -0.080l$$

$$\int_0^l \cos^2 \frac{\pi x}{l} \, dx = \frac{l}{2}$$

$$\int_0^l \cos^2 \frac{3\pi x}{l} \, dx = \frac{l}{2}$$

$$\int_0^l \cos \frac{\pi x}{l} \cos \frac{3\pi x}{l} \, dx = 0$$

Using these expressions, the total potential energy given by Eq. (2.61) can be reduced to the form

$$U + V = \frac{EI_0\pi^4}{l^3}(0.216a^2 - 1.080ab + 11.016b^2) - \frac{P\pi^2}{4l}(a^2 + 9b^2)$$

$$(2.63)$$

As before, the deflected shape is an equilibrium configuration if the total potential energy has a stationary value. In this case $U + V$ is a function of two variables, a and b. The partial derivatives of $U + V$ with respect to a and b must therefore vanish for the energy to have a stationary value. Thus

$$\frac{\partial(U + V)}{\partial a} = \frac{EI_0\pi^4}{l^3}(0.432a - 1.080b) - \frac{P\pi^2 a}{2l} = 0$$

$$\frac{\partial(U + V)}{\partial b} = \frac{EI_0\pi^4}{l^3}(-1.080a + 22.032b) - \frac{9P\pi^2 b}{2l} = 0$$

Introducing the notation $P_0 = \pi^2 EI_0/l^2$, these equations can be rewritten in the form

$$\left(0.432 - 0.50\frac{P}{P_0}\right)a - 1.080b = 0$$

$$-1.080a + \left(22.032 - 4.50\frac{P}{P_0}\right)b = 0 \tag{2.64}$$

Equations (2.64) are two linear homogeneous equations. As such, they possess a trivial solution

$$a = b = 0$$

and a nontrivial solution, which is obtained by setting their determinant equal to zero. Thus

$$\begin{vmatrix} 0.432 - 0.50\dfrac{P}{P_0} & -1.080 \\ -1.080 & 22.032 - 4.50\dfrac{P}{P_0} \end{vmatrix} = 0$$

Expansion of the determinant leads to the polynomial equation

$$2.25\left(\frac{P}{P_0}\right)^2 - 12.96\frac{P}{P_0} + 8.35 = 0$$

The smaller of the two solutions to this equation is

$$\frac{P}{P_0} = 0.735$$

from which

$$P_{cr} = \frac{0.735\pi^2 EI_0}{l^2}$$

Whereas the answer obtained using a single term in the approximate deflection curve was in error by 33%, this solution differs from the exact answer by only 13%.

2.8 GALERKIN'S METHOD

In the previous two articles, the Rayleigh–Ritz method was used to carry out approximate stability analyses. A similar technique for obtaining approximate solutions is the Galerkin method. The main difference between the two procedures is that the Galerkin method deals directly with the differential equation, whereas the Ritz method is concerned with the energy of the system.

The requirement that the total potential energy of a hinged-hinged column have a minimum value was shown, in Article 2.5, to lead to the condition

$$\int_0^l (EIy^{\text{IV}} + Py'')(\delta y)\, dx + [(EIy'')(\delta y')]_0^l = 0 \tag{2.65}$$

The first term in this expression consists of the left-hand side of the column differential equation multiplied by a small arbitrary change in the displacement function. The second term contains the natural boundary conditions for the member.

It is possible to approximate the deflection of the column by a series consisting of n independent functions $g_i(x)$ each multiplied by an undetermined coefficient a_i. Thus

$$\begin{aligned} y_{\text{approx}} &= a_1 g_1(x) + a_2 g_2(x) + \cdots + a_n g_n(x) \\ &= \sum_{i=1}^n a_i g_i(x) \end{aligned} \tag{2.66}$$

If each of the functions $g_i(x)$ satisfied both the geometric and natural boundary conditions, then the second term in Eq. (2.65) vanishes when y in that equation is replaced with y_{approx}. In order to make also the first term in Eq. (2.65) equal to zero, the coefficients a_i must be chosen in such a way that y_{approx} satisfies the differential equation.

Letting the operator, which produces the left-hand side of the column differential equation, when applied to y, be represented by Q, that is,

$$Q = EI\frac{d^4}{dx^4} + P\frac{d^2}{dx^2} \tag{2.67}$$

and letting the series used to approximate the column deflection be represented by ϕ, that is,

$$\phi = \sum_{i=1}^n a_i g_i(x) \tag{2.68}$$

the requirement that the first term in Eq. (2.65) vanish for y_{approx} can be expressed in the form

$$\int_0^l Q(\phi)\, \delta\phi\, dx = 0 \tag{2.69}$$

Since ϕ is a function of n parameters a_i, its variation is given by

$$\begin{aligned} \delta\phi &= \frac{\partial\phi}{\partial a_1}\delta a_1 + \frac{\partial\phi}{\partial a_2}\delta a_2 + \cdots + \frac{\partial\phi}{\partial a_n}\delta a_n \\ &= g_1(x)\,\delta a_1 + g_2(x)\,\delta a_2 + \cdots + g_n(x)\,\delta a_n \\ &= \sum_{i=1}^n g_i(x)\,\delta a_i \end{aligned} \tag{2.70}$$

Making use of this relationship, Eq. (2.69) can be rewritten as

$$\int_0^l Q(\phi) \sum_{i=1}^n g_i(x)\, \delta a_i\, dx = 0 \qquad (2.71)$$

It has been assumed that the n functions $g_i(x)$ used to approximate y are independent of each other. The only way that Eq. (2.71) can therefore be identically equal to zero is for each of the n terms in the equation to vanish individually. Thus

$$\int_0^l Q(\phi)g_i(x)\, \delta a_i\, dx - 0 \quad \text{for } i - 1, 2, \ldots, n$$

and in view of the fact that a_i is arbitrary

$$\int_0^l Q(\phi)g_i(x)\, dx = 0 \quad \text{for } i = 1, 2, \ldots, n \qquad (2.72)$$

The relationships given by Eq. (2.72) are referred to as Galerkin equations. For a given problem any assumed deflection function that satisfies the boundary conditions and the Galerkin equations will be an approximate solution of the problem. If there are n terms in the assumed deflection function, there will be n equations of the type given by (2.72). In an equilibrium problem these n equations can be solved for the n unknown coefficients in the assumed deflection function. In a linear buckling problem the n equations will be homogeneous, and the critical load is obtained by setting their determinant equal to zero.

To illustrate the use of the Galerkin method, the critical load of the hinged-fixed column, shown in Fig. 2-11, will be obtained. The first step is to choose a deflected shape that satisfies the boundary conditions. Such a function can usually be obtained by taking a power series and evaluating as many arbitrary constants as possible from the boundary conditions. This

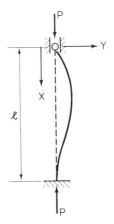

Fig. 2-11   Hinged-fixed column.

procedure was used in Article 2.6 to obtain a suitable deflected shape for a fixed-free column. However, in this instance an alternative approach will be tried. The deflection curve of a transversely loaded beam with boundary conditions similar to those of the column will be used. The deflection of a uniformly loaded beam hinged at $x = 0$ and fixed at $x = l$ is

$$y = A(xl^3 - 3lx^3 + 2x^4) \tag{2.73}$$

This function satisfies all the boundary conditions of the fixed-hinged column and will therefore be used to approximate its deflected shape.

The second step in the Galerkin method is to establish equilibrium by requiring that the assumed deflection function satisfy Eq. (2.72). If ϕ is given by the expression in (2.73), then $Q(\phi)$ is, in accordance with (2.67), equal to

$$Q(\phi) = A[48EI + P(24x^2 - 18lx)]$$

Furthermore, in view of (2.68),

$$g(x) = xl^3 - 3lx^3 + 2x^4$$

Substitution of these two expressions into Eq. (2.72) leads to

$$\int_0^l A[48EI(xl^3 - 3lx^3 + 2x^4) + P(24x^3l^3 - 72x^5l \tag{2.74}$$
$$+ 48x^6 - 18l^4x^2 + 54l^2x^4 - 36lx^5)] \, dx = 0$$

which, after one has carried out the indicated integration, reduces to

$$A\left(\frac{36EIl^5}{5} - \frac{12Pl^7}{35}\right) = 0$$

Hence one obtains for the critical load of the member

$$P_{cr} = \frac{21EI}{l^2}$$

For comparison, the exact buckling load of the hinged-fixed column is $20.2EI/l^2$.

2.9 METHOD OF FINITE DIFFERENCES

Introduction

The finite-difference method is a numerical technique for obtaining approximate solutions to differential equations (Ref. 2.2). In the method the differential equation is replaced by a set of equivalent algebraic equations that are usually easier to solve than the differential equation. The basis of the finite-difference technique is that a derivative of a function at a point can be approximated by an algebraic expression consisting of the value of the function at that point and at several nearby points. In view of this fact it is possible to replace the derivatives in a differential equation with algebraic expressions and thus transform the differential equation into an algebraic equation.

As a rule, differential equations describe the behavior of continuous systems, whereas algebraic equations describe the behavior of lumped-parameter systems. The replacement of a continuous function in a differential equation with an algebraic expression consisting of the value of that function at several discrete points is thus equivalent to replacing a continuous system with one consisting of a discrete number of mass points. The finite-difference method is therefore similar to the energy method in that both simplify the solution of the problem by reducing the number of degrees of freedom. The energy method does this by approximating the behavior of the system, that is, assuming a deflected shape, while the finite-difference technique simplifies the system itself.

In general, if a continuous system is replaced by n discrete mass points, the unknown function is replaced by n algebraic variables, and the differential equation is replaced by n simultaneous algebraic equations in these variables. Since the derivative of the unknown function at a point is approximated by an expression consisting of the value of the function at that point and at several neighboring points, the closer the points are to one another the better is the agreement between the derivative and its algebraic approximation, and the more accurate will be the solution to the problem. However, as the number of points increases so does the number of simultaneous equations that must be solved.

Due to the large amount of numerical work involved, the finite-difference method is particularly suited for use when a high-speed electronic computer is available.

The main disadvantage of the method is that it gives numerical values of the unknown function at discrete points instead of an analytical expression that is valid for the entire system. If an analytical expression is needed, it must be obtained by fitting a curve to the discrete values obtained in the solution. This shortcoming is more pronounced in equilibrium problems than in eigenvalue problems, because generally applicable relationships can usually be obtained for critical loads, whereas continuous expressions for deflection functions are never obtained. In spite of the aforementioned disadvantage, the finite-difference procedure, because of its wide range of applicability, is an extremely useful method of analysis.

Difference Ratios

The derivative of a function, at a point, can be expressed approximately in terms of the value of the function at that point and its value at one or more nearby points. Such an expression is known as a difference ratio. Consider

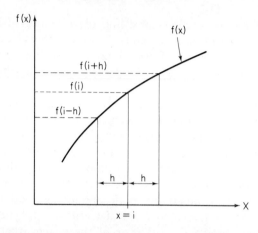

Fig. 2-12   Difference ratios.

the function, $f(x)$, plotted in Fig. 2-12, whose value is known at $x = i$ and at several evenly spaced points to the right and to the left of $x = i$. The first derivative of $f(x)$ at a point x can be approximated by

$$\frac{df}{dx} \simeq \frac{f(x + \Delta x) - f(x)}{\Delta x}$$

At $x = i$ this expression can be rewritten in the form

$$\left(\frac{df}{dx}\right)_{x=i} \cong \Delta f_i = \frac{f_{i+h} - f_i}{h} \tag{2.75}$$

in which f_i and f_{i+h} are the values of the function $f(x)$ at $x = i$, and at $x = i + h$, h is the distance between these two points, and Δf_i is the approximation of the derivative df/dx at $x = i$. It is obvious that the difference between the derivative and its approximation Δf will decrease as h decreases.

The approximation of the derivative df/dx given by Eq. (2.75) involves the function f at $x = i$ and at the point to the right of $x = i$. It is therefore known as the forward difference. A similar expression involving the function f at $x = i$ and at $x = i - h$ is

$$\Delta f_i = \frac{f_i - f_{i-h}}{h} \tag{2.76}$$

This form of the approximation is known as the backward difference. A third possible expression involving points on either side of $x = i$ is

$$\Delta f_i = \frac{f_{i+h} - f_{i-h}}{2h} \tag{2.77}$$

It is known as the central difference. Of the three approximations, the central difference is the most accurate for a given spacing h. The remaining discussion dealing with the approximation of higher derivatives will therefore be limited to central differences.

Once the first difference has been defined, the second difference can be obtained by taking the difference of the first difference. If Δ is defined as the difference operator that corresponds to the differential operator d/dx, then

$$\Delta^2 f_i = \Delta(\Delta f_i) = \frac{\Delta(f_{i+h/2} - f_{i-h/2})}{h} = \frac{\Delta f_{i+h/2} - \Delta f_{i-h/2}}{h}$$

$$= \frac{\dfrac{f_{i+h} - f_i}{h} - \dfrac{f_i - f_{i-h}}{h}}{h} \tag{2.78}$$

$$= \frac{f_{i+h} - 2f_i + f_{i-h}}{h^2}$$

Expression (2.78) gives the second central difference at the point $x = i$.

In a similar manner the third and fourth central differences can be derived:

$$\Delta^3 f_i = \Delta^2(\Delta f_i) = \frac{\Delta^2 f_{i+h} - \Delta^2 f_{i-h}}{2h}$$

$$= \frac{\dfrac{f_{i+2h} - 2f_{i+h} + f_i}{h^2} - \dfrac{f_i - 2f_{i-h} + f_{i-2h}}{h^2}}{2h} \tag{2.79}$$

$$= \frac{f_{i+2h} - 2f_{i+h} + 2f_{i-h} - f_{i-2h}}{2h^3}$$

$$\Delta^4 f_i = \Delta^2(\Delta^2 f_i) = \frac{\Delta^2 f_{i+h} - 2\Delta^2 f_i + \Delta^2 f_{i-h}}{h^2}$$

$$= \frac{\dfrac{f_{i+2h} - 2f_{i+h} + f_i}{h^2} - 2\left(\dfrac{f_{i+h} - 2f_i + f_{i-h}}{h^2}\right) + \dfrac{f_i - 2f_{i-h} + f_{i-2h}}{h^2}}{h^2}$$

$$= \frac{f_{i+2h} - 4f_{i+h} + 6f_i - 4f_{i-h} + f_{i-2h}}{h^4} \tag{2.80}$$

The "computational molecules" in Fig. 2-13 give a pictorial representation

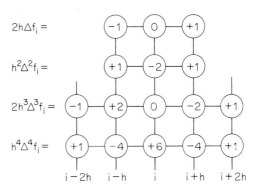

Fig. 2-13 Computational molecules for difference ratios.

of Eqs. (2.77), (2.78), (2.79), and (2.80). This very convenient way of representing difference ratios is due to Bickley (Ref. 2.3).

2.10 CALCULATION OF THE CRITICAL LOAD BY FINITE DIFFERENCES

In this article the finite-difference method will be used to determine the
critical load of the hinged-hinged column shown in Fig. 2-14a. The solution

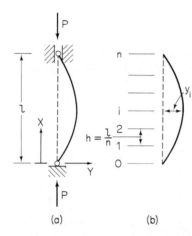

Fig. 2-14 Hinged-hinged column
subdivided into *n* equal segments.

(a)   (b)

follows the general outline of a similar analysis presented by Salvadori (Ref.
2.4). The differential equation and boundary conditions for a hinged-hinged
column are

$$y'' + \frac{P}{EI}y = 0 \tag{2.81}$$

and

$$y(0) = y(l) = 0 \tag{2.82}$$

To obtain the corresponding difference relations, the span of the member is
divided into *n* equal segments of length $h = l/n$ and the deflection at the end
of the *i*th segment is denoted by y_i (Fig. 2-14b). According to Eq. (2.78), the
second derivative at point *i* can be approximated by the difference ratio

$$\Delta^2 y_i = \frac{y_{i+h} - 2y_i + y_{i-h}}{h^2} \tag{2.83}$$

in which y_{i+1} and y_{i-1} are the deflections at points on either side of point *i*.
If (2.83) is substituted for the second derivative in Eq. (2.81), one obtains

$$y_{i+h} - 2y_i + y_{i-h} + \frac{Ph^2}{EI}y_i = 0 \tag{2.84}$$

the difference equation at point *i*.

The differential equation is an exact expression of the condition of equilibrium. By satisfying it, one establishes equilibrium everywhere along the member. By comparison, the difference equation expresses the equilibrium condition only approximately, and by satisfying it one attempts to establish equilibrium only at the point $x = i$.

First approximation n = 2

Let the member be divided into two equal parts of length $h = l/2$, and let the ends of these segments be denoted by $i = 0$, 1, and 2, as shown in Fig. 2-15. In this case, it is necessary to write the difference equation only at the

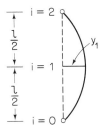

Fig. 2-15 Approximation with $n = 2$.

point $i = 1$. At the two boundary points, both deflection and curvature vanish and the equation is satisfied identically. Writing Eq. (2.84) at $i = 1$ gives

$$y_2 - 2y_1 + y_0 + \frac{Pl^2}{4EI}y_1 = 0 \qquad (2.85)$$

From the boundary conditions

$$y_0 = y_2 = 0$$

Thus
$$y_1\left(\frac{Pl^2}{4EI} - 2\right) = 0 \qquad (2.86)$$

As is typical in linear buckling problems, Eq. (2.86) leads to the trivial solution of equilibrium at any load, provided $y_1 = 0$, and to the critical load

$$P_{cr} = \frac{8EI}{l^2} \qquad (2.87)$$

Comparison of this result with the exact solution, $9.87EI/l^2$, shows the finite-difference approximation to be in error by about 19%. To obtain a more accurate solution, it is necessary to satisfy the difference equation at more than one interior point.

Second approximation n = 3

If the member is divided into three equal segments of length $h = l/3$, as shown in Fig. 2-16, there will be two interior points, $i = 1$ and 2, at which the

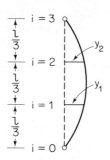

Fig. 2-16 Approximation with $n = 3$.

difference equation can be written. Writing Eq. (2.84) at $i = 1$ leads to

$$y_2 - 2y_1 + y_0 + \lambda y_1 = 0 \qquad (2.88)$$

and at $i = 2$ one obtains

$$y_3 - 2y_2 + y_1 + \lambda y_2 = 0 \qquad (2.89)$$

in which $\lambda = Pl^2/9EI$.

Making use of the boundary conditions and rearranging terms, Eqs. (2.88) and (2.89) can be rewritten in the form

$$(\lambda - 2)y_1 + y_2 = 0$$
$$y_1 + (\lambda - 2)y_2 = 0$$

These equations are linear and homogeneous. As such they have a trivial solution $y_1 = y_2 = 0$ and a nontrivial solution that is obtained by setting their determinant equal to zero. That is,

$$\begin{vmatrix} \lambda - 2 & 1 \\ 1 & \lambda - 2 \end{vmatrix} = 0 \qquad (2.90)$$

Expanding Eq. (2.90) leads to

$$\lambda^2 - 4\lambda + 3 = 0 \qquad (2.91)$$

a polynomial equation whose smallest root is the critical load. The roots of Eq. (2.91) are

$$\lambda_1 = 1, \qquad \lambda_2 = 3$$

from which

$$P_1 = \frac{9EI}{l^2}, \qquad P_2 = \frac{27EI}{l^2}$$

Hence the critical load is

$$P_{cr} = \frac{9EI}{l^2} \tag{2.92}$$

This solution differs from the Euler load by 9 %. The 19 % error that existed when the difference equation was satisfied at only one interior point has thus been reduced to 9 % by satisfying the difference equation at two interior points.

Third approximation n = 4

If the member is divided into four equal parts of length $h = l/4$, as shown in Fig. 2-17, there will be three interior points at which the difference equation

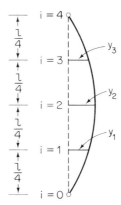

Fig. 2-17 Approximation with $n = 4$.

can be written. However, taking into account the fact that the buckling mode of a hinged-hinged column is symmetrical, that is, $y_1 = y_3$, the number of equations that must be written is reduced to two. At $i = 1$, Eq. (2.84) leads to

$$y_2 - 2y_1 + y_0 + \frac{Pl^2}{16EI} y_1 = 0 \tag{2.93}$$

and at $i = 2$ one obtains

$$y_3 - 2y_2 + y_1 + \frac{Pl^2}{16EI} y_2 = 0 \tag{2.94}$$

Making use of the boundary conditions and symmetry, these equations can be rewritten as

$$y_1(\lambda - 2) + y_2 = 0$$
$$y_1(2) + y_2(\lambda - 2) = 0 \tag{2.95}$$

where $\lambda = Pl^2/16EI$. Setting the determinant of Eqs. (2.95) equal to zero gives the quadratic equation

$$\lambda^2 - 4\lambda + 2 = 0 \tag{2.96}$$

whose smallest root is $\lambda = 0.59$. Hence

$$P_{cr} = 9.4\frac{EI}{l^2} \tag{2.97}$$

This answer differs from the Euler load by 5%.

By continuing to increase the degrees of freedom and satisfying the difference equation at more and more points, the accuracy of the solution can be improved to any desirable degree. However, this process entails the solution of a large number of simultaneous equations. As indicated by Salvadori (Ref. 2.4), a quicker and much simpler way of increasing the accuracy of the solution is afforded by Richardson's extrapolation scheme.

It can be shown that the error, e, of the approximate solution is roughly proportional to the square of the mesh size, h. Thus

$$e = Ch^2 \tag{2.98}$$

in which C is a constant. If n_1 and n_2 are the number of sections into which a member has been divided, and $h_1 = l/n_1$ and $h_2 = l/n_2$ are the corresponding mesh sizes, and if β_1 and β_2 are the approximations of the exact solution, β, obtained thus, then the corresponding errors are

$$e_1 = \beta - \beta_1 = C\frac{l^2}{n_1^2}$$

and

$$e_2 = \beta - \beta_2 = C\frac{l^2}{n_2^2}$$

Elimination of C between these relations leads to

$$\beta = \frac{n_1^2\beta_1 - n_2^2\beta_2}{n_1^2 - n_2^2} \tag{2.99}$$

Equation (2.99) gives the extrapolated value of the solution provided the approximations β_1 and β_2 are approaching the exact solution monotonically. It is usually possible to obtain a monotonic convergence by choosing a proper sequence of n's.

To illustrate the effectiveness of Richardson's extrapolation scheme, the approximate results obtained for the hinged-hinged column, letting $n = 3$

and 4, will be substituted into Eq. (2.99). Thus

$$\beta = \frac{9(9) - 16(9.4)}{9 - 16} = 9.85$$

from which

$$P_{cr} = 9.85\frac{EI}{l^2} \tag{2.100}$$

This solution differs from the Euler load by only 0.2 %.

Each of the approximate solutions together with the percentage of error between it and the exact answer are given in Table 2-1. These results indicate that a simple extrapolation has increased the accuracy of the solution considerably. A similar increase in accuracy could have been obtained without the extrapolation formula only by dividing the member into a very large number of intervals and by solving the resulting large number of simultaneous equations.

Table 2-1 Summary of finite-difference solutions for hinged-hinged column

Case	$\lambda = \dfrac{P_{cr}l^2}{EI}$	% Error
Approx. with		
$n = 2$	8	19
3	9	9
4	9.4	5
Extrapolation		
of $n = 3, 4$	9.85	0.2
Exact		
solution	9.87	0

2.11 HIGHER-ORDER DERIVATIVES

The solution by finite differences of an equation involving higher-order derivatives will now be considered. The column shown in Fig. 2-18a is built in at its lower end and simply supported at its upper end. Its behavior is governed by the differential equation

$$y^{IV} + \frac{P}{EI}y'' = 0 \tag{2.101}$$

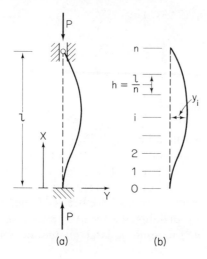

Fig. 2-18   Fixed-hinged column sub-divided into n equal segments.

(a)   (b)

and by the boundary conditions

$$y(0) = y'(0) = y(l) = y''(l) = 0 \qquad (2.102)$$

To obtain the finite-difference formulation of the problem, the member is divided into n equal segments of length $h = l/n$ (Fig. 2-18b). The difference equation at any point $x = i$ is obtained by substituting the central-difference ratios given by Eqs. (2.78) and (2.80) for the derivatives in Eq. (2.101). Thus

$$y_{i+2h} - 4y_{i+h} + 6y_i - 4y_{i-h} + y_{i-2h} + \frac{Ph^2}{EI}(y_{i+h} - 2y_i + y_{i-h}) = 0$$

$$(2.103)$$

First approximation n = 2

Let the member be divided into two equal parts of length $h = l/2$, as shown in Fig. 2-19, and let the ends of these segments be denoted by $i = 0$, 1, and 2. Two additional segments extending from $i = 0$ to $i = -1$ and from $i = 2$ to $i = 3$ are formed by prolonging the axis of the member a distance $l/2$ beyond each end (see figure). It is necessary to imagine the member to be extended in this manner because the fourth difference ratio of the deflection at $i = 1$ involves the deflection at points two intervals away from $i = 1$.

Writing Eq. (2.103) at $i = 1$ gives

$$y_3 \quad 4y_2 + 6y_1 - 4y_0 + y_{-1} + \frac{Pl^2}{4EI}(y_2 - 2y_1 + y_0) = 0 \qquad (2.104)$$

Since the deflections at the end of the member must vanish,

$$y_0 = y_2 = 0 \qquad (2.105)$$

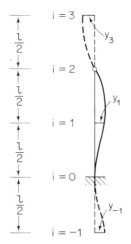

Fig. 2-19 Approximation with $n = 2$.

The condition of zero slope at $x = 0$ leads to

$$\frac{y_1 - y_{-1}}{l} = 0$$

from which

$$y_{-1} = y_1 \tag{2.106}$$

The fourth boundary condition of zero moment at $x = l$ requires that

$$\frac{y_3 - 2y_2 + y_1}{(l/2)^2} = 0$$

In view of the fact that $y_2 = 0$, this can be reduced to

$$y_3 = -y_1 \tag{2.107}$$

The results obtained and expressed by Eqs. (2.106) and (2.107) can be summarized as follows: If the end of a member is fixed, the deflection at a distance h outside the support can be assumed to be equal to the deflection at a distance h inside the support. For a hinged end the deflection at a distance h outside the support is approximated by the negative of the deflection at a distance h inside the support. In other words, the deflection function must be symmetric about a normal to the member at the support for a fixed end and antisymmetric about the same normal for a hinged end.

Substituting Eqs. (2.105), (2.106), and (2.107) into Eq. (2.104) and simplifying, one obtains

$$y_1\left(6 - \frac{Pl^2}{2EI}\right) = 0 \tag{2.108}$$

Equation (2.108) gives the trivial solution of equilibrium at any load, provided $y_1 = 0$, and the critical load

$$P_{cr} = \frac{12EI}{l^2} \tag{2.109}$$

This solution differs from the exact answer, $20.2EI/l^2$, by 41%.

Second approximation n = 3

Let the member be divided into three equal parts of length $h = l/3$, and let the axis of the member be extended beyond each support a distance $l/3$, as shown in Fig. 2-20. The ends of the segments thus formed are labeled from

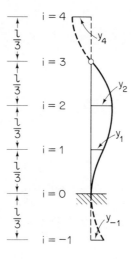

Fig. 2-20 Approximation with $n = 3$.

$i = -1$ to $i = 4$, inclusively. Writing Eq. (2.103) at $i = 1$ gives

$$y_3 - 4y_2 + 6y_1 - 4y_0 + y_{-1} + \frac{Pl^2}{9EI}(y_2 - 2y_1 + y_0) = 0 \tag{2.110}$$

and at $i = 2$ one obtains

$$y_4 - 4y_3 + 6y_2 - 4y_1 + y_0 + \frac{Pl^2}{9EI}(y_3 - 2y_2 + y_1) = 0 \tag{2.111}$$

With the aid of the boundary conditions given by Eqs. (2.105), (2.106), and (2.107), these equations reduce to

$$y_1(7 - 2\lambda) + y_2(\lambda - 4) = 0$$
$$y_1(\lambda - 4) + y_2(5 - 2\lambda) = 0 \tag{2.112}$$

To obtain the nontrivial solution of Eqs. (2.112), their determinant is set equal to zero. This leads to the quadratic equation

$$3\lambda^2 - 16\lambda + 19 = 0 \tag{2.113}$$

whose smallest root is $\lambda = 1.78$. Hence

$$P_{cr} = \frac{16.1EI}{l^2} \tag{2.114}$$

This answer differs from the exact solution of $20.2EI/l^2$ by 20%.

   To improve the accuracy of the solution further, Richardson's extrapolation formula can now be applied. Substituting the results given by (2.109) and (2.114) for $n = 2$ and $n = 3$ into Eq. (2.99), one obtains

$$\beta = \frac{4(12) - 9(16.1)}{4 - 9} = 19.4$$

and $$P_{cr} = 19.4\frac{EI}{l^2} \tag{2.115}$$

Compared to the approximate solution for $n = 3$, which is in error by 20%, the extrapolated solution differs from the exact answer by only 4%.

2.12 UNEVENLY SPACED PIVOTAL POINTS

In some problems it is convenient to divide the member into segments of unequal length. This makes it necessary to have expressions for the derivatives of a function in terms of the value of the function at unevenly spaced intervals. For the function $f(x)$, given by the curve in Fig. 2-21, the first

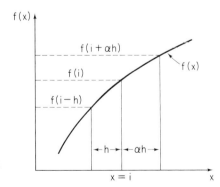

Fig. 2-21 Unevenly spaced pivotal points.

central difference, at the point $x = i$, is

$$\Delta f_i = \frac{f(i + \alpha h) - f(i - h)}{h(\alpha + 1)} \tag{2.116}$$

in which $f(i + \alpha h)$ and $f(i - h)$ are the values of $f(x)$ at $x = i + \alpha h$ and $x = i - h$, respectively. The second central difference, obtained by taking the difference of the first difference, is

$$\Delta^2 f_i = \Delta(\Delta f_i) = \Delta\left(\frac{f_{i+\alpha h/2} - f_{i-h/2}}{\frac{1}{2}h(\alpha + 1)}\right)$$

$$= \frac{\Delta f_{i+\alpha h/2} - \Delta f_{i-h/2}}{\frac{1}{2}h(\alpha + 1)}$$

$$= \frac{\left(\dfrac{f_{i+\alpha h} - f_i}{\alpha h}\right) - \left(\dfrac{f_i - f_{i-h}}{h}\right)}{\frac{1}{2}h(\alpha + 1)} \tag{2.117}$$

$$= \frac{2[f_{i+\alpha h} - f_i(1 + \alpha) + \alpha f_{i-h}]}{h^2 \alpha(\alpha + 1)}$$

To illustrate the use of unevenly spaced pivotal points, the critical load of the stepped column in Fig. 2-22a will be determined.* The column is

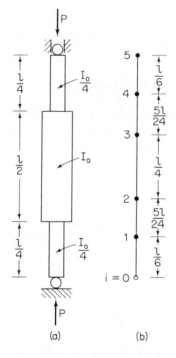

(a)   (b)

Fig. 2-22 Column with varying moment of inertia subdivided into segments of unequal length.

hinged at both ends and has a moment of inertia equal to I_0 for the central half of the span and to $I_0/4$ for the remaining parts of the member. Let the

*The solution of a similar problem can be found in Ref. 2.2.

member be subdivided into five parts, as shown in Fig. 2-22b. The ends of the segments thus formed, called *pivotal points*, are denoted by $i = 0, 1, 2, 3, 4,$ and 5. The consequence of subdividing the member in this manner is that each pivotal point is at the center of a length of column for which I is constant.

The differential equation and the boundary conditions for a hinged-hinged column are

$$y'' + \frac{P}{EI}y = 0 \tag{2.118}$$

and

$$y(0) = y(l) = 0 \tag{2.119}$$

Substitution of the difference ratio for the second derivative given by Eq. (2.117) into (2.118) leads to

$$\frac{2}{\alpha(\alpha + 1)}[f_{i+\alpha h} - f_i(1 + \alpha) + \alpha f_{i-h}] + \frac{Ph^2}{EI}y_i = 0 \tag{2.120}$$

the difference equation at the point $x = i$.

Due to the symmetric shape of the deflection curve, the difference equation need be written only at the points $i = 1$ and $i = 2$. At $i = 1$

$$h = \frac{l}{6}, \qquad \alpha = 1.25$$

and Eq. (2.120) becomes

$$\frac{2}{(1.25)(2.25)}(y_2 - 2.25y_1 + 1.25y_0) + \frac{Pl^2}{36EI_0/4}y_1 = 0 \tag{2.121}$$

At $i = 2$

$$h = \frac{5l}{24}, \qquad \alpha = 1.2$$

and the difference equation is

$$\frac{2}{(1.2)(2.2)}(y_3 - 2.2y_2 + 1.2y_1) + \frac{25Pl^2}{576EI_0}y_2 = 0 \tag{2.122}$$

In view of the boundary conditions, $y_0 = 0$, and, as a result of symmetry, $y_3 = y_2$. Hence Eqs. (2.121) and (2.122) can be reduced to the form

$$y_1(\lambda - 1.60) + y_2(0.71) = 0$$
$$y_1(0.91) + y_2(0.39\lambda - 0.91) = 0 \tag{2.123}$$

in which $\lambda = Pl^2/9EI_0$.

To obtain the nontrivial solution to these equations, their determinant must be made to vanish. This leads to the quadratic equation

$$0.39\lambda^2 - 1.53\lambda + 0.81 = 0 \tag{2.124}$$

whose smallest root is $\lambda = 0.63$. Hence

$$P_{cr} = 0.57\frac{EI_0}{l^2} \tag{2.125}$$

This solution differs from the exact buckling load, $0.65EI_0/l^2$, by 12.3%.

2.13 MATRIX STIFFNESS METHOD— FLEXURAL MEMBERS

Introduction

The matrix method is a numerical technique that uses matrix algebra to analyze structural systems. It idealizes the system as an assembly of discrete elements connected to one another at points called nodes. For example, the beam in Fig. 2-23 is shown subdivided into two elements, elements *ab* and *bc*. Associated with each element are generalized displacements, δ, used to describe its deformation, and the corresponding generalized forces, q. The term generalized denotes the fact that q can be a moment as well as a force and δ a rotation as well as a deflection. The q's are internal forces as far as the overall structure is concerned, but they are external forces when individual elements are considered. Since they refer to the element, the q's are called *element forces*, and the δ's are called *element displacements*.

The load–deformation characteristics of an element can be given by means of the matrix equation

$$\begin{bmatrix} q_1 \\ q_2 \\ q_3 \\ q_4 \end{bmatrix} = \begin{bmatrix} k_{11} & k_{12} & k_{13} & k_{14} \\ k_{21} & k_{22} & k_{23} & k_{24} \\ k_{31} & k_{32} & k_{33} & k_{34} \\ k_{41} & k_{42} & k_{43} & k_{44} \end{bmatrix} \begin{bmatrix} \delta_1 \\ \delta_2 \\ \delta_3 \\ \delta_4 \end{bmatrix} \tag{2.126}$$

in which the stiffness influence coefficient k_{ij} is the force q_i due to a unit displacement δ_j when all other δ's are zero. The matrix made up of these influence coefficients is called the element stiffness matrix.

A relation similar to Eq. (2.126), expressing the load–deformation characteristics of the overall structure, is

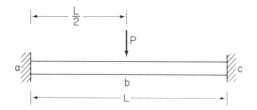

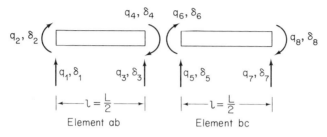

Element force and displacement notation

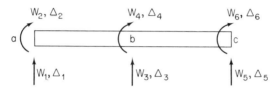

Structure force and displacement notation

Fig. 2-23 Nodal forces and displacements for a beam.

$$
\begin{bmatrix} W_1 \\ W_2 \\ W_3 \\ W_4 \\ W_5 \\ W_6 \end{bmatrix} = \begin{bmatrix} K_{11} & K_{12} & K_{13} & K_{14} & K_{15} & K_{16} \\ K_{21} & K_{22} & K_{23} & K_{24} & K_{25} & K_{26} \\ K_{31} & K_{32} & K_{33} & K_{34} & K_{35} & K_{36} \\ K_{41} & K_{42} & K_{43} & K_{44} & K_{45} & K_{46} \\ K_{51} & K_{52} & K_{53} & K_{54} & K_{55} & K_{56} \\ K_{61} & K_{62} & K_{63} & K_{64} & K_{65} & K_{66} \end{bmatrix} \begin{bmatrix} \Delta_1 \\ \Delta_2 \\ \Delta_3 \\ \Delta_4 \\ \Delta_5 \\ \Delta_6 \end{bmatrix}
\tag{2.127}
$$

or in abbreviated form

$$
[W] = [K][\Delta]
\tag{2.128}
$$

The displacements Δ_j and the loads W_i that make up the displacement matrix $[\Delta]$ and the load matrix $[W]$ are depicted in Fig. 2-23. They are the generalized structure node point displacements and the corresponding generalized structure loads that act at these node points. The matrix $[K]$ that relates the structure loads $[W]$ to the structure displacements $[\Delta]$ is known as the structure stiffness matrix.

The analysis of a structure by the matrix method consists of two steps. In the first, the structure stiffness matrix $[K]$ is synthesized from the stiffness matrices of the individual elements. This is usually accomplished by applying at each node the conditions of equilibrium and deformation compatibility. In the second step the structure displacements and the external reactions are obtained from the structure stiffness matrix $[K]$ and the load matrix $[W]$. To illustrate these procedures, let us use the matrix method to determine the midspan deflection and fixed-end moments for the beam in Fig. 2-23.

Formation of Element Stiffness Matrices

To form the structure stiffness matrix, the stiffness matrices of the individual elements must first be constructed. The stiffness matrix for element *ab* will be of the form given by Eq. (2.126). The first column of the matrix is obtained by applying a unit translation, δ_1, to the left end of the element and keeping δ_2, δ_3, and δ_4 at zero (see Fig. 2-24a). According to the definition of a

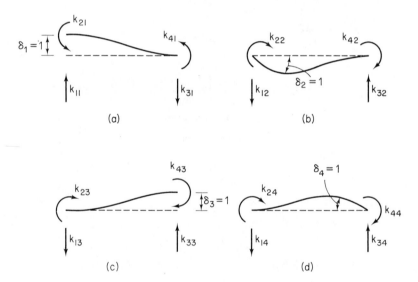

Fig. 2-24   Components of element stiffness matrix.

stiffness influence coefficient, k_{21} and k_{41} are the moments induced at the left and right ends of the member by the unit translation δ_1. From the slope–deflection equation

$$k_{21} = k_{41} = -\frac{6EI}{l^2}$$

The shears, k_{11} and k_{31}, that are also induced by the unit translation δ_1 are obtained by considering moment equilibrium of the element. They are equal to

$$k_{11} = +\frac{12EI}{l^3}, \qquad k_{31} = -\frac{12EI}{l^3}$$

In a similar manner, by applying unit displacements δ_2, δ_3, and δ_4 (Figs. 2-24b, c and d), the remaining terms in the element stiffness matrix can be evaluated. The entire matrix, for element ab, is

$$[k]_{ab} = \begin{bmatrix} \dfrac{12EI}{l^3} & -\dfrac{6EI}{l^2} & -\dfrac{12EI}{l^3} & -\dfrac{6EI}{l^2} \\[2mm] -\dfrac{6EI}{l^2} & \dfrac{4EI}{l} & \dfrac{6EI}{l^2} & \dfrac{2EI}{l} \\[2mm] -\dfrac{12EI}{l^3} & \dfrac{6EI}{l^2} & \dfrac{12EI}{l^3} & \dfrac{6EI}{l^2} \\[2mm] -\dfrac{6EI}{l^2} & \dfrac{2EI}{l} & \dfrac{6EI}{l^2} & \dfrac{4EI}{l} \end{bmatrix} \qquad (2.129)$$

Except for different subscripts on the q's and δ's, the two beam elements are identical. The stiffness matrix for element bc, $[k]_{bc}$, is therefore identical to $[k]_{ab}$.

Before proceeding with the synthesis of the structure stiffness matrix $[K]$ from the stiffness matrices of the individual elements, it is useful to combine the latter into a single composite element stiffness matrix $[k]$. Thus

$$\begin{Bmatrix} q_1 \\ q_2 \\ q_3 \\ q_4 \\ q_5 \\ q_6 \\ q_7 \\ q_8 \end{Bmatrix} = \frac{EI}{l} \begin{bmatrix} \frac{12}{l^2} & -\frac{6}{l} & -\frac{12}{l^2} & -\frac{6}{l} & & & & \\ -\frac{6}{l} & 4 & \frac{6}{l} & 2 & & & & \\ -\frac{12}{l^2} & \frac{6}{l} & \frac{12}{l^2} & \frac{6}{l} & & & & \\ -\frac{6}{l} & 2 & \frac{6}{l} & 4 & & & & \\ & & & & \frac{12}{l^2} & -\frac{6}{l} & -\frac{12}{l^2} & -\frac{6}{l} \\ & & & & -\frac{6}{l} & 4 & \frac{6}{l} & 2 \\ & & & & -\frac{12}{l^2} & \frac{6}{l} & \frac{12}{l^2} & \frac{6}{l} \\ & & & & -\frac{6}{l} & 2 & \frac{6}{l} & 4 \end{bmatrix} \begin{Bmatrix} \delta_1 \\ \delta_2 \\ \delta_3 \\ \delta_4 \\ \delta_5 \\ \delta_6 \\ \delta_7 \\ \delta_8 \end{Bmatrix}$$

$$(2.130)$$

or
$$[q] = [k][\delta] \tag{2.131}$$

Formation of Structure Stiffness Matrix, Method A: Equilibrium and Compatibility

The structure stiffness matrix can be obtained from the element stiffness matrices by applying the conditions of equilibrium and compatibility at each node. Equilibrium is satisfied if

$$W_1 = q_1, \qquad W_2 = q_2, \qquad W_3 = q_3 + q_5$$
$$W_4 = q_4 + q_6, \qquad W_5 = q_7, \qquad W_6 = q_8 \tag{2.132}$$

Putting these relations into matrix form gives

$$\begin{bmatrix} W_1 \\ W_2 \\ W_3 \\ W_4 \\ W_5 \\ W_6 \end{bmatrix} = \begin{bmatrix} 1 & 0 & 0 & 0 & 0 & 0 & 0 & 0 \\ 0 & 1 & 0 & 0 & 0 & 0 & 0 & 0 \\ 0 & 0 & 1 & 0 & 1 & 0 & 0 & 0 \\ 0 & 0 & 0 & 1 & 0 & 1 & 0 & 0 \\ 0 & 0 & 0 & 0 & 0 & 0 & 1 & 0 \\ 0 & 0 & 0 & 0 & 0 & 0 & 0 & 1 \end{bmatrix} \begin{bmatrix} q_1 \\ q_2 \\ q_3 \\ q_4 \\ q_5 \\ q_6 \\ q_7 \\ q_8 \end{bmatrix} \tag{2.133}$$

or simply
$$[W] = [A][q] \tag{2.134}$$

Equation (2.134) can be regarded as a linear transformation in which the matrix $[A]$ transforms the element forces into structure loads. In a similar manner, the compatibility relations

$$\delta_1 = \Delta_1, \qquad \delta_2 = \Delta_2, \qquad \delta_3 = \delta_5 = \Delta_3$$
$$\delta_4 = \delta_6 = \Delta_4, \qquad \delta_7 = \Delta_5, \qquad \delta_8 = \Delta_6$$

can be expressed by the matrix equation

$$\begin{bmatrix} \delta_1 \\ \delta_2 \\ \delta_3 \\ \delta_4 \\ \delta_5 \\ \delta_6 \\ \delta_7 \\ \delta_8 \end{bmatrix} = \begin{bmatrix} 1 & 0 & 0 & 0 & 0 & 0 \\ 0 & 1 & 0 & 0 & 0 & 0 \\ 0 & 0 & 1 & 0 & 0 & 0 \\ 0 & 0 & 0 & 1 & 0 & 0 \\ 0 & 0 & 1 & 0 & 0 & 0 \\ 0 & 0 & 0 & 1 & 0 & 0 \\ 0 & 0 & 0 & 0 & 1 & 0 \\ 0 & 0 & 0 & 0 & 0 & 1 \end{bmatrix} \begin{bmatrix} \Delta_1 \\ \Delta_2 \\ \Delta_3 \\ \Delta_4 \\ \Delta_5 \\ \Delta_6 \end{bmatrix} \tag{2.135}$$

or
$$[\delta] = [B][\Delta] \tag{2.136}$$

in which $[B]$ is the matrix that transforms the structure deformations into element deformations.

All the information necessary to transform the composite element stiffness matrix into the structure stiffness matrix is now available. Starting with Eq. (2.134) and making use of relations (2.131) and (2.136), one can write

$$[W] = [A][q] = [A][k][\delta] = [A][k][B][\Delta]$$

Comparison of this result with the relationship in (2.128) indicates that

$$[K] = [A][k][B] \tag{2.137}$$

Hence $[K]$, the structure stiffness matrix, is obtained from $[k]$, the composite element stiffness matrix, by premultiplying the latter by $[A]$ and postmultiplying it by $[B]$.

It will now be shown that $[A]$ and $[B]$ are related to one another and that only one of these two matrices is needed to transform $[k]$ into $[K]$. The strain energy stored in a structure is equal to the work performed by the external loads acting on the structure. Thus

$$U = \tfrac{1}{2}[\Delta]^T[W] \tag{2.138}$$

However, the strain energy is also equal to the work performed by the element forces acting on the elements of the structure. That is,

$$U = \tfrac{1}{2}[\delta]^T[q] \tag{2.139}$$

Hence
$$\tfrac{1}{2}[\Delta]^T[W] = \tfrac{1}{2}[\delta]^T[q] \tag{2.140}$$

Substitution of $[A][q]$ for $[W]$ and $[\Delta]^T[B]^T$ for $[\delta]^T$ leads to

$$\tfrac{1}{2}[\Delta]^T[A][q] = \tfrac{1}{2}[\Delta]^T[B]^T[q] \tag{2.141}$$

or
$$[A] = [B]^T \tag{2.142}$$

Hence $[B]^T$ is equal to $[A]$ and Eq. (2.137), which prescribes the manner in which $[K]$ is synthesized from $[k]$, becomes

$$[K] = [B]^T[k][B] \tag{2.143}$$

If the operation indicated by (2.143) is carried out using the element stiffness matrix given in (2.130) and the transformation matrix given by

(2.135), one obtains

$$[K] = \frac{EI}{l} \begin{array}{cccccc} \Delta_1 & \Delta_2 & \Delta_3 & \Delta_4 & \Delta_5 & \Delta_6 \\ \left[\begin{array}{cccccc} \dfrac{12}{l^2} & -\dfrac{6}{l} & -\dfrac{12}{l^2} & -\dfrac{6}{l} & 0 & 0 \\[2mm] -\dfrac{6}{l} & 4 & \dfrac{6}{l} & 2 & 0 & 0 \\[2mm] -\dfrac{12}{l^2} & \dfrac{6}{l} & \dfrac{24}{l^2} & 0 & -\dfrac{12}{l^2} & \dfrac{6}{l} \\[2mm] -\dfrac{6}{l} & 2 & 0 & 8 & \dfrac{6}{l} & 2 \\[2mm] 0 & 0 & -\dfrac{12}{l^2} & \dfrac{6}{l} & \dfrac{12}{l^2} & \dfrac{6}{l} \\[2mm] 0 & 0 & -\dfrac{6}{l} & 2 & \dfrac{6}{l} & 4 \end{array} \right] \end{array} \qquad (2.144)$$

the structure stiffness matrix for the entire beam.

Formation of Structure Stiffness Matrix, Method B: Transformation of Coordinates

In the foregoing, the structure stiffness matrix was obtained from the element stiffness matrices by applying conditions of equilibrium and deformation compatibility at the nodes. Alternatively, the synthesis of $[K]$ from $[k]$ can be seen as a transformation of coordinates. The element stiffness matrix is written in terms of element deformations, and the structure stiffness matrix in terms of structure deformations. A transformation from one matrix to the other, as given by Eq. (2.143), can therefore be considered to be a transformation from element to structure coordinates. The matrix $[B]$, which is used to carry out the transformation, is commonly referred to as the *transformation matrix*. It is made up of the direction cosines between the structure and element coordinate axes.

In the relation

$$[\delta] = [B][\Delta] \qquad (2.145)$$

the matrix $[B]$ transforms structure deformation vectors into element deformation vectors. Since the element and structure force vectors coincide with the corresponding element and structure deformation vectors, the forces must transform in precisely the same manner at the deformations. That is,

$$[q] = [B][W] \qquad (2.146)$$

Substitution of Eqs. (2.145) and (2.146) into the element stiffness relation

$$[q] = [k][\delta] \tag{2.147}$$

leads to

$$[B][W] = [k][B][\Delta] \tag{2.148}$$

or

$$[W] = [B]^{-1}[k][B][\Delta] \tag{2.149}$$

Since $[B]$ represents an orthogonal transformation, that is,

$$[B]^T = [B]^{-1} \tag{2.150}$$

Eq. (2.149) can be rewritten as

$$[W] = [B]^T[k][B][\Delta] \tag{2.151}$$

from which

$$[K] = [B]^T[k][B] \tag{2.152}$$

This relation, arrived at earlier by considering equilibrium and compatibility, has now been shown to also represent a transformation of coordinates. However, the main difference between methods A and B is not the manner in which Eq. (2.152) is interpreted. Rather it is in the procedure used to carry out the calculation of $[K]$ that the primary distinction lies.

The transformation from element to structure coordinates, represented by Eq. (2.152), can be carried out either before or after combining the stiffness matrices corresponding to the individual elements. In the preceding calculations the individual element stiffness matrices were first combined to form the composite element stiffness matrix, and this matrix was then transformed into the structure stiffness matrix. However, it sometimes requires less computer effort to transform each of the element stiffness matrices individually into structure coordinates, and then combine the transformed matrices into a structure stiffness matrix. The latter procedure, which is usually referred to as the *direct stiffness method*, will now be illustrated.

To obtain $[K]$ for the beam in Fig. 2-23, transformation matrices are required for each of the two elements. These matrices are obtained from equations that relate the element to the structure coordinates. Thus

$$\begin{bmatrix} \delta_1 \\ \delta_2 \\ \delta_3 \\ \delta_4 \end{bmatrix} = \begin{bmatrix} 1 & 0 & 0 & 0 \\ 0 & 1 & 0 & 0 \\ 0 & 0 & 1 & 0 \\ 0 & 0 & 0 & 1 \end{bmatrix} \begin{bmatrix} \Delta_1 \\ \Delta_2 \\ \Delta_3 \\ \Delta_4 \end{bmatrix} = [B]_{ab}[\Delta]_{ab} \tag{2.153}$$

and

$$\begin{bmatrix} \delta_5 \\ \delta_6 \\ \delta_7 \\ \delta_8 \end{bmatrix} = \begin{bmatrix} 1 & 0 & 0 & 0 \\ 0 & 1 & 0 & 0 \\ 0 & 0 & 1 & 0 \\ 0 & 0 & 0 & 1 \end{bmatrix} \begin{bmatrix} \Delta_3 \\ \Delta_4 \\ \Delta_5 \\ \Delta_6 \end{bmatrix} = [B]_{bc}[\Delta]_{bc} \qquad (2.154)$$

define the transformation matrices $[B]_{ab}$ and $[B]_{bc}$. The terms in the transformation matrices are the direction cosines between the element and structure deformation vectors. Since these vectors coincide for the structure being considered, the transformation matrices are both identity matrices.

The relationships between element and structure deformations given by Eqs. (2.153) and (2.154) are of course identical to those given by Eq. (2.135). The only difference is that these relations are now considered to be transformations of the deformation vectors from one coordinate system to another, whereas they were previously looked on as being equations of deformation compatibility.

Using the transformation matrices $[B]_{ab}$ and $[B]_{bc}$, and carrying out the operations indicated by Eq. (2.152) on each of the two element stiffness matrices $[k]_{ab}$ and $[k]_{bc}$, one obtains

$$[K]_{ab} = \frac{EI}{l} \begin{array}{cccc} \Delta_1 & \Delta_2 & \Delta_3 & \Delta_4 \end{array}$$

$$[K]_{ab} = \frac{EI}{l} \begin{bmatrix} \dfrac{12}{l^2} & -\dfrac{6}{l} & -\dfrac{12}{l^2} & -\dfrac{6}{l} \\ -\dfrac{6}{l} & 4 & \dfrac{6}{l} & 2 \\ -\dfrac{12}{l^2} & \dfrac{6}{l} & \dfrac{12}{l^2} & \dfrac{6}{l} \\ -\dfrac{6}{l} & 2 & \dfrac{6}{l} & 4 \end{bmatrix} \begin{array}{c} W_1 \\ W_2 \\ W_3 \\ W_4 \end{array} \qquad (2.155)$$

$$[K]_{bc} = \frac{EI}{l} \begin{array}{cccc} \Delta_3 & \Delta_4 & \Delta_5 & \Delta_6 \end{array}$$

$$[K]_{bc} = \frac{EI}{l} \begin{bmatrix} \dfrac{12}{l^2} & -\dfrac{6}{l} & -\dfrac{12}{l^2} & -\dfrac{6}{l} \\ -\dfrac{6}{l} & 4 & \dfrac{6}{l} & 2 \\ -\dfrac{12}{l^2} & \dfrac{6}{l} & \dfrac{12}{l^2} & \dfrac{6}{l} \\ -\dfrac{6}{l} & 2 & \dfrac{6}{l} & 4 \end{bmatrix} \begin{array}{c} W_3 \\ W_4 \\ W_5 \\ W_6 \end{array} \qquad (2.156)$$

The stiffness matrix $[K]$ of the entire structure is now constructed by combining $[K]_{ab}$ and $[K]_{bc}$, that is, by placing the individual terms from $[K]_{ab}$ and $[K]_{bc}$ into their correct position in the matrix $[K]$. The row and column of $[K]$ into which any term from $[K]_{ab}$ and $[K]_{bc}$ goes is indicated in (2.155) and (2.156). These designations are obtained from the law of matrix multiplication. The row and column of any term in $[K]_{mn}$ is obtained from the corresponding row in $[B]^T_{mn}$ and the corresponding column in $[B]_{mn}$.

Combination of $[K]_{ab}$ and $[K]_{bc}$ in the manner described leads to

$$[K] = \frac{EI}{l} \begin{array}{cccccc} \Delta_1 & \Delta_2 & \Delta_3 & \Delta_4 & \Delta_5 & \Delta_6 \end{array}$$

$$[K] = \frac{EI}{l}\begin{bmatrix} \dfrac{12}{l^2} & -\dfrac{6}{l} & -\dfrac{12}{l^2} & -\dfrac{6}{l} & 0 & 0 \\[2mm] -\dfrac{6}{l} & 4 & \dfrac{6}{l} & 2 & 0 & 0 \\[2mm] -\dfrac{12}{l^2} & \dfrac{6}{l} & \dfrac{24}{l^2} & 0 & -\dfrac{12}{l^2} & -\dfrac{6}{l} \\[2mm] -\dfrac{6}{l} & 2 & 0 & 8 & \dfrac{6}{l} & 2 \\[2mm] 0 & 0 & -\dfrac{12}{l^2} & \dfrac{6}{l} & \dfrac{12}{l^2} & \dfrac{6}{l} \\[2mm] 0 & 0 & -\dfrac{6}{l} & 2 & \dfrac{6}{l} & 4 \end{bmatrix}\begin{matrix} W_1 \\[2mm] W_2 \\[2mm] W_3 \\[2mm] W_4 \\[2mm] W_5 \\[2mm] W_6 \end{matrix} \qquad (2.157)$$

The dashed lines indicate the manner in which the element matrices have been combined to form the structure matrix. Whenever a term such as W_3, Δ_3 appears in two element matrices, the corresponding terms in the structure matrix is equal to the sum of the former. The structure stiffness matrix formed by superposing element matrices is of course identical to the one given in (2.144).

Structure Deflections and Element Forces

Equation (2.157) relates all possible structure nodal displacements to the corresponding structure node point loads. Before attempting to solve for any of these displacements, it is convenient to distinguish between those that are unknown and those that are fixed as a result of the boundary conditions. This is accomplished by rearranging and then partitioning the deformation matrix $[\Delta]$ into two submatrices $[\Delta]_a$ and $[\Delta]_b$. Included in $[\Delta]_a$ are the unknown nodal displacements and in $[\Delta]_b$ the nodal displacements prescribed by the boundary conditions. The load matrix $[W]$ and the stiffness matrix $[K]$ are then rearranged and partitioned accordingly. Thus

$$\begin{bmatrix} W_a \\ \cdots \\ W_b \end{bmatrix} = \begin{bmatrix} K_{aa} & \vdots & K_{ab} \\ \cdots & & \cdots \\ K_{ba} & \vdots & K_{bb} \end{bmatrix}\begin{bmatrix} \Delta_a \\ \cdots \\ \Delta_b \end{bmatrix} \qquad (2.158)$$

in which the submatrix $[W]_a$ contains the loads corresponding to the unknown nodal displacements and the submatrix $[W]_b$ the reactions at the known nodal displacements.

In many problems the nodal displacements prescribed by the boundary conditions are all zero. Equation (2.158) can then be separated into the following two relations:

$$[W_a] = [K_{aa}][\Delta_a] \tag{2.159}$$

and

$$[W_b] = [K_{ba}][\Delta_a] \tag{2.160}$$

If one multiplies both sides of Eq. (2.159) by $[K_{aa}]^{-1}$, one obtains

$$[\Delta_a] = [K_{aa}]^{-1}[W_a] \tag{2.161}$$

from which the unknown nodal displacements $[\Delta_a]$ can be determined. Once $[\Delta_a]$ has been obtained, the reactions $[W_b]$ can be found using Eq. (2.160).

For the fixed-end beam in Fig. 2-23, $\Delta_1 = \Delta_2 = \Delta_5 = \Delta_6 = 0$. Consequently, $[\Delta_a]$ consists of Δ_3 and Δ_4, and Eq. (2.159) takes the form

$$\begin{bmatrix} W_3 \\ W_4 \end{bmatrix} = \frac{EI}{l} \begin{bmatrix} \frac{24}{l^2} & 0 \\ 0 & 8 \end{bmatrix} \begin{bmatrix} \Delta_3 \\ \Delta_4 \end{bmatrix} \tag{2.162}$$

Inverting the stiffness matrix and noting that $W_4 = 0$, one obtains

$$\begin{bmatrix} \Delta_3 \\ \Delta_4 \end{bmatrix} = \frac{l}{24EI} \begin{bmatrix} l^2 & 0 \\ 0 & 3 \end{bmatrix} \begin{bmatrix} W_3 \\ 0 \end{bmatrix} \tag{2.163}$$

from which the midspan deflection Δ_3 is found to be

$$\Delta_3 = \frac{W_3 l^3}{24EI} = \frac{W_3 L^3}{192EI} \tag{2.164}$$

Having obtained $[\Delta_a]$, the reactions $[W_b]$ can be determined using Eq. (2.160). Thus

$$\begin{bmatrix} W_1 \\ W_2 \\ W_5 \\ W_6 \end{bmatrix} = \frac{EI}{l} \begin{bmatrix} -\frac{12}{l^2} & -\frac{6}{l} \\ \frac{6}{l} & 2 \\ -\frac{12}{l^2} & \frac{6}{l} \\ -\frac{6}{l} & 2 \end{bmatrix} \begin{bmatrix} \frac{W_3 l^3}{24EI} \\ 0 \end{bmatrix} \tag{2.165}$$

and the fixed-end moments W_2 and W_6 are

$$W_2 = \frac{6EI}{l^2} \frac{W_3 l^3}{24EI} = \frac{W_3 l}{4} = \frac{W_3 L}{8} \qquad (2.166)$$

and
$$W_6 = -\frac{6EI}{l^2} \frac{W_3 l^3}{24EI} = -\frac{W_3 l}{4} = -\frac{W_3 L}{8} \qquad (2.167)$$

In the preceding pages the matrix stiffness method has been used to obtain the deflection and reactons for a simple beam in bending. As a rule, matrix methods are intended to be used to analyze complex structures. The deflection of a simple beam should obviously be obtained by traditional procedures and not by matrix analysis. However, a relatively simple problem is especially well suited for illustrating basic principles. It is with this object in mind that the preceding problem, as well as those that follow, is presented.

2.14 MATRIX STIFFNESS METHOD— COMPRESSION MEMBERS

Introduction

The stiffness method utilized in Article 2.13 to analyze a flexural member will now be used to study the behavior of a member that is subject to axial loading as well as bending (Ref. 2.5). Within the limitations of small displacements and elastic stresses, the stiffness of a flexural member is a constant, and the linear relationship $[Q] = [K][\Delta]$ describes its behavior. By comparison, the stiffness of a member subject to both axial load and bending is a function of the axial load. It will later be demonstrated that the force–deflection relation of such a member takes the form

$$[Q] = \{[K] + P[K_1]\}[\Delta] \qquad (2.168)$$

in which $[Q]$ contains the transverse loads that cause bending, $[\Delta]$ contains the corresponding bending deformations, and P is the axial load. The stiffness matrix in this equation consists of two parts, $[K]$, the standard stiffness matrix of a member subject only to flexure, and $[K_1]$, a matrix which accounts for the effect that the axial load P has on the stiffness of the flexural member.

Equation (2.168) can be used to obtain the deflection of a beam column. In addition, the equation can be used to obtain the critical load of an axially loaded member. By definition, the critical load is that axial load at which the bending stiffness of the member vanishes. Rewriting Eq. (2.168) in the form

$$[\Delta] = \{[K] + P[K_1]\}^{-1}[Q]$$

it becomes obvious that the bending stiffness vanishes; that is, $[\Delta]$ increases without bound for finite values of $[Q]$ only when the inverse of the stiffness matrix becomes infinitely large. Since the inverse of a matrix is obtained by dividing the adjoint matrix by the determinant, the inverse will blow up when the determinant vanishes. The critical load can thus be found by setting the determinant of the stiffness matrix equal to zero.

Element Stiffness Matrix for Beam Column

Consider an element of a beam column subject to an axial load P and a set of loads $[q]$, as shown in Fig. 2-25a. The corresponding displacements $[\delta]$

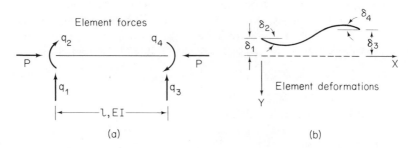

Fig. 2-25 Beam column element forces and displacements.

are depicted in Fig. 2-25b. It is our purpose to find a matrix relationship between the loads $[q]$ and the deformations $[\delta]$ in the presence of the axial load P. As long as the deformations are small and the material obeys Hooke's law, the deformations corresponding to a given set of loads $[q]$ and P are uniquely determined, regardless of the order of application of the loads. The deformations $[\delta]$ can therefore be determined by applying first the entire axial load P and then the loads $[q]$. Under these circumstances the relation of $[q]$ to $[\delta]$ is linear, and the stiffness matrix can be evaluated using the principle of conservation of energy.

The element is assumed to be loaded in two stages. During the first stage only the axial load P is applied, and during the second stage the element is bent by the $[q]$ forces while P remains constant. Since the element is in equilibrium at the end of stage one as well as at the end of stage two, the external work must be equal to the strain energy not only for the entire loading process but also for stage two by itself. The external work corresponding to the second loading stage is

$$W_e = \frac{1}{2}[\delta]^T[q] + \frac{P}{2}\int_0^l (y')^2\, dx \qquad (2.169)$$

in which the first term represents the work of the $[q]$ forces and the second term the work due to P. Since the ends of the member approach each other during bending, the axial force does positive work when it is a compression force and negative work if it is a tension force. The strain energy stored in the member during stage two is due only to bending. Thus

$$U = \frac{EI}{2} \int_0^l (y'')^2 \, dx \tag{2.170}$$

Equating the strain energy to the external work gives

$$\frac{1}{2} [\delta]^T [q] + \frac{P}{2} \int_0^l (y')^2 \, dx = \frac{EI}{2} \int_0^l (y'')^2 \, dx \tag{2.171}$$

Making use of the relationship $[q] = [k][\delta]$, in which $[k]$ is the element stiffness matrix, Eq. (2.171) becomes

$$[\delta]^T [k][\delta] = EI \int_0^l (y'')^2 \, dx - P \int_0^l (y')^2 \, dx \tag{2.172}$$

To evaluate $[k]$, it is necessary to put the right-hand side of Eq. (2.172) into matrix form. This can be accomplished if the deflection y is assumed to be given by

$$y = A + Bx + Cx^2 + Dx^3 \tag{2.173}$$

The choice of a deflection function is an extremely important step. A cubic is chosen in this instance because such a function satisfies the conditions of constant shear and linearly varying bending moment that exist in the beam element. Taking the coordinate axes in the directions shown in Fig. 2-25b, the boundary conditions for the element are

$$y = -\delta_1, \qquad y' = \delta_2 \quad \text{at } x = 0$$
$$y = -\delta_3, \qquad y' = \delta_4 \quad \text{at } x = l$$

Substitution of these conditions into Eq. (2.173) makes it possible to evaluate the four arbitrary constants and to obtain the following expression for y:

$$y = -\delta_1 + \delta_2 x + \frac{3(\delta_1 - \delta_3)}{l^2} x^2 - \frac{2\delta_2 + \delta_4}{l} x^2$$
$$+ \frac{\delta_2 + \delta_4}{l^2} x^3 + \frac{2(\delta_3 - \delta_1)}{l^3} x^3 \tag{2.174}$$

Equation (2.174) can be rewritten in matrix form as

$$y = \left[\left(\frac{3x^2}{l^2} - \frac{2x^3}{l^3} - 1 \right) \left(x - \frac{2x^2}{l} + \frac{x^3}{l^2} \right) \left(\frac{2x^3}{l^3} - \frac{3x^2}{l^2} \right) \left(\frac{x^3}{l^2} - \frac{x^2}{l} \right) \right] \begin{bmatrix} \delta_1 \\ \delta_2 \\ \delta_3 \\ \delta_4 \end{bmatrix} \tag{2.175}$$

or $y = [A][\delta]$

Differentiating the expression in (2.175) gives

$$y' = [C][\delta] \tag{2.176}$$

and

$$y'' = [D][\delta] \tag{2.177}$$

in which

$$[C] = \left(\frac{6x}{l^2} - \frac{6x^2}{l^3}\right)\left(1 - \frac{4x}{l} + \frac{3x^2}{l^2}\right)\left(\frac{6x^2}{l^3} - \frac{6x}{l^2}\right)\left(\frac{3x^2}{l^2} - \frac{2x}{l}\right) \tag{2.178}$$

and

$$[D] = \left(\frac{6}{l^2} - \frac{12x}{l^3}\right)\left(-\frac{4}{l} + \frac{6x}{l^2}\right)\left(\frac{12x}{l^3} - \frac{6}{l^2}\right)\left(\frac{6x}{l^2} - \frac{2}{l}\right) \tag{2.179}$$

In view of (2.176) and (2.177) one can write

$$(y')^2 = [\delta]^T[C]^T[C][\delta] \tag{2.180}$$

and

$$(y'')^2 = [\delta]^T[D]^T[D][\delta] \tag{2.181}$$

Substitution of these relations into (2.172) gives

$$[\delta]^T[k][\delta] = [\delta]^T\left\{EI\int_0^l [D]^T[D]\, dx - P\int_0^l [C]^T[C]\, dx\right\}[\delta]$$

from which

$$[k] = EI\int_0^l [D]^T[D]\, dx - P\int_0^l [C]^T[C]\, dx \tag{2.182}$$

Using the expressions given in (2.178) and (2.179) for $[C]$ and $[D]$ and carrying out the operations indicated in (2.182), one obtains

$$[k] = EI\begin{bmatrix} \frac{12}{l^3} & -\frac{6}{l^2} & -\frac{12}{l^3} & -\frac{6}{l^2} \\ -\frac{6}{l^2} & \frac{4}{l} & \frac{6}{l^2} & \frac{2}{l} \\ -\frac{12}{l^3} & \frac{6}{l^2} & \frac{12}{l^3} & \frac{6}{l^2} \\ -\frac{6}{l^2} & \frac{2}{l} & \frac{6}{l^2} & \frac{4}{l} \end{bmatrix} - P\begin{bmatrix} \frac{6}{5l} & -\frac{1}{10} & -\frac{6}{5l} & -\frac{1}{10} \\ -\frac{1}{10} & \frac{2l}{15} & +\frac{1}{10} & -\frac{l}{30} \\ -\frac{6}{5l} & +\frac{1}{10} & \frac{6}{5l} & \frac{1}{10} \\ -\frac{1}{10} & -\frac{l}{30} & \frac{1}{10} & \frac{2l}{15} \end{bmatrix} \tag{2.183}$$

Equation (2.183) gives the stiffness matrix of a beam column element. The matrix consists of two parts: the first is the conventional stiffness matrix of a flexural element derived in Article 2.13, and the second is a matrix representing the effect of axial loading on the bending stiffness. The latter matrix is sometimes referred to as an initial-stress stiffness matrix. As the name implies, this matrix accounts for the influence that an initial constant axial load has on the subsequent bending characteristics of a member. The matrix was derived for an axial compression force. It could serve equally well for a member with an initial tension force if the sign preceding the second matrix were changed from minus to plus.

Calculations involving the stiffness matrix of a beam column element are considerably simplified if every term in the matrix has the same dimensions. This can be accomplished by modifying the force and displacement matrices so that the terms in the former all have the dimension of force and those in the latter the dimension of distance. Thus

$$
\begin{bmatrix} q_1 \\ \dfrac{q_2}{l} \\ q_3 \\ \dfrac{q_4}{l} \end{bmatrix} = \left\{ \dfrac{EI}{l^3} \begin{bmatrix} 12 & -6 & -12 & -6 \\ -6 & 4 & 6 & 2 \\ -12 & 6 & 12 & 6 \\ -6 & 2 & 6 & 4 \end{bmatrix} - \dfrac{P}{l} \begin{bmatrix} \dfrac{6}{5} & -\dfrac{1}{10} & -\dfrac{6}{5} & -\dfrac{1}{10} \\ -\dfrac{1}{10} & \dfrac{2}{15} & \dfrac{1}{10} & -\dfrac{1}{30} \\ -\dfrac{6}{5} & \dfrac{1}{10} & \dfrac{6}{5} & \dfrac{1}{10} \\ -\dfrac{1}{10} & -\dfrac{1}{30} & \dfrac{1}{10} & \dfrac{2}{15} \end{bmatrix} \right\} \begin{bmatrix} \delta_1 \\ \delta_2 l \\ \delta_3 \\ \delta_4 l \end{bmatrix}
$$

$$(2.184)$$

This form of the stiffness matrix is especially useful when the stiffness matrix must be inverted.

Calculation of the Critical Load

As an illustration, the stiffness method will be used to determine the critical load of the column shown in Fig. 2-26. The member has a length L and a uniform flexural rigidity EI and for the purpose of the analysis is subdivided into two elements. The positive deformations and the corresponding forces, for both the entire member and the individual elements, are defined in the figure.

The stiffness matrix of each element can be constructed in accordance with Eq. (2.184). Hence

$$
[k]_{ab} = \dfrac{EI}{l^3} \begin{array}{cccc} \delta_1 & \delta_2 l & \delta_3 & \delta_4 l \end{array} \\ \begin{bmatrix} 12 & -6 & -12 & -6 \\ -6 & 4 & 6 & 2 \\ -12 & 6 & 12 & 6 \\ -6 & 2 & 6 & 4 \end{bmatrix} - \dfrac{P}{l} \begin{array}{cccc} \delta_1 & \delta_2 l & \delta_3 & \delta_4 l \end{array} \\ \begin{bmatrix} \dfrac{6}{5} & -\dfrac{1}{10} & -\dfrac{6}{5} & -\dfrac{1}{10} \\ -\dfrac{1}{10} & \dfrac{2}{15} & \dfrac{1}{10} & -\dfrac{1}{30} \\ -\dfrac{6}{5} & \dfrac{1}{10} & \dfrac{6}{5} & \dfrac{1}{10} \\ -\dfrac{1}{10} & -\dfrac{1}{30} & \dfrac{1}{10} & \dfrac{2}{15} \end{bmatrix} \begin{array}{c} q_1 \\ \dfrac{q_2}{l} \\ q_3 \\ \dfrac{q_4}{l} \end{array}
$$

$$(2.185)$$

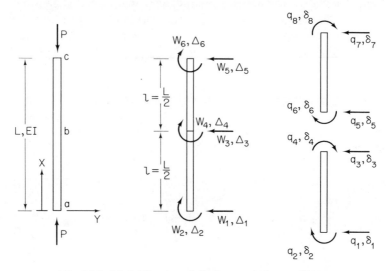

Fig. 2-26   Nodal forces and displacements for a column.

$$[k]_{bc} = \frac{EI}{l^3}
\begin{array}{cccc}
\delta_5 & \delta_6 l & \delta_7 & \delta_8 l
\end{array}
\begin{bmatrix}
12 & -6 & -12 & -6 \\
-6 & 4 & 6 & 2 \\
-12 & 6 & 12 & 6 \\
-6 & 2 & 6 & 4
\end{bmatrix}
- \frac{P}{l}
\begin{array}{cccc}
\delta_5 & \delta_6 l & \delta_7 & \delta_8 l
\end{array}
\begin{bmatrix}
\dfrac{6}{5} & -\dfrac{1}{10} & -\dfrac{6}{5} & -\dfrac{1}{10} \\[2mm]
-\dfrac{1}{10} & \dfrac{2}{15} & \dfrac{1}{10} & -\dfrac{1}{30} \\[2mm]
-\dfrac{6}{5} & \dfrac{1}{10} & \dfrac{6}{5} & \dfrac{1}{10} \\[2mm]
-\dfrac{1}{10} & -\dfrac{1}{30} & \dfrac{1}{10} & \dfrac{2}{15}
\end{bmatrix}
\begin{array}{c}
q_5 \\ \dfrac{q_6}{l} \\ q_7 \\ \dfrac{q_8}{l}
\end{array}$$

$$(2.186)$$

The structure stiffness matrix for the entire column will be obtained by transforming the individual element stiffness matrices from element to structure coordinates and then combining the resulting matrices. The transformation matrices that relate the structure deformations to the element deformations are

$$[B]_{ab} =
\begin{array}{cccc}
\delta_1 & \delta_2 l & \delta_3 & \delta_4 l
\end{array}
\begin{bmatrix}
1 & 0 & 0 & 0 \\
0 & 1 & 0 & 0 \\
0 & 0 & 1 & 0 \\
0 & 0 & 0 & 1
\end{bmatrix}
\begin{array}{c}
\Delta_1 \\ \Delta_2 l \\ \Delta_3 \\ \Delta_4 l
\end{array}$$

$$\begin{array}{cccc} \delta_5 & \delta_6 l & \delta_7 & \delta_8 l \end{array}$$

and $\qquad [B]_{bc} = \begin{bmatrix} 1 & 0 & 0 & 0 \\ 0 & 1 & 0 & 0 \\ 0 & 0 & 1 & 0 \\ 0 & 0 & 0 & 1 \end{bmatrix} \begin{array}{l} \Delta_3 \\ \Delta_4 l \\ \Delta_5 \\ \Delta_6 l \end{array}$

Carrying out for each element the transformation of coordinates in accordance with (2.152), one obtains

$$\begin{array}{cccc} \Delta_1 & \Delta_2 l & \Delta_3 & \Delta_4 l \end{array} \qquad\qquad \begin{array}{cccc} \Delta_1 & \Delta_2 l & \Delta_3 & \Delta_4 l \end{array}$$

$$[K]_{ab} = \frac{EI}{l^3} \begin{bmatrix} 12 & -6 & -12 & -6 \\ -6 & 4 & 6 & 2 \\ -12 & 6 & 12 & 6 \\ -6 & 2 & 6 & 4 \end{bmatrix} - \frac{P}{l} \begin{bmatrix} \frac{6}{5} & \frac{1}{10} & -\frac{6}{5} & -\frac{1}{10} \\ -\frac{1}{10} & \frac{2}{15} & \frac{1}{10} & -\frac{1}{30} \\ -\frac{6}{5} & \frac{1}{10} & \frac{6}{5} & \frac{1}{10} \\ -\frac{1}{10} & -\frac{1}{30} & \frac{1}{10} & \frac{2}{15} \end{bmatrix} \begin{array}{l} W_1 \\ \frac{W_2}{l} \\ W_3 \\ \frac{W_4}{l} \end{array}$$

$$(2.187)$$

$$\begin{array}{cccc} \Delta_3 & \Delta_4 l & \Delta_5 & \Delta_6 l \end{array} \qquad\qquad \begin{array}{cccc} \Delta_3 & \Delta_4 l & \Delta_5 & \Delta_6 l \end{array}$$

$$[K]_{bc} = \frac{EI}{l^3} \begin{bmatrix} 12 & -6 & -12 & -6 \\ -6 & 4 & 6 & 2 \\ -12 & 6 & 12 & 6 \\ -6 & 2 & 6 & 4 \end{bmatrix} - \frac{P}{l} \begin{bmatrix} \frac{6}{5} & \frac{1}{10} & -\frac{6}{5} & -\frac{1}{10} \\ -\frac{1}{10} & \frac{2}{15} & \frac{1}{10} & -\frac{1}{30} \\ -\frac{6}{5} & \frac{1}{10} & \frac{6}{5} & \frac{1}{10} \\ -\frac{1}{10} & -\frac{1}{30} & \frac{1}{10} & \frac{2}{15} \end{bmatrix} \begin{array}{l} W_3 \\ \frac{W_4}{l} \\ W_5 \\ \frac{W_6}{l} \end{array}$$

$$(2.188)$$

Since the transformation matrix for each element is an identity matrix, the transformation from element to structure coordinates does not bring about a change in the magnitude of any of the terms inside the stiffness matrices. However, these terms now represent structure loads per unit structure deformations, whereas they represented element forces per unit element deformations before. Accordingly, the row and column designations in (2.187) and (2.188) are Δ and W, whereas they were δ and q in (2.185) and (2.186).

Superimposing the matrices in (2.187) and (2.188), one obtains the structure stiffness matrix for the entire member. Thus

$$
\begin{bmatrix} W_1 \\ \dfrac{W_2}{l} \\ W_3 \\ \dfrac{W_4}{l} \\ W_5 \\ \dfrac{W_6}{l} \end{bmatrix} = \left\{ \dfrac{EI}{l^3} \begin{bmatrix} 12 & -6 & -12 & -6 & 0 & 0 \\ -6 & 4 & 6 & 2 & 0 & 0 \\ -12 & 6 & 24 & 0 & -12 & -6 \\ -6 & 2 & 0 & 8 & 6 & 2 \\ 0 & 0 & -12 & 6 & 12 & 6 \\ 0 & 0 & -6 & 2 & 6 & 4 \end{bmatrix} \right.
$$

$$
\left. - \dfrac{P}{l} \begin{bmatrix} \dfrac{6}{5} & -\dfrac{1}{10} & -\dfrac{6}{5} & -\dfrac{1}{10} & 0 & 0 \\ -\dfrac{1}{10} & \dfrac{2}{15} & \dfrac{1}{10} & -\dfrac{1}{30} & 0 & 0 \\ -\dfrac{6}{5} & \dfrac{1}{10} & \dfrac{12}{5} & 0 & -\dfrac{6}{5} & -\dfrac{1}{10} \\ -\dfrac{1}{10} & -\dfrac{1}{30} & 0 & \dfrac{4}{15} & \dfrac{1}{10} & -\dfrac{1}{30} \\ 0 & 0 & -\dfrac{6}{5} & \dfrac{1}{10} & \dfrac{6}{5} & \dfrac{1}{10} \\ 0 & 0 & -\dfrac{1}{10} & -\dfrac{1}{30} & \dfrac{1}{10} & \dfrac{2}{15} \end{bmatrix} \right\} \begin{bmatrix} \Delta_1 \\ \Delta_2 l \\ \Delta_3 \\ \Delta_4 l \\ \Delta_5 \\ \Delta_6 l \end{bmatrix}
\qquad (2.189)
$$

This matrix is valid for any boundary conditions. Using it, the critical load will now be determined for both a fixed-fixed and a hinged-hinged member.

1. Fixed-fixed column

For a fixed-end column, all Δ's with the exception of Δ_3 vanish. Consequently, the stiffness matrix given in (2.189) reduces to

$$
W_3 = \left(\dfrac{24EI}{l^3} - \dfrac{12}{5}\dfrac{P}{l} \right) \Delta_3
\qquad (2.190)
$$

from which

$$
\Delta_3 = \dfrac{1}{\left(\dfrac{24EI}{l^3} - \dfrac{12}{5}\dfrac{P}{l} \right)} W_3
\qquad (2.191)
$$

At the critical load the bending stiffness of the member vanishes; that is,

Δ_3 becomes infinitely large for finite values of W_3. Hence the quantity inside the parentheses must vanish at the critical load. That is,

$$\frac{24EI}{l^2} - \frac{12}{5}\frac{P}{l} = 0$$

from which

$$P_{cr} = \frac{10EI}{l^2} = \frac{40EI}{L^2} \tag{2.192}$$

The exact solution to this problem is $P_{cr} = 39.44EI/L^2$.

2. Hinged-hinged column

For a hinged-hinged column, $\Delta_1 = \Delta_4 = \Delta_5 = 0$. Crossing out the columns and rows of the stiffness matrix corresponding to the zero deformations gives

$$\begin{bmatrix} \dfrac{W_2}{l} \\ W_3 \\ \dfrac{W_6}{l} \end{bmatrix} = \left\{ \frac{EI}{l^3} \begin{bmatrix} 4 & 6 & 0 \\ 6 & 24 & -6 \\ 0 & -6 & 4 \end{bmatrix} - \frac{P}{l} \begin{bmatrix} \dfrac{2}{15} & \dfrac{1}{10} & 0 \\ \dfrac{1}{10} & \dfrac{12}{5} & -\dfrac{1}{10} \\ 0 & -\dfrac{1}{10} & \dfrac{2}{15} \end{bmatrix} \right\} \begin{bmatrix} \Delta_2 l \\ \Delta_3 \\ \Delta_6 l \end{bmatrix}$$

By recognizing that $\Delta_6 = -\Delta_2$, the stiffness matrix can be further reduced to

$$\begin{bmatrix} \dfrac{W_2}{l} \\ W_3 \end{bmatrix} = \left\{ \frac{EI}{l^3} \begin{bmatrix} 4 & 6 \\ 12 & 24 \end{bmatrix} - \frac{P}{l} \begin{bmatrix} \dfrac{2}{15} & \dfrac{1}{10} \\ \dfrac{1}{5} & \dfrac{12}{5} \end{bmatrix} \right\} \begin{bmatrix} \Delta_2 l \\ \Delta_3 \end{bmatrix} \tag{2.193}$$

As in the previous example, the criterion for finding the critical load is that the bending stiffness must vanish, or the inverse of the stiffness matrix must blow up. Hence the denominator of $[K]^{-1}$, which is the determinant of $[K]$, must be equal to zero. That is,

$$\begin{vmatrix} \dfrac{4EI}{l^3} - \dfrac{2P}{15l} & \dfrac{6EI}{l^3} - \dfrac{P}{10l} \\ \dfrac{12EI}{l^3} - \dfrac{Pl}{5} & \dfrac{24EI}{l^3} - \dfrac{12P}{5l} \end{vmatrix} = 0 \tag{2.194}$$

To simplify the numerical computations, divide each term by EI/l^3 and introduce the notation

$$\lambda = \frac{Pl^2}{5EI}$$

Equation (2.194) then takes the form

$$\begin{vmatrix} 4 - \frac{2}{3}\lambda & 6 - \frac{\lambda}{2} \\ 12 - \lambda & 24 - 12\lambda \end{vmatrix} = 0 \qquad (2.195)$$

Expansion of (2.195) leads to the equation

$$7.5\lambda^2 - 52\lambda + 24 = 0$$

whose smallest root is $\lambda = 0.49$. This gives

$$P_{cr} = \frac{2.45EI}{l^2} = \frac{9.8EI}{L^2} \qquad (2.196)$$

The exact value of the critical load is of course $9.87EI/L^2$.

References

2.1   S. P. TIMOSHENKO, *The Collected Papers of Stephen P. Timoshenko* (New York: McGraw-Hill Book Company, 1953), p. 1.

2.2   M. G. SALVADORI and M. L. BARON, *Numerical Methods in Engineering*, 2nd ed. (Englewood Cliffs, N.J.: Prentice-Hall, Inc., 1961).

2.3   W. G. BICKLEY, "Finite Difference Formulae for the Square Lattice," *Quarterly Journal of Mechanics and Applied Mathematics*, Vol. 1, 1948.

2.4   M. G. SALVADORI, "Numerical Computation of Buckling Loads by Finite Differences," *Transactions, ASCE*, Vol. 116, 1951.

2.5   H. C. MARTIN, "Large Deflection and Stability Analysis by the Direct Stiffness Method," *Jet Propulsion Laboratory, California Institute of Technology, Pasadena, Calif.*, Technical Report, No. 32-931, Aug. 1966.

Problems

2.1   Determine an approximate value for the critical load of an axially loaded column, hinged at one end and fixed at the other, using the energy method. Approximate the deflected shape of the column by the deflection curve of a uniformly loaded beam whose boundary conditions are the same as those of the column.

2.2   Using the energy method, determine an approximate value for the critical load of the column shown in Fig. P2-1.

2.3   (a) Use the energy method to determine the critical load of a hinged-hinged column that is supported along its entire length by an elastic foundation, as shown in Fig. P2-2. As the column deflects the foundation exerts a force of

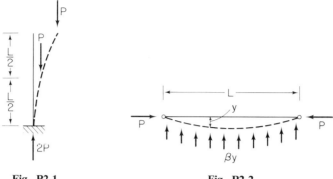

Fig. P2-1   Fig. P2-2

β pounds per unit length per unit lateral deflection on the column. Assume that the deflection of the column is given by the infinite series $y = \sum_{n=1}^{\infty} a_n \sin(n\pi x/l)$.

$$\left[P_{cr} = \frac{\pi^2 EI}{l^2} \left(m^2 + \frac{\beta l^4}{m^2 \pi^4 EI} \right) \right]$$

(b) Plot a curve of P_{cr}/P_e versus $\beta l^2/P_e$ and use it to discuss the variation of the critical load and the mode shape with the stiffness of the foundation β. (Hint: To obtain the desired curve it is necessary to determine the number of half-waves m that lead to the minimum critical load for any given value of β. This can be accomplished by letting m take on successively higher values, starting with 1, and plotting the critical load versus β for each case.)

2.4 Determine an approximate value for the critical load of a hinged-hinged column whose moment of inertia varies linearly from I_0 to $4I_0$ as shown in Fig. P2-3. Use the energy method and assume that the deflection is given by $y = a \sin(\pi x/l)$.

$$\left(P_{cr} = \frac{5\pi^2 EI_0}{2l^2} \right)$$

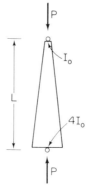

Fig. P2-3

2.5 Solve Problem 2.4 using the method of finite differences. Obtain solutions with the column divided into two and three segments and extrapolate these results using Richardson's method.

2.6 Solve Problem 2.1 using the matrix method. Divide the member into two elements. (Note: The smallest root of a cubic equation must be obtained to find the critical load.)

2.7 Solve Problem 2.2 using the matrix method. Divide the member into two elements. (Note: The smallest root of a quartic equation must be obtained to find the critical load.)

3
BEAM COLUMNS

3.1 INTRODUCTION

Beam columns are members that are subjected to both bending and axial compression. The bending may be caused either by moments applied to the ends of the member, as indicated in Fig. 3-1a, or it may be due to transverse

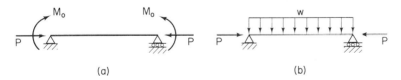

Fig. 3-1 Beam column.

loads acting directly on the member, as shown in Fig. 3-1b. Thus vertical members in rigid frames that are both bent and compressed are beam columns. The eccentrically loaded column investigated in Article 1.11 was in essence also a beam column. However, our concern at that time was different from what it is now. The reason we studied an eccentrically loaded member in Article 1.11 was to learn what effect small amounts of bending, caused by unavoidable imperfections, have on axially loaded columns. By comparison, we are now concerned with members where both the bending and the axial compression are due to intentionally applied loads. In other words, bending is now a primary effect, whereas in the analysis of the eccentrically loaded column it was a secondary effect.

3.2   BEAM COLUMN WITH CONCENTRATED LATERAL LOAD

Let us begin by considering a simply supported member of length l that is simultaneously acted on by a transverse load Q and axial forces P, as shown in Fig. 3-2. It is assumed that the material behaves according to Hooke's law,

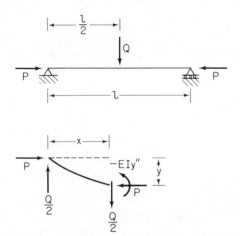

Fig. 3-2 Beam column with concentrated load.

that deformations remain small, and that the member is laterally braced so that it can only bend in the vertical plane. The case of a member that is not braced in this manner and which can therefore bend laterally as well as vertically is considered in Chapter 5.

If the coordinate axes are taken as indicated in the figure, the external moment, at a distance x from the origin, is

$$M = \frac{Qx}{2} + Py$$

Equating this expression to the internal resisting moment $-EIy''$ gives

$$EI\frac{d^2y}{dx^2} + Py = -\frac{Qx}{2}$$

or

$$\frac{d^2y}{dx^2} + k^2y = -\frac{Qx}{2EI} \tag{3.1}$$

in which

$$k^2 = \frac{P}{EI} \tag{3.2}$$

The general solution to Eq. (3.1) is

$$y = A \sin kx + B \cos kx - \frac{Qx}{2P} \tag{3.3}$$

where A and B are arbitrary constants. The boundary condition

$$y = 0 \quad \text{at } x = 0$$

leads to

$$B = 0$$

and from the condition that

$$\frac{dy}{dx} = 0 \quad \text{at } x = \frac{l}{2}$$

one obtains

$$A = \frac{Q}{2kP} \frac{1}{\cos(kl/2)}$$

Substitution of these results in Eq. (3.3) gives

$$y = \frac{Q}{2Pk} \left[\frac{\sin kx}{\cos(kl/2)} - kx \right] \tag{3.4}$$

Instead of considering the deformation of the entire member, it is convenient from hereon to limit our attention to the midspan deflection δ. Letting $x = l/2$ in (3.4), one obtains

$$\delta = \frac{Q}{2Pk} \left[\frac{\sin(kl/2)}{\cos(kl/2)} - \frac{kl}{2} \right]$$

or

$$\delta = \frac{Q}{2Pk} (\tan u - u) \tag{3.5}$$

where

$$u = \frac{kl}{2} \tag{3.6}$$

Multiplying and dividing the expression in (3.5) by $l^3/24EI$ gives

$$\delta = \frac{Ql^3}{48EI} \frac{24EI}{kPl^3} (\tan u - u)$$

$$= \frac{Ql^3}{48EI} \frac{3}{(kl/2)^3} (\tan u - u) \tag{3.7}$$

$$= \frac{Ql^3}{48EI} \frac{3(\tan u - u)}{u^3}$$

The left-hand factor in this relation is the deflection that would exist if the transverse load Q were acting by itself. Accordingly, we introduce the notation

$$\delta_0 = \frac{Ql^3}{48EI} \tag{3.8}$$

and rewrite Eq. (3.7) as

$$\delta = \delta_0 \frac{3(\tan u - u)}{u^3} \tag{3.9}$$

To further simplify the expression for δ, let us make use of the power series expansion of $\tan u$, which is

$$\tan u = u + \frac{u^3}{3} + \frac{2}{15}u^5 + \frac{17}{315}u^7 + \cdots$$

Substitution of this series for $\tan u$ in Eq. (3.9) gives

$$\delta = \delta_0\left(1 + \frac{2}{5}u^2 + \frac{17}{105}u^4 + \cdots\right) \tag{3.10}$$

In view of (3.2) and (3.6)

$$u^2 = \frac{P}{EI}\frac{l^2}{4}\frac{\pi^2}{\pi^2} = 2.46\frac{P}{P_{cr}} \tag{3.11}$$

and Eq. (3.10) can be rewritten as

$$\delta = \delta_0\left[1 + 0.984\frac{P}{P_{cr}} + 0.998\left(\frac{P}{P_{cr}}\right)^2 + \cdots\right]$$

or very nearly

$$\delta = \delta_0\left[1 + \frac{P}{P_{cr}} + \left(\frac{P}{P_{cr}}\right)^2 + \cdots\right] \tag{3.12}$$

Since the sum of the geometric series inside the brackets is $1/[1 - (P/P_{cr})]$, (3.12) reduces to

$$\delta = \delta_0\frac{1}{1 - (P/P_{cr})} \tag{3.13}$$

Equation (3.13) approximates very closely the maximum deflection of a simply supported member that is simultaneously bent by a transverse load Q and an axial force P. The equation indicates that the maximum deflection of the member is equal to δ_0, the maximum deflection that would exist if only Q were acting, multiplied by an amplification factor that depends on the ratio P/P_{cr}. The effect of the axial load is thus to magnify the deflection that would exist in the beam if it, the axial force, were not present. Equation (3.13) also shows that the deflection of the beam column increases without bound as P/P_{cr} approaches unity. In other words, the resistance of the member to lateral deformation vanishes as the axial load approaches the critical load. It is thus possible to determine the critical load of a member by finding the axial load at which its bending stiffness vanishes.

Having made some general observations regarding beam columns, let us now consider in detail their load–deflection characteristics. In Fig. 3-3a the

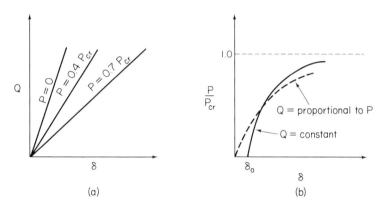

Fig. 3-3   Beam column load–deflection characteristics.

variation of δ with Q, as given by Eq. (3.13), is shown plotted for $P = 0$, $P = 0.4P_{cr}$, and $P = 0.7P_{cr}$. Since the bending stiffness of a member is proportional to the slope of its load–deflection relation, these curves clearly demonstrate that an increase in axial load produces a decrease in bending stiffness. The curves also show that the relation between Q and δ, which we know to be linear when $P = 0$, remains linear even when $P \neq 0$, provided P is a constant. However, if P is allowed to vary, as is the case in Fig. 3-3b, the load–deflection relation is not linear. This is true regardless of whether Q remains constant (solid curve) or increases as P increases (dashed curve). The deflection of a beam column is thus a linear function of Q but a nonlinear function of P. If both P and Q increase simultaneously, the load–deflection relation is nonlinear.

Having determined how the presence of an axial load affects the lateral deflection of a transversely loaded member, we shall now consider how the bending moment is affected by axial compression. The maximum bending moment in the member is

$$M_{\max} = \frac{Ql}{4} + P\delta \tag{3.14}$$

which, in view of (3.8) and (3.13), can be written as

$$M_{max} = \frac{Ql}{4} + \frac{PQl^3}{48EI}\frac{1}{1-(P/P_{cr})}$$

or

$$M_{max} = \frac{Ql}{4}\left[1 + \frac{Pl^2}{12EI}\frac{1}{1-(P/P_{cr})}\right] \tag{3.15}$$

Simplifying the term inside the bracket gives

$$M_{max} = \frac{Ql}{4}\left[1 + 0.82P/P_{cr}\frac{1}{1-(P/P_{cr})}\right]$$

from which

$$M_{max} = \frac{Ql}{4}\frac{1-(0.18P/P_{cr})}{1-(P/P_{cr})} \tag{3.16}$$

The left-hand factor in (3.16) is the maximum moment that would exist if no axial force were present. Thus, letting

$$M_0 = \frac{Ql}{4} \tag{3.17}$$

the maximum moment in the beam column can be given as

$$M_{max} = M_0\frac{1-(0.18P/P_{cr})}{1-(P/P_{cr})} \tag{3.18}$$

Equation (3.18) shows that the effect of axial compression on the bending moment is very similar to the effect that an axial load has on the deflection. Like the deflection, the moment that exists in the absence of axial compression is amplified by the presence of an axial load. It is also interesting to note the similarity between the amplification factor for moment and the corresponding amplification factor for deflection.

3.3 BEAM COLUMN WITH DISTRIBUTED LATERAL LOAD

Let us now consider the case of a simply supported member bent by a uniformly distributed lateral load w and a set of axial forces P, as shown in Fig. 3-4. As before, we assume that the material obeys Hooke's law, that deformations remain small, and that the member is restrained against lateral buckling. In Article 3.2 the investigation was carried out by setting up and

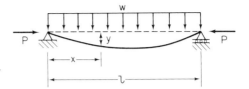

Fig. 3-4 Beam column with laterally distributed load.

solving the governing differential equation. To illustrate an alternative method of analysis, we shall now use the Rayleigh–Ritz method.

In a beam column, bending and axial compression usually proceed simultaneously. However, the bending deformations can be assumed to be independent of the axial deformations as long as deformations in general remain small. The analysis of a beam column by the energy method is therefore similar to the analysis of an axially loaded member. That is, the energy of axial compression is omitted and only bending energy is considered (see Article 2.2).

The strain energy that is stored in the member as it bends is

$$U = \frac{EI}{2} \int_0^l \left(\frac{d^2y}{dx^2}\right)^2 dx$$

and the potential energy of the external loads is

$$V = -w \int_0^l y\, dx - \frac{P}{2} \int_0^l \left(\frac{dy}{dx}\right)^2 dx$$

Thus the total energy in the system is

$$U + V = \frac{EI}{2} \int_0^l \left(\frac{d^2y}{dx^2}\right)^2 dx - w \int_0^l y\, dx - \frac{P}{2} \int_0^l \left(\frac{dy}{dx}\right)^2 dx \qquad (3.19)$$

To satisfy the boundary conditions, the deflection y is assumed to be of the form

$$y = \delta \sin \frac{\pi x}{l} \qquad (3.20)$$

where δ is the midspan deflection. Substitution of this expression into Eq. (3.19) gives

$$U + V = \frac{EI\delta^2\pi^4}{2l^4} \int_0^l \sin^2 \frac{\pi x}{l}\, dx - w\delta \int_0^l \sin \frac{\pi x}{l}\, dx$$
$$- \frac{P\delta^2\pi^2}{2l^2} \int_0^l \cos^2 \frac{\pi x}{l}\, dx \qquad (3.21)$$

To evaluate (3.21), we make use of the following definite integrals:

$$\int_0^l \sin^2 \frac{\pi x}{l} \, dx = \int_0^l \cos^2 \frac{\pi x}{l} \, dx = \frac{l}{2}$$

$$\int_0^l \sin \frac{\pi x}{l} \, dx = \frac{2l}{\pi}$$

Thus Eq. (3.21) becomes

$$U + V = \frac{EI \, \delta^2 \pi^4}{4 \quad l^3} - \frac{2w\delta l}{\pi} - \frac{P\delta^2 \pi^2}{4l} \tag{3.22}$$

For the system to be in equilibrium the derivative of $U + V$ with respect to δ must vanish. That is,

$$\frac{\partial(U + V)}{\partial \delta} = \frac{EI\delta\pi^4}{2l^3} - \frac{2wl}{\pi} - \frac{P\delta\pi^2}{2l} = 0$$

from which

$$\delta = \frac{4wl^4}{\pi} \frac{1}{EI\pi^4 - P\pi^2 l^2} \tag{3.23}$$

If the numerator and denominator of (3.23) are multiplied by $5/384EI$, one obtains

$$\delta = \frac{5wl^4}{384EI} \frac{1536EI}{5\pi} \frac{1}{EI\pi^4 - P\pi^2 l^2}$$

which reduces to

$$\delta = \frac{5wl^4}{384EI} \frac{1536}{5\pi^5} \frac{1}{1 - (P/P_{cr})}$$

or very nearly to

$$\delta = \frac{5wl^4}{384EI} \frac{1}{1 - (P/P_{cr})} \tag{3.24}$$

The left-hand factor in this relation is the deflection that would exist if the lateral load w were acting by itself. Thus we let

$$\delta_0 = \frac{5wl^4}{384EI} \tag{3.25}$$

and rewrite (3.24) as

$$\delta = \delta_0 \frac{1}{1 - (P/P_{cr})} \tag{3.26}$$

Equation (3.26) gives the maximum deflection of a simply supported beam that is bent simultaneously by a distributed transverse load w and axial forces P. Since the assumed shape for y was not exact, the deflection given by (3.26) is only an approximation. However, it has been shown by Timoshenko and Gere (Ref. 1.2), who solved the problem rigorously, that the approximate solution differs from the exact answer only slightly.

The maximum moment in the member is

$$M_{max} = \frac{wl^2}{8} + P\delta \qquad (3.27)$$

In view of (3.25) and (3.26) this expression can be written as

$$M_{max} = \frac{wl^2}{8} + \frac{5Pwl^4}{384EI} \frac{1}{1 - (P/P_{cr})}$$

or

$$M_{max} = \frac{wl^2}{8}\left[1 + \frac{5Pl^2}{48EI} \frac{1}{1 - (P/P_{cr})}\right]$$

Simplifying the term inside the brackets, one obtains

$$M_{max} = \frac{wl^2}{8}\left[1 + 1.03P/P_{cr} \frac{1}{1 - (P/P_{cr})}\right]$$

from which

$$M_{max} = \frac{wl^2}{8}\left[\frac{1 + (0.03P/P_{cr})}{1 - (P/P_{cr})}\right] \qquad (3.28)$$

The term outside the brackets is the maximum moment that would exist if no axial force were present. If one lets

$$M_0 = \frac{wl^2}{8} \qquad (3.29)$$

(3.28) can be written in the form

$$M_{max} = M_0 \frac{1 + (0.03P/P_{cr})}{1 - (P/P_{cr})} \qquad (3.30)$$

The maximum deflection of the beam column given by Eq. (3.26) and the maximum moment given by Eq. (3.30) are thus both equal to the product of two terms, the maximum deflection or moment that would exist if only lateral load were present and an amplification factor that accounts for the effect of the axial load. What is perhaps most significant in these relations is their similarity to the corresponding expressions for deflection and moment obtained previously for a concentrated lateral load. It is at least partially due to this similarity that a relatively simple design criterion can be formulated for beam columns.

3.4 EFFECT OF AXIAL LOAD ON BENDING STIFFNESS SLOPE–DEFLECTION EQUATION

The slope–deflection equation provides a convenient way of expressing the bending stiffness of a member. The equation, which is derived in any standard text on indeterminate structures (Ref. 3.1), gives the moment M_A induced at end A of a beam AB by end rotations θ_A and θ_B and by a displacement Δ of one end relative to the other. The equation usually takes the form

$$M_A = C_1\theta_A + C_2\theta_B + C_3\Delta \tag{3.31}$$

where C_1, C_2, and C_3 are stiffness influence coefficients.

In conventional linear structural analysis, it is customary to neglect the effect of axial forces on the bending stiffness of flexural members and to determine the constants C_1, C_2, and C_3 accordingly. It has been shown, in Articles 3.2 and 3.3, that this simplification is valid as long as the axial load remains small in comparison with the critical load of the member. However, when the ratio of the axial load to the critical load becomes sizeable, the bending stiffness is markedly reduced by the presence of axial compression, and it is no longer reasonable to neglect this reduction in determining the stiffness.

In this article, a form of the slope–deflection equation that includes the effect of axial compression on the bending stiffness will be developed. In other words, the constants A, B, and C in the slope-deflection equation will be evaluated for a member simultaneously bent and axially compressed. It is convenient in making these calculations to deal separately with the joint rotations θ and the member rotation Δ/l. Let us consider a single member of a framework, shown in Fig. 3-5, on which axial compression loads are acting and whose ends have been rotated through angles θ_A and θ_B, thereby inducing moments M_A and M_B at the ends. Since joint translations will be considered separately later, it is assumed that the ends of the member do not translate laterally relative to one another. The coordinate axes are taken in the directions indicated, and moments acting on the ends of the member and end rotations are assumed to be positive when clockwise, as in the slope–deflection sign convention.

The moment at a distance x from the origin is

$$M = M_A + Py - (M_A + M_B)\frac{x}{l}$$

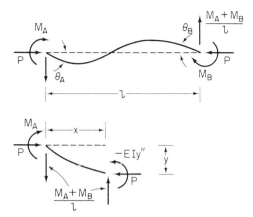

Fig. 3-5 End moments due to joint rotations.

Equating this expression to the internal resisting moment $-EI(d^2y/dx^2)$ gives

$$EI\frac{d^2y}{dx^2} + Py = M_A\left(\frac{x}{l} - 1\right) + M_B\frac{x}{l}$$

or

$$\frac{d^2y}{dx^2} + k^2y = \frac{M_A}{EI}\left(\frac{x}{l} - 1\right) + \frac{M_B}{EI}\frac{x}{l} \tag{3.32}$$

where

$$k^2 = \frac{P}{EI} \tag{3.33}$$

The general solution to Eq. (3.32) is

$$y = A\sin kx + B\cos kx + \frac{M_A}{P}\left(\frac{x}{l} - 1\right) + \frac{M_B}{P}\frac{x}{l} \tag{3.34}$$

where A and B are arbitrary constants.

The boundary condition

$$y = 0 \quad \text{at } x = 0$$

leads to

$$B = \frac{M_A}{P}$$

and from the condition that

$$y = 0 \quad \text{at } x = l$$

one obtains

$$A = -\frac{M_A}{P}\frac{\cos kl}{\sin kl} - \frac{M_B}{P}\frac{1}{\sin kl}$$

Substitution of these results in Eq. (3.34) gives

$$y = \frac{M_A}{P}\left(-\frac{\cos kl}{\sin kl}\sin kx + \cos kx + \frac{x}{l} - 1\right)$$
$$- \frac{M_B}{P}\left(-\frac{\sin kx}{\sin kl} + \frac{x}{l}\right)$$

(3.35)

from which

$$y' = \frac{M_A}{P}\left(\frac{1}{l} - k\frac{\sin kl \sin kx + \cos kl \cos kx}{\sin kl}\right)$$
$$+ \frac{M_B}{P}\left(\frac{1}{l} - \frac{k\cos kx}{\sin kl}\right)$$

(3.36)

Making use of the identity

$$\cos(\alpha - \beta) = \sin \alpha \sin \beta + \cos \alpha \cos \beta$$

and multiplying the numerator and denominator of the second term in each parenthesis of (3.36) by l, one obtains

$$y' = \frac{M_A}{Pl}\left[1 - \frac{kl \cos k(l - x)}{\sin kl}\right] + \frac{M_B}{Pl}\left(1 - \frac{kl \cos kx}{\sin kl}\right)$$

(3.37)

The end rotation at A is obtained by setting $x = 0$. Thus

$$\theta_A = \frac{M_A}{Pl}(1 - kl \cot kl) + \frac{M_B}{Pl}(1 - kl \csc kl)$$

(3.38)

If numerator and denominator in (3.38) are multiplied by l, and k^2EI is substituted for P, one obtains

$$\theta_A = \frac{M_A l}{k^2 l^2 EI}(1 - kl \cot kl) + \frac{M_B l}{k^2 l^2 EI}(1 - kl \csc kl)$$

or $\qquad \theta_A = \frac{M_A}{K}\phi_n - \frac{M_B}{K}\phi_f$

(3.39)

where $\qquad\qquad K = \frac{EI}{l}$

(3.40)

$$\phi_n = \frac{1}{(kl)^2}(1 - kl \cot kl)$$

(3.41)

$$\phi_f = \frac{1}{(kl)^2}(kl \csc kl - 1)$$

(3.42)

In a similar manner, the rotation at end B of the member can be obtained. Setting $x = l$ in Eq. (3.37) gives

$$\theta_B = \frac{M_A}{Pl}(1 - kl \csc kl) + \frac{M_B}{Pl}(1 - kl \cot kl)$$

from which

$$\theta_B = \frac{M_A l}{k^2 EIl^2}(1 - kl \csc kl) + \frac{M_B l}{k^2 EIl^2}(1 - kl \cot kl)$$

or
$$\theta_B = -\frac{M_A}{K}\phi_f + \frac{M_B}{K}\phi_n \tag{3.43}$$

where K, ϕ_f, and ϕ_n are defined in (3.40) through (3.42).

Solving Eqs. (3.39) and (3.43) for M_A and M_B, one obtains

$$M_A = \frac{K(\theta_A \phi_n + \theta_B \phi_f)}{\phi_n^2 - \phi_f^2} \tag{3.44}$$

and
$$M_B = \frac{K(\theta_B \phi_n + \theta_A \phi_f)}{\phi_n^2 - \phi_f^2} \tag{3.45}$$

Letting

$$\alpha_n = \frac{\phi_n}{\phi_n^2 - \phi_f^2}, \qquad \alpha_f = \frac{\phi_f}{\phi_n^2 - \phi_f^2} \tag{3.46}$$

(3.44) and (3.45) can be put into the same form as (3.31). That is,

$$M_A = \frac{EI}{l}(\alpha_n \theta_A + \alpha_f \theta_B) \tag{3.47}$$

and
$$M_B = \frac{EI}{l}(\alpha_n \theta_B + \alpha_f \theta_A) \tag{3.48}$$

Equations (3.47) and (3.48) give the relation between end moments M_A and M_B and end rotations θ_A and θ_B for a member subject to both bending and axial compression. Let us now consider for the same type of member the relation between the end moments and a relative joint displacement Δ.

The deformation, shown in Fig. 3-6, is brought about by displacing the ends of the member relative to one another a distance Δ and keeping the end rotations θ_A and θ_B at zero. As a consequence of this deformation, negative moments are induced at both ends of the member. Equating internal and

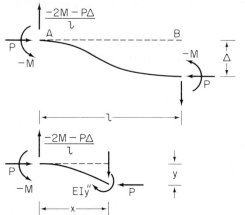

Fig. 3-6 End moments due to relative joint displacement.

external moments, at a distance x from the origin, gives

$$EI\frac{d^2y}{dx^2} + Py = M\left(\frac{2x}{l} - 1\right) + \frac{Px\Delta}{l}$$

or

$$\frac{d^2y}{dx^2} + k^2y = \frac{M}{EI}\left(\frac{2x}{l} - 1\right) + \frac{k^2x\Delta}{l} \qquad (3.49)$$

where $k^2 = P/EI$. The solution to Eq. (3.49) is

$$y = A\sin kx + B\cos kx + \frac{M}{P}\left(\frac{2x}{l} - 1\right) + \frac{x\Delta}{l} \qquad (3.50)$$

From the condition that $y = 0$ at $x = 0$ one obtains

$$B = \frac{M}{P}$$

and letting $y = \Delta$ at $x = l$ gives

$$A = -\frac{M}{P}\frac{\cos kl + 1}{\sin kl}$$

Substitution of these results in Eq. (3.50) gives

$$y = \frac{M}{P}\left[-\frac{\sin kx}{\sin kl}(1 + \cos kl) + \cos kx + \frac{2x}{l} - 1\right] + \frac{x\Delta}{l} \qquad (3.51)$$

and

$$y' = \frac{M}{P}\left[-\frac{k\cos kx}{\sin kl}(1 + \cos kl) - k\sin kx + \frac{2}{l}\right] + \frac{\Delta}{l} \qquad (3.52)$$

Furthermore, the condition $dy/dx = 0$ at $x = l$ leads to

$$0 = \frac{M}{P}\left[-\frac{k \cos kl}{\sin kl}(1 + \cos kl) - k \sin kl + \frac{2}{l}\right] + \frac{\Delta}{l}$$

or

$$\frac{\Delta}{l} = -\frac{M}{P}\left[-\frac{k(\sin^2 kl + \cos^2 kl)}{\sin kl} - \frac{k \cos kl}{\sin kl} + \frac{2}{l}\right] \qquad (3.53)$$

Making use of the identity $\sin^2 \alpha + \cos^2 \alpha = 1$ and multiplying the numerator and denominator of the first two terms inside the bracket of (3.53) by l, one obtains

$$\frac{\Delta}{l} = -\frac{M}{Pl}(-kl \csc kl - kl \cot kl + 2)$$

from which

$$\frac{\Delta}{l} = -\frac{M}{K}(\phi_n - \phi_f) \qquad (3.54)$$

If numerator and denominator are now multiplied by $\phi_n + \phi_f$, one gets

$$\frac{\Delta}{l} = -\frac{M}{K}\frac{\phi_n^2 - \phi_f^2}{\phi_n + \phi_f}$$

or, in view of (3.46),

$$M = -K\frac{\Delta}{l}(\alpha_n + \alpha_f) \qquad (3.55)$$

Equation (3.55) gives the relation between end moments and relative joint displacement when an axial load is present. Combining this expression with (3.47), we obtain the complete stiffness relation for a member that is subject to both bending and axial compression. That is,

$$M_A = \frac{EI}{l}\left[\alpha_n\theta_A + \alpha_f\theta_B - (\alpha_n + \alpha_f)\frac{\Delta}{l}\right] \qquad (3.56)$$

Equation (3.56) is the slope–deflection equation adjusted to include the effect of axial compression. In Chapter 4, we shall see how this equation can be used to determine the critical load of a framework. So that the equation can be used efficiently, numerical values of α_n and α_f calculated by Winter, Hsu, Koo, and Loh (Ref. 3.2) are given in the Appendix.

To see what Eq. (3.56) tells us about the effect of axial compression on the bending stiffness of a flexural member, let us consider the variation of α_n with kl plotted in Fig. 3-7. The quantity α_n can be shown to be given by

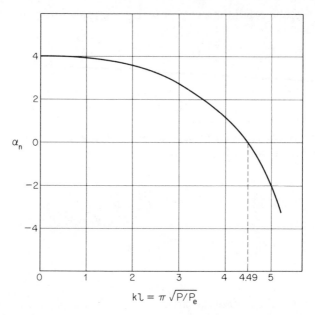

Fig. 3-7   Variation of bending stiffness with ratio of axial load to critical load.

$$\alpha_n = M_A \frac{l}{EI\theta_A}$$

if θ_B and Δ are set equal to zero in Eq. (3.56). Thus α_n is proportional to the moment M_A that is needed to maintain a rotation θ_A when $\theta_B = \Delta = 0$. In other words, α_n is a measure of the bending stiffness of the member. If the quantity kl is rewritten in the form

$$kl = l\sqrt{\frac{P}{EI}} = \pi\sqrt{\frac{Pl^2}{\pi^2 EI}} = \pi\sqrt{\frac{P}{P_e}}$$

where P_e is the Euler load, it becomes evident that kl is a measure of the ratio of the axial load to the Euler load. The curve in Fig. 3-7 thus gives the variation of the bending stiffness with the ratio of axial load to critical load.

When $kl = 0$, that is, when there is no axial load, $\alpha_n = 4$. This value of α_n is used in routine structural analysis where the effect of axial compression on the bending stiffness is neglected. Between $kl = 0$ and $kl = 4.49$, α_n decreases as kl increases. The bending stiffness is thus reduced by an increase in the magnitude of the axial load. At $kl = 4.49$ or $P = 2.04P_e$, $\alpha_n = 0$. The reason the bending stiffness vanishes at this load is that the member which we have considered up to this point is in effect hinged at one support and fixed at the other, and therefore has a critical load of $P = 2.04P_e$. For values of kl

greater than 4.49, α_n is negative, which means that the moment and the rotation are oppositely directed. Values of kl in excess of 4.49 correspond to members that are elastically restrained by other members at the end to which the rotation is applied. Another way of putting the same idea is to say that $kl < 4.49$ corresponds to cases where θ_A is induced by the adjacent member and $kl > 4.49$ to cases where θ_A is resisted by the adjacent member.

3.5 FAILURE OF BEAM COLUMNS

Up to this point in our study of beam columns, we did not concern ourselves with the subject of failure, and it was therefore possible to limit the analysis to elastic behavior. Now, however, we are specifically interested in determining the failure load, and, since failure involves yielding, it becomes necessary to introduce the complexities of inelastic behavior into the investigation. When studying the behavior of columns in Chapter 1, it was pointed out that problems which involve inelastic bending do not possess closed–form solutions. They must either be solved numerically, which entails lengthy and time-consuming calculations, or approximate answers must be sought by making simplifying assumptions. In this article we shall study the failure of beam columns using the latter of these two approaches to the problem.

Let us consider the simply supported, symmetrically loaded member shown in Fig. 3-8a. The member is simultaneously bent and compressed by

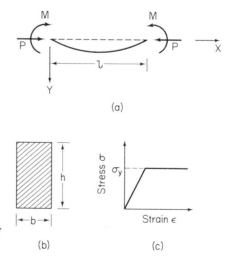

Fig. 3-8 Idealized beam column of Jezek.

equal end couples M and axial forces P. It has been demonstrated by Jezek (Refs. 3.3 and 3.4) that a closed-form solution for the load–deflection characteristics, beyond the proportional limit, can be obtained provided the following assumptions are introduced.

1. The cross section of the member is rectangular (Fig. 3-8b).
2. The material is an ideal elastic-plastic material (Fig. 3-8c).
3. The bending deflection of the member takes the form of a half-sinewave.

The reason inelastic bending is difficult to analyze is that the relation of stress to strain varies in a complicated manner both along the member and across the section, once the proportional limit has been exceeded. It is with this problem in mind that Jezek introduces the foregoing assumptions. Assumption 3 makes it possible to predict the behavior of the entire member from a consideration of the stresses at only a single cross section, and assumptions 1 and 2 greatly simplify the manner in which stress and strain vary at that one section. In addition to these major idealizations, the following assumptions are made:

4. Deformations are finite but still small enough so that the curvature can be approximated by the second derivative.
5. The member is initially straight.
6. Bending takes place about the major principal axis.

If the coordinate axes are taken as indicated in Fig. 3-8a, the external bending moment at a distance x from the origin is

$$M_{ext} = M + Py \tag{3.57}$$

This expression is valid regardless of whether the elastic limit of the material has been exceeded or not. The characteristics of the internal resisting moment do, however, depend on the state of stress in the member. As long as Hooke's law remains valid, the internal moment is given by the well-known relation

$$M_{int} = -EI\frac{d^2y}{dx^2} \tag{3.58}$$

To determine the relation between load and deflection up to the proportional limit, we equate (3.58) to (3.57). Thus

$$M + Py = -EI\frac{d^2y}{dx^2} \tag{3.59}$$

If the deflection is now assumed to be of the form

$$y = \delta \sin\frac{\pi x}{l} \tag{3.60}$$

the curvature can be written as

$$\frac{d^2y}{dx^2} = -\frac{\delta\pi^2}{l^2}\sin\frac{\pi x}{l} \tag{3.61}$$

Substitution of (3.61) into (3.59) gives

$$M + Py = EI\frac{\delta\pi^2}{l^2}\sin\frac{\pi x}{l}$$

which reduces to

$$M + P\delta = \frac{EI\delta\pi^2}{l^2} \tag{3.62}$$

at midspan.

Assuming that M is proportional to P, we introduce the notation

$$e = \frac{M}{P} \tag{3.63}$$

and rewrite Eq. (3.62) in the form

$$P(e + \delta) = \frac{\delta EI\pi^2}{l^2}$$

or

$$P(e + \delta) = \delta P_E \tag{3.64}$$

where $P_E = \pi^2 EI/l^2$ is the Euler load of the member. If both sides of (3.64) are divided by the depth h and the terms rearranged, one obtains

$$\frac{\delta}{h} = \frac{e}{h}\frac{1}{\dfrac{P_E}{P} - 1}$$

or

$$\frac{\delta}{h} = \frac{e}{h}\frac{1}{\dfrac{\sigma_E}{\sigma_0} - 1} \tag{3.65}$$

where $\sigma_E = P_E/bh$ is the Euler stress and $\sigma_0 = P/bh$ is the average axial stress.

As long as stresses remain elastic, Eq. (3.65) gives the correct load–deflection relationship for the member. To determine the load at which Eq. (3.65) becomes invalid, one must consider the maximum stress in the member. That latter is

$$\sigma_{\max} = \frac{P}{bh} + \frac{M + P\delta}{bh^2/6} \tag{3.66}$$

or, substituting Pe for M and σ_0 for P/bh,

$$\sigma_{\max} = \sigma_0\left[1 + \frac{6(e + \delta)}{h}\right] \tag{3.67}$$

The elastic load–deflection relation given by (3.65) becomes invalid when σ_{max} as given by (3.67) equals the yield stress.

Of the three expressions, (3.57), (3.58), and (3.60), used to determine the elastic load–deflection relation, only (3.58), the moment–curvature relation, must be revised when the elastic limit is exceeded. To determine the inelastic moment–curvature expression that is used in place of (3.58) in the inelastic range, let us consider the stress distributions depicted in Fig. 3-9. As indicated,

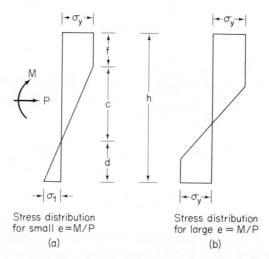

Stress distribution
for small $e = M/P$

(a)

Stress distribution
for large $e = M/P$

(b)

Fig. 3-9   Stress distribution for beam column in inelastic range. (Adapted from Ref. 1.12.)

two different distributions of stress are possible. If the ratio $e = M/P$ is relatively small, yielding occurs only on the concave side of the member prior to failure. This case is depicted in Fig. 3-9a. On the other hand, if e is relatively large, both the convex as well as the concave side of the member will have started to yield before the maximum load is reached (see Fig. 3-9b). To simplify the analysis, we shall restrict ourselves to small values of e and thus limit our concern to the stress distribution in Fig. 3-9a.

Equilibrium of forces in the x direction gives

$$P = b\left(\sigma_y f + \frac{\sigma_y c}{2} - \frac{\sigma_1 d}{2}\right)$$

which, after dividing both sides by bh, can be written as

$$\sigma_0 = \frac{1}{h}\left(\sigma_y f + \frac{\sigma_y c}{2} - \frac{\sigma_1 d}{2}\right) \tag{3.68}$$

The distances c, d, and f are defined in Fig. 3-9a, and σ_y and σ_1 are, respectively, the yield stress acting at the extreme fiber on the concave side of the member and the tensile stress acting at the extreme fiber on the convex side.

The internal moment is obtained by taking the moment of all the forces about the centroidal axis. Thus

$$M_{\text{int}} = \left[\sigma_y f \left(\frac{h}{2} - \frac{f}{2} \right) + \frac{\sigma_y c}{2} \left(\frac{h}{2} - f - \frac{c}{3} \right) + \frac{\sigma_1 d}{2} \left(\frac{h}{2} - \frac{d}{3} \right) \right] b \qquad (3.69)$$

Noting that $f + c + d = h$, Eqs. (3.68) and (3.69) can be solved for c. After some fairly involved algebraic manipulations, which are not reproduced here, one obtains

$$c = \frac{9 \left[\frac{h}{2} \left(\frac{\sigma_y}{\sigma_0} - 1 \right) - \frac{M_{\text{int}}}{P} \right]^2}{2 \sigma_0 h \left(\frac{\sigma_y}{\sigma_0} - 1 \right)^3} \qquad (3.70)$$

From Fig. 3-9a it is evident that

$$\epsilon_y = \frac{c}{\rho} \qquad (3.71)$$

where ρ is the radius of curvature.

Thus
$$\frac{d^2 y}{dx^2} = \frac{\epsilon_y}{c} \qquad (3.72)$$

from which
$$\frac{d^2 y}{dx^2} = \frac{\sigma_y}{Ec} \qquad (3.73)$$

Finally, substituting the expression for c given in (3.70) into (3.73) leads to

$$y'' = \frac{2 \sigma_0 h \left(\frac{\sigma_y}{\sigma_0} - 1 \right)^3}{9E \left[\frac{h}{2} \left(\frac{\sigma_y}{\sigma_0} - 1 \right) - \frac{M_{\text{int}}}{P} \right]^2} \qquad (3.74)$$

This is the inelastic moment–curvature relation that must be used in place of Eq. (3.58) once the stresses have exceeded the proportional limit.

In view of (3.57), (3.61), and (3.63), the curvature and moment at midspan are given by

$$(y'')_{l/2} = \frac{\delta \pi^2}{l^2}$$

and
$$(M_{\text{int}})_{l/2} = P(e + \delta)$$

Substitution of these expressions into (3.74) leads to

$$\delta\left[\frac{h}{2}\left(\frac{\sigma_y}{\sigma_0}-1\right)-e-\delta\right]^2 = \frac{2hl^2\sigma_0}{9E\pi^2}\left(\frac{\sigma_y}{\sigma_0}-1\right)^3$$

or

$$\frac{\delta}{h}\left[\frac{1}{2}\left(\frac{\sigma_y}{\sigma_0}-1\right)-\frac{e}{h}-\frac{\delta}{h}\right]^2 = \frac{2l^2\sigma_0}{9E\pi^2h^2}\left(\frac{\sigma_y}{\sigma_0}-1\right)^3 \qquad (3.75)$$

Since the Euler stress can be expressed as

$$\sigma_E = \frac{\pi^2 EI}{Al^2} = \frac{\pi^2 Eh^2}{12l^2}$$

Eq. (3.75) can also be written in the form

$$\frac{\delta}{h}\left[\frac{1}{2}\left(\frac{\sigma_y}{\sigma_0}-1\right)-\frac{\delta}{h}-\frac{e}{h}\right]^2 = \frac{1}{54}\frac{\sigma_0}{\sigma_E}\left(\frac{\sigma_y}{\sigma_0}-1\right)^3 \qquad (3.76)$$

Equation (3.76) gives the load–deflection relation in the inelastic range. It can be used from the onset of yielding up to failure, provided failure occurs before yielding commences on the convex side of the member.

With the aid of Eqs. (3.65) and (3.76) it is possible to obtain the entire load–deflection curve, from the beginning of loading to failure, for any member that falls within the limitations outlined at the start of the analysis.

As an example, let us consider a simply supported, rectangular, steel beam column with the following dimensions and properties:

length $l = 120$ in.
radius of gyration $r = 1$ in.
ratio of moment to axial load $e = 1.15$ in.
yield stress $\sigma_y = 34$ ksi
modulus of elasticity $E = 30 \times 10^3$ ksi

Based on this data

$$h = 2\sqrt{3}\text{ in.}, \qquad \frac{e}{h} = 0.33$$

and

$$\sigma_E = \frac{\pi^2 E}{(l/r)^2} = 20.6 \text{ ksi}$$

The load–deflection data for the elastic range, obtained using Eq. (3.65), are given in columns 1 and 2 of Table 3.1a. Corresponding to each set of values for σ_0 and δ/h listed in the table, the maximum stress has been determined using Eq. (3.67). The latter is given in column 3 of the table. It is evident from these data that the maximum stress in the member reaches 34 ksi, the

Table 3-1   Load–deflection data for beam column

1	2	3		1	2
σ_0 (ksi)	δ/h	σ_{max} (ksi)		σ_0 (ksi)	δ/h
2	0.036	6.4		8.0	0.21
4	0.080	14		8.5	0.24
6	0.137	23		9.0	0.30
8	0.212	34		9.1	0.35
10	0.314	—		9.0	0.40
12	0.463	—			
14	0.710	—		(b) Inelastic Range Eq. (3.76)	
16	1.150	—			

(a) Elastic range Eqs. (3.65) and (3.67)

yield stress, at approximately $\sigma_0 = 8$ ksi. As a result, Eq. (3.76), the inelastic load–deflection relation, must be used to obtain deflections for axial stresses in excess of 8 ksi. The load–deflection data for the inelastic range, obtained using Eq. (3.76), are listed in Table 3-1b.

The entire load–deflection curve, including both the elastic and the inelastic portions, is plotted in Fig. 3-10. The solid line represents the actual behavior of the member. A dashed line denoting the invalid part of the elastic curve is also included for comparison. Up to $\sigma_0 = 8$ ksi, the material obeys Hooke's law and the deformations are relatively small. However, as soon as yielding spreads beyond $\sigma_0 = 8$ ksi, there occurs a noticeable decrease in the stiffness of the member. This decrease builds up fairly rapidly until at approximately $\sigma_0 = 9.1$ ksi the member is no longer able to resist an increase in load. In other words, $\sigma_0 = 9.1$ ksi represents the maximum load that the member can support.

The results obtained here for a rectangular section and for a perfect elastic-plastic material are typical of the behavior exhibited by other shapes and other materials. However, the determination of the maximum load for most other sections and materials involves considerably more effort than was required to analyze the rectangular section with the perfect elastic-plastic material. In the majority of instances, closed-form solutions of the type presented here are out of the question, and numerical methods are the only means available for obtaining the maximum load. One such numerical solution for the maximum load of a structural-steel I beam is given by Galambos and Ketter (Ref. 3.5).

In view of the fact that the determination of the maximum load of a beam column is invariably complex and time consuming, the load at which yielding

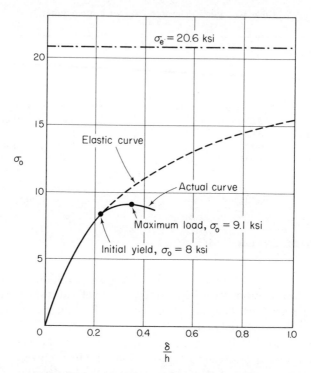

Fig. 3-10 Load–deflection curve for beam column.

begins has often been used in place of the maximum load as the limit of structural usefulness. The load corresponding to initial yielding is an attractive design criteria, because it is relatively easy to obtain and it gives a conservative estimate of the actual collapse load. However, it does have the disadvantage of being often too conservative. Fortunately, there has been developed an alternative semiempirical design criterion that is both accurate and relatively easy to use. This design criterion, the interaction equation, is considered in the following article.

3.6 DESIGN OF BEAM COLUMNS
INTERACTION EQUATION

In Article 3.5 the collapse load of a beam column was calculated. To simplify the analysis as much as possible, a very idealized member was chosen, a rectangular section made out of a perfect elastic-plastic material. Nevertheless, fairly lengthy and complicated calculations were needed to obtain the desired result. Had we attempted to determine the maximum load for some other member, the calculations would have been even more complex and far more time consuming. The impracticability of obtaining the collapse load of a beam column by purely theoretical procedures and the need for an empirical design formula are thus self-evident.

When a member is subject to a combined loading, such as bending and axial compression, an interaction equation provides a convenient way of approximating the ultimate strength (Ref. 3.6). Knowing the strength of the member in both pure compression and pure bending and knowing that the member can resist less compression and less bending when both of these loads are present, then if either is acting by itself, one can estimate how much bending and compression can be resisted if both are present. Such an approximation can then be verified experimentally.

To develop an interaction equation for combined bending and axial compression, let us introduce the ratios P/P_u and M/M_u, where

P = axial load acting on the member at failure when both axial compression and bending are present

P_u = ultimate load of the member when only axial compression is present, that is, the buckling load of the member

M = maximum primary bending moment acting on the member at failure when both bending and axial compression exist; this excludes the amplification in the moment due to presence of the axial load

M_u = ultimate bending moment when only bending exists, that is, the plastic moment of the section

Let us now calculate the above ratios for the rectangular beam column analyzed in Article 3.5. For that member the axial stress at failure was found to be $\sigma_0 = 9.1$ ksi and the Euler stress is $\sigma_E = 20.6$ ksi. Thus

$$\frac{P}{P_u} = \frac{\sigma_0}{\sigma_E} = \frac{9.1}{20.6} = 0.44$$

The ratio of the maximum primary moment at failure to the plastic moment of the section can be written in the form

$$\frac{M}{M_u} = \frac{\sigma_0(bh)e}{\sigma_y \dfrac{bh^2}{4}} = \frac{4\sigma_0}{\sigma_y}\frac{e}{h}$$

Substitution of $e/h = 0.33$, $\sigma_0 = 9.1$, and $\sigma_y = 34$ gives

$$\frac{M}{M_u} = \frac{4 \times 9.1 \times 0.33}{34.0} = 0.35$$

The ratios $P/P_u = 0.44$ and $M/M_u = 0.35$ give the maximum values of P and M that the rectangular beam column with $e/h = 0.33$ analyzed in Article 3.5 can resist. In Fig. 3-11 this result is shown plotted as point A on a

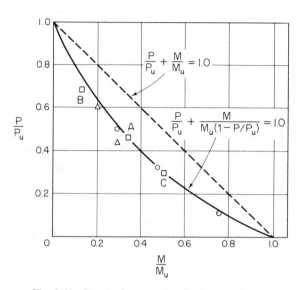

Fig. 3-11   Interaction equation for beam column.

graph whose ordinate is P/P_u and whose abscissa is M/M_u. Calculations similar to those leading to point A have been carried out by Jezek (Refs. 3.3 and 3.4) for rectangular beam columns with various values of e/h, and the results thus obtained are tabulated by Bleich (Ref. 1.12). Points B and C in the figure have been plotted using these data. In addition to these results, depicted by square points, the figure includes three circular points giving the maximum loads for structural-steel I beams and two triangular points that correspond to aluminum-alloy tubes. The data used to plot the circular points were obtained by Galambos and Ketter (Ref. 3.5) using a numerical integration method, and the failure loads represented by the triangular points were obtained experimentally by Clark (Ref. 3.7).

The lack of scatter exhibited by the failure loads plotted in Fig. 3-11 indicates that in all probability a single analytical expression can be found which will predict the maximum load for a variety of different beam columns. Such a relation, which is also simple enough to be useful in routine engineering, will now be developed.

It is fairly obvious that $P/P_u = 1.0$ when $M/M_u = 0$ and that $M/M_u = 1.0$ when $P/P_u = 0$. The desired curve must therefore pass through the points $(1, 0)$, $(0, 1)$. The simplest expression that satisfies this criterion is the straight line

$$\frac{P}{P_u} + \frac{M}{M_u} = 1.0 \tag{3.77}$$

depicted by the dashed line in Fig. 3-11. All the theoretically and experimentally obtained failure loads included in the figure fall below this curve. It can therefore be concluded that Eq. (3.77) gives an unconservative estimate of the maximum strength of beam columns and is not a satisfactory design criterion.

The reason for the discrepancy between Eq. (3.77) and the actual failure loads is that M, in the equation, is only the primary part of the total moment that acts on the member. In other words, M does not include the secondary moment produced by the product of the axial load and the lateral deflection. It was shown in Article 3.2 that the presence of an axial load amplifies the primary bending moment roughly by the ratio $1/[1 - (P/P_e)]$. If this factor is incorporated into Eq. (3.77), one obtains

$$\frac{P}{P_u} + \frac{M}{M_u[1 - (P/P_e)]} = 1.0 \tag{3.78}$$

This relation is shown plotted as a solid line in Fig. 3-11. It is evident that Eq. (3.78) agrees much better with the actual failure loads than did the straight line and that Eq. (3.78) appears to offer a satisfactory design criterion.

Although agreement has been shown to exist between Eq. (3.78) and only a limited number of cases, Eq. (3.78) is actually able to predict the ultimate load for a large variety of situations. The equation is applicable to I beams as well as rectangular sections, and to aluminum as well as steel. Furthermore, it makes no difference whether the primary moment is due to eccentric axial loading or to transverse loads or to a combination of the two. The only restriction is that the maximum moment occur at or near the center of the beam. Equation (3.78) is still applicable if this condition is not satisfied. However, a suitable factor must be introduced in the moment term of the equation (Ref. 3.8). In view of the fact that Eq. (3.78) is both simple to apply and remarkably accurate for a large number of different situations, it is used extensively as a design criterion for beam columns.

References

3.1   J. I. Parcel and R. B. B. Moorman, *Analysis of Statically Indeterminate Structures* (New York: John Wiley & Sons, Inc., 1955).

3.2   G. Winter, P. T. Hsu, B. Koo, and M. H. Loh, "Buckling of Trusses and Rigid Frames," *Cornell University Engineering Experimental Station Bulletin, No. 36*, Ithaca, N.Y., 1948.

3.3 K. Jezek, "Näherungsberechnung der Tragkraft exzentrisch gedrückter Stahlstäbe," *Der Stahlbau*, Vol. 8, 1935.

3.4 K. Jezek, "Die Tragfähigkeit axial gedrückter und auf Biegung beanspruchter Stahlstäbe," *Der Stahlbau*, Vol. 9, 1936.

3.5 T. V. Galambos and R. L. Ketter, "Columns Under Combined Bending and Thrust," *Transactions, ASCE*, Vol. 120, 1955.

3.6 F. R. Shanley and E. I. Ryder, "Stress Ratios," *Aviation*, Vol. 36, No. 6, 1937.

3.7 J. W. Clark, "Eccentrically Loaded Columns," *Transactions, ASCE*, Vol. 120, 1955.

3.8 W. McGuire, *Steel Structures* (Englewood Cliffs, N.J.: Prentice-Hall, Inc., 1968).

Problems

3.1 Obtain expressions for the maximum deflection and maximum moment of a beam column whose ends are built in and that is loaded with a concentrated load at midspan as shown in Fig. P3-1.

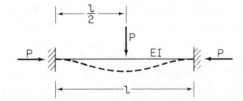

Fig. P3-1

3.2 Determine the maximum moment for a beam column that is bent in a reverse curve as shown in Fig. P3-2, when

Fig. P3-2

(a) $P/P_e = 0.2$
(b) $P/P_e = 0.8$
where $P_e = \pi^2 EI/L^2$. In view of the foregoing results, what can be concluded regarding the maximum moment in a beam column with reverse curvature?

3.3 The load P at which yielding commences in the beam column shown in Fig.

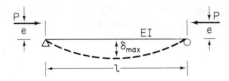

Fig. P3-3

P3-3 is given by the implicit relation

$$\sigma_y = \frac{P}{A}\left[1 + \frac{ec}{r^2}\sec\left(\frac{L}{2r}\sqrt{\frac{P}{EA}}\right)\right]$$

Noting that

$$\sigma_y = \sigma_{max} = \frac{P}{A} + P\frac{(e + \sigma_{max})c}{I}$$

derive the relation.

The terms used in the relations are defined as follows:

A = cross-sectional area
c = distance from neutral axis to extreme fiber
r = radius of gyration
σ_y = yield stress
σ_{max} = maximum stress

4
BUCKLING
OF FRAMES

4.1 INTRODUCTION

When considering the subject of column stability in Chapter 1, it was desirable to limit our concern to individual members with very idealized boundary conditions. However, many columns found in actual engineering structures occur neither as isolated members nor are their ends hinged, fixed, or free. Instead, these members are usually part of a larger framework, and their ends are elastically restrained by the members to which they are attached. To make our study of columns complete, it is thus desirable that we consider the behavior of framed columns as well as the characteristics of isolated members.

In a framework, the members are as a rule rigidly connected to one another at the joints. Consequently, no single compression member can buckle without all the members in the frame becoming simultaneously deformed. In other words, the elastic restraint at the end of a given compression member depends not only on the members framing directly into it but on each and every member in the entire system. To obtain the critical load of one or more compression members that are part of a larger framework, it is thus necessary to investigate the stability of the entire frame acting as a single unit.

In this chapter we shall consider several methods for obtaining the critical loading of a frame. This will be followed by a brief summary of approximate procedures for estimating the critical load of a framed column when a rigorous stability analysis of the entire frame is not warranted.

4.2 MODES OF BUCKLING

Let us begin the study of frame buckling by considering the single-story single-bay frame in Fig. 4-1. The external loads P are assumed to act directly

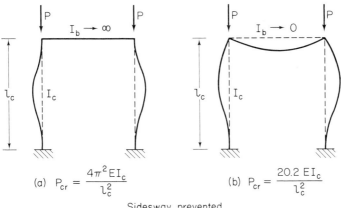

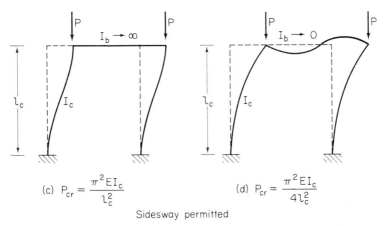

Fig. 4-1   Buckling modes of portal frame.

over the columns so that there is no bending moment in any member of the frame prior to buckling. When analyzing frames, it is useful to divide them into two categories: those in which sidesway is prevented (parts a and b of the figure) and those in which the upper joints are free to move horizontally (parts c and d). We need not be concerned with the way in which sidesway is prevented, only with whether it is prevented from taking place or not.

We consider first the frame in which sidesway is prevented. At the critical load this frame buckles as indicated by the solid line in the figure. It is self-evident in this simple structure that buckling takes place when the applied load is equal to the critical load of the columns. It is also obvious that the upper end of each column is elastically restrained by the beam to which the column is rigidly connected, and that the critical load of the column therefore depends not only on the column stiffness, but also on the stiffness of the beam. The problem is greatly simplified if we assume the beam to be infinitely rigid. The beam must then remain straight while the frame deforms (part a), and the columns can neither rotate nor translate at their upper ends. Under these circumstances the columns behave as if they were fixed at both extremities, and the critical load of the frame is equal to four times the Euler load of the columns. Alternatively, the beam can be assumed to be infinitely flexible. The beam is then unable to offer any rotational restraint to the upper end of the column (part b). In this case the columns behave as if they were fixed at one end and hinged at the other, and the critical load of the frame is approximately equal to twice the Euler load of the columns.

For an actual frame the flexibility of the beam must lie somewhere between the two extreme conditions just considered. The critical load of such a frame, in which sidesway is prevented, can therefore be bracketed as follows:

$$2P_e < P_{cr} < 4P_e \tag{4.1}$$

where P_{cr} is the critical value of the applied load and P_e is the Euler load of the columns.

The line of reasoning that has just been applied to frames in which sidesway is prevented can also be applied to frames whose upper joints are free to move laterally. If the beam is infinitely rigid, the frame buckles in the manner indicated in part c. The upper ends of the columns are free to translate, but they cannot rotate. Hence the critical load of the frame is equal to the Euler load of the columns. On the other hand, if the beam is infinitely flexible, the upper ends of the columns are free to both rotate and translate, as indicated in part d. In this case the columns act as if they were fixed at the base and free at the top, and the critical load of the frame is equal to one fourth the Euler load of the columns. The critical load of the frame whose upper joints are free to translate laterally must therefore lie between P_e and $\frac{1}{4}P_e$. That is,

$$\tfrac{1}{4}P_e < P_{cr} < P_e \tag{4.2}$$

Comparison of the results in (4.1) for symmetric buckling with those given in (4.2) for sidesway buckling indicates that the load required to cause symmetric buckling is larger than the one needed for sidesway regardless of the stiffness of the members. It can therefore be concluded that the portal frame in Fig. 4-1 will always buckle in the sidesway mode unless it is laterally braced, in which case it must buckle in the symmetric mode. It has been shown

by Bleich (Ref. 1.12) that this conclusion is valid for multistory frames as well
as for single-story frames.

4.3 CRITICAL LOAD OF A FRAME USING NEUTRAL EQUILIBRIUM

In Article 4.2 we discussed the qualitative aspects of the buckling characteristics of a single-story single-bay frame. Let us now, by means of the method
of neutral equilibrium, calculate the critical load of such a frame. Depending
on whether the frame is laterally restrained or not, buckling will take place
in the symmetric or in the sidesway mode. We shall consider first the case of a
laterally unrestrained frame.

Sidesway Buckling

The frame in Fig. 4-2a is fixed at the base and free to translate laterally at
the top. It is assumed that the frame's material behaves according to Hooke's

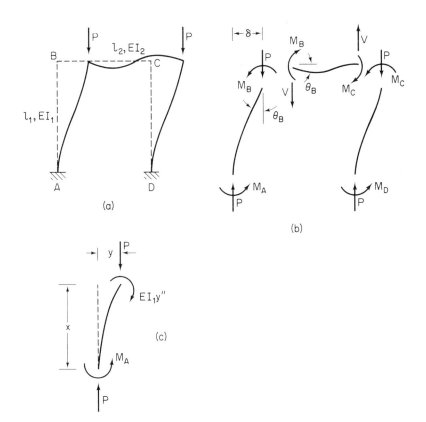

Fig. 4-2 Sidesway buckling.

law, that the deformations remain small, and that there is no primary bending present in the frame prior to buckling. To differentiate the column properties from the beam properties, the subscript 1 is used to denote the former and the subscript 2 to denote the latter.

When the frame buckles it assumes the shape indicated by the solid lines in Fig. 4-2a. The forces acting on each of the individual members when the frame is thus deformed are shown in Fig. 4-2b. It should be noted that the shears V that arise from the bending of the horizontal member are neglected in comparison to the applied load P when dealing with the vertical members. Taking the coordinate axes as shown in Fig. 4-2c, the equation of moment equilibrium for the vertical member is

$$EI_1 \frac{d^2y}{dx^2} + Py = M_A \tag{4.3}$$

or

$$\frac{d^2y}{dx^2} + k_1^2 y = \frac{M_A}{EI_1} \tag{4.4}$$

where $k_1^2 = P/EI_1$. The solution of Eq. (4.4) is

$$y = A \sin k_1 x + B \cos k_1 x + \frac{M_A}{P} \tag{4.5}$$

From the condition

$$y = 0 \quad \text{at } x = 0$$

one obtains

$$B = -\frac{M_A}{P}$$

and the condition

$$\frac{dy}{dx} = 0 \quad \text{at } x = 0$$

leads to

$$A = 0$$

Thus

$$y = \frac{M_A}{P}(1 - \cos k_1 x) \tag{4.6}$$

Denoting the horizontal displacement of the column at $x = l_1$ by δ, Eq. (4.6) can be rewritten in the form

$$\delta = \frac{M_A}{P}(1 - \cos k_1 l_1) \tag{4.7}$$

Moment equilibrium of the member requires that

$$\delta = \frac{M_A + M_B}{P} \tag{4.8}$$

Substitution of this relation in (4.7) leads to

$$M_A \cos k_1 l_1 + M_B = 0 \tag{4.9}$$

A second equation, representing the equilibrium condition of the horizontal member, will now be derived. Applying the slope–deflection relationship to this member, we obtain

$$M_B = \frac{2EI_2}{l_2}(2\theta_B + \theta_C) \tag{4.10}$$

or, since $\theta_C = \theta_B$,

$$M_B = \frac{6EI_2}{l_2}\theta_B \tag{4.11}$$

The compatibility condition at joint B requires that θ_B as given by Eq. (4.11) be equal to the slope dy/dx at $x = l_1$ obtained from Eq. (4.6). Thus

$$\frac{M_B l_2}{6EI_2} = \frac{M_A}{k_1 EI_1} \sin k_1 l_1$$

from which

$$\frac{6I_2}{k_1 I_1 l_2} M_A \sin k_1 l_1 - M_B = 0 \tag{4.12}$$

Equations (4.9) and (4.12) are the equilibrium conditions for the frame. Ordinarily, a frame with n members would require n such equations. However, in this case, because the vertical members are identical, two equations suffice. To determine the stability condition, we set the determinant of Eqs. (4.9) and (4.12) equal to zero. This leads to

$$\frac{\tan k_1 l_1}{k_1 l_1} = -\frac{I_1 l_2}{6I_2 l_1} \tag{4.13}$$

The critical load is the smallest root of this equation.

For example, let us suppose that

$$I_1 = I_2 = I$$
$$l_1 = l_2 = l$$

For this case, Eq. (4.13) reduces to

$$\frac{\tan kl}{kl} = -\frac{1}{6}$$

from which

$$kl = 2.71$$

and

$$P_{cr} = \frac{7.34EI}{l^2}$$

This is the critical load for a fixed-base portal frame free to move laterally at the top. It should be noted that this critical load does fall, as it should, between the limits established for the sidesway mode in Article 4.2.

Symmetric Buckling

If the frame is prevented from translating laterally at the top, buckling will occur in the symmetric mode, as indicated in Fig. 4-3a. The forces acting on

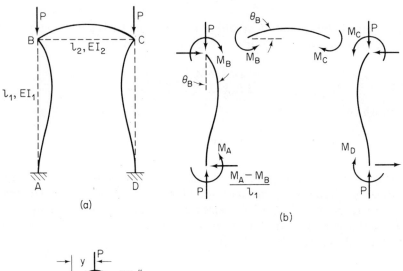

(a)

(b)

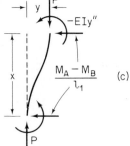

(c)

Fig. 4-3 Symmetric buckling.

individual members when this mode of buckling occurs are shown in Fig. 4-3b. Moment equilibrium for the vertical member (Fig. 4-3c) requires that

$$EI_1\frac{d^2y}{dx^2} + Py = M_A - (M_A - M_B)\frac{x}{l_1} \tag{4.14}$$

or

$$\frac{d^2y}{dx^2} + k_1^2 y = \frac{M_A}{EI_1}\left(1 - \frac{x}{l_1}\right) + \frac{M_B}{EI_1}\left(\frac{x}{l_1}\right) \tag{4.15}$$

where $k_1^2 = P/EI_1$. The solution to Eq. (4.15) is

$$y = A \sin k_1 x + B \cos k_1 x + \frac{M_A}{P}\left(1 - \frac{x}{l_1}\right) + \frac{M_B}{P}\left(\frac{x}{l_1}\right) \tag{4.16}$$

From the condition

$$y = 0 \quad \text{at } x = 0$$

we obtain

$$B = -\frac{M_A}{P}$$

and the condition

$$\frac{dy}{dx} = 0 \quad \text{at } x = 0$$

leads to

$$A = \frac{M_A - M_B}{k_1 P l_1}$$

Thus

$$\begin{aligned} y &= \frac{M_A}{P}\left(\frac{1}{k_1 l_1}\sin k_1 x - \cos k_1 x + 1 - \frac{x}{l_1}\right) \\ &\quad + \frac{M_B}{P}\left(\frac{x}{l_1} - \frac{1}{k_1 l_1}\sin k_1 x\right) \end{aligned} \tag{4.17}$$

Since the upper end of the member cannot translate laterally

$$y = 0 \quad \text{at } x = l_1$$

and Eq. (4.17) reduces to

$$M_A(\sin k_1 l_1 - k_1 l_1 \cos k_1 l_1) + M_B(k_1 l_1 - \sin k_1 l_1) = 0 \tag{4.18}$$

As before, a second equation is obtained by considering the horizontal member. Applying the slope–deflection equation, we can write

$$M_B = \frac{2EI_2}{l_2}(2\theta_B + \theta_C) \tag{4.19}$$

or, since $\theta_C = -\theta_B$,

$$M_B = \frac{2EI_2}{l_2}\theta_B \tag{4.20}$$

Compatibility of slopes at joint B requires that θ_B of the horizontal member be equal to $-dy/dx$ at $x = l_1$ of the vertical member. That is

$$\frac{M_B l_2}{2EI_2} = -\frac{M_A}{P}\left(\frac{1}{l_1}\cos k_1 l_1 + k_1 \sin k l_1 - \frac{1}{l_1}\right) - \frac{M_B}{P}\left(\frac{1}{l_1} - \frac{1}{l_1}\cos k_1 l_1\right)$$

from which

$$M_A(\cos k_1 l_1 + k_1 l_1 \sin k_1 l_1 - 1) + M_B\left(1 - \cos k_1 l_1 + \frac{I_1 l_1 k_1^2 l_2}{2I_2}\right) = 0 \tag{4.21}$$

To obtain the stability condition, we set the determinant of Eqs. (4.18) and (4.21) equal to zero. This leads to the equation

$$2 - 2\cos k_1 l_1 - k_1 l_1 \sin k_1 l_1 + \frac{l_2 I_1 k_1}{2I_2}\left(\sin k_1 l_1 - k_1 l_1 \cos k_1 l_1\right) = 0 \tag{4.22}$$

The critical load is obtained from the smallest root of this equation.
Setting $I_1 = I_2 = I$ and $l_1 = l_2 = l$ in (4.22), one obtains

$$kl \sin kl + 4\cos kl + (kl)^2 \cos kl = 4$$

from which

$$kl = 5.02$$

and

$$P_{cr} = \frac{25.2EI}{l^2}$$

This is the critical load for a fixed-base portal frame whose beam has the same stiffness as the columns and that is laterally restrained. As previously predicted, this load is considerably larger than the critical load for the same frame when sidesway is not prevented.

4.4   CALCULATION OF CRITICAL LOADING USING SLOPE–DEFLECTION EQUATIONS

In Article 4.3 the critical loading of a portal frame was obtained by writing a differential equation for the column and a slope–deflection equation for the beam and by solving these equations simultaneously. Although this procedure could, in theory, be used on any size frame, in actuality it becomes prohibitively complex when applied to any but a single-bay single-story frame. However, it has been demonstrated by Winter, Hsu, Koo, and Loh (Ref. 3.2) that a significant reduction in the complexity of the calculations is obtained if one uses the slope–deflection equations for axially loaded bars, developed in Article 3.4, for each and every member of the frame. To illustrate this method, let us consider the two-story frame depicted in Fig. 4-4. It is assumed

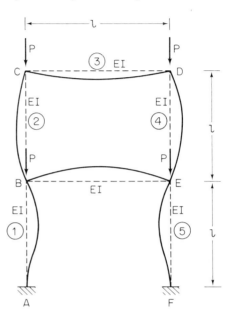

Fig. 4-4 Buckling of two-story frame.

that sidesway is prevented and that the flexural stiffness EI/l is the same for each member. Accordingly, the frame is completely symmetric and only one half need be considered in the analysis.

Numbering the different members as indicated in the figure and letting $K = EI/l$, the moments, according to Eq. (3.56), are given by

$$M_{BA} = K(\alpha_{n1}\theta_B)$$
$$M_{BE} = K(\alpha_{n2}\theta_B + \alpha_{f2}\theta_E)$$
$$M_{BC} = K(\alpha_{n3}\theta_B + \alpha_{f3}\theta_C) \qquad (4.23)$$
$$M_{CB} = K(\alpha_{n3}\theta_C + \alpha_{f3}\theta_B)$$
$$M_{CD} = K(\alpha_{n4}\theta_C + \alpha_{f4}\theta_D)$$

Since the two horizontal members do not have any primary axial loading

$$\alpha_{n2} = \alpha_{n4} = 4$$
$$\alpha_{f2} = \alpha_{f4} = 2$$

Furthermore, due to symmetry

$$\theta_C = -\theta_B$$
$$\theta_D = -\theta_C$$

Thus

$$M_{BA} = K(\alpha_{n1}\theta_B)$$
$$M_{BE} = K(2\theta_B)$$
$$M_{BC} = K(\alpha_{n3}\theta_B + \alpha_{f3}\theta_C) \qquad (4.24)$$
$$M_{CB} = K(\alpha_{n3}\theta_C + \alpha_{f3}\theta_B)$$
$$M_{CD} = K(2\theta_C)$$

The equations of moment equilibrium at joints B and C are

$$M_{BA} + M_{BE} + M_{BC} = 0 \qquad (4.25)$$
$$M_{CB} + M_{CD} = 0 \qquad (4.26)$$

Substituting the moments in (4.24) into these relations gives

$$\theta_B(\alpha_{n1} + \alpha_{n3} + 2) + \theta_C(\alpha_{f3}) = 0 \qquad (4.27)$$
$$\theta_B(\alpha_{f3}) + \theta_C(\alpha_{n3} + 2) = 0 \qquad (4.28)$$

To obtain the stability condition, we set the determinant of these equations equal to zero. This leads to

$$(\alpha_{n3} + 2)(\alpha_{n1} + \alpha_{n3} + 2) - (\alpha_{f3})^2 = 0 \qquad (4.29)$$

Using the values of α and kl given in the Appendix, Eq. (4.29) can be solved by trial and error for the critical loading. Since $k_1 = \sqrt{2P/EI}$ and $k_3 = \sqrt{P/EI}$ it follows that $k_1 = k_3\sqrt{2}$. A trial-and-error procedure eventually leads to the result

$$k_3 l = 3.55$$

and

$$P_{cr} = \frac{12.6EI}{l^2}$$

4.5 STABILITY OF A FRAME BY MATRIX ANALYSIS

The matrix method used in Article 2.14 to analyze the stability of an individual compression member has been shown by Hartz (Ref. 4.1) to be equally well suited for determining the critical loading of an entire frame. As an illustration, let us consider the stability of the simple portal frame shown in

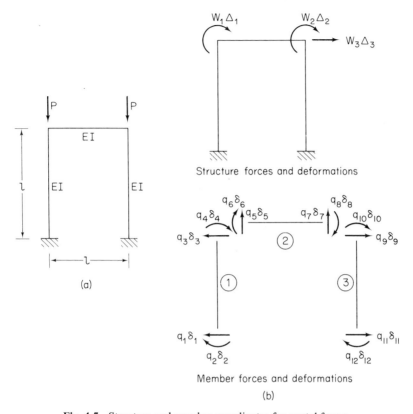

Fig. 4-5 Structure and member coordinates for portal frame.

Fig. 4-5a. Each member of the frame has a length l and stiffness EI, and the frame is fixed at the base, free to move laterally at the top, and loaded as indicated in the figure. For the sake of simplicity we let each member consist of only a single element. Positive element and structure nodal deformations and forces are defined in Fig. 4-5b.

In accordance with Eq. (2.184) the stiffness matrices for the columns are given by

$$[k_1] = [k_3] = \frac{EI}{l^3}\begin{pmatrix} 12 & -6 & -12 & -6 \\ -6 & 4 & 6 & 2 \\ -12 & 6 & 12 & 6 \\ -6 & 2 & 6 & 4 \end{pmatrix} - \frac{P}{l}\begin{pmatrix} \dfrac{6}{5} & -\dfrac{1}{10} & -\dfrac{6}{5} & -\dfrac{1}{10} \\[2mm] -\dfrac{1}{10} & \dfrac{2}{15} & \dfrac{1}{10} & -\dfrac{1}{30} \\[2mm] -\dfrac{6}{5} & \dfrac{1}{10} & \dfrac{6}{5} & \dfrac{1}{10} \\[2mm] -\dfrac{1}{10} & -\dfrac{1}{30} & \dfrac{1}{10} & \dfrac{2}{15} \end{pmatrix}$$

$$(4.30)$$

and the stiffness matrix for the beam takes the form

$$[k_2] = \frac{EI}{l^3} \begin{pmatrix} 12 & -6 & -12 & -6 \\ -6 & 4 & 6 & 2 \\ -12 & 6 & 12 & 6 \\ -6 & 2 & 6 & 4 \end{pmatrix} \tag{4.31}$$

As indicated in (2.184), the coefficients in these matrices all have the dimensions of force per unit distance.

To obtain the structure stiffness matrix, the element stiffness matrices are first transformed to structure coordinates and then combined. The transformation from element to structure coordinates is carried out in accordance with Eq. (2.145). That is,

$$[K_n] = [B_n]^T [k_n][B_n] \tag{4.32}$$

in which $[B_n]$, the transformation matrix for the nth element, is defined by Eq. (2.141) as

$$[\delta_n] = [B_n][\Delta_n] \tag{4.33}$$

Accordingly, the transformation matrices for elements 1, 2, and 3 of the frame are

$$[B_1] = \begin{matrix} \Delta_1 & \Delta_2 & \Delta_3 \\ \begin{pmatrix} 0 & 0 & 0 \\ 0 & 0 & 0 \\ 0 & 0 & -1 \\ 1 & 0 & 0 \end{pmatrix} & \begin{matrix} \delta_1 \\ \delta_2 \\ \delta_3 \\ \delta_4 \end{matrix} \end{matrix} \tag{4.34}$$

$$[B_2] = \begin{matrix} \Delta_1 & \Delta_2 & \Delta_3 \\ \begin{pmatrix} 0 & 0 & 0 \\ 1 & 0 & 0 \\ 0 & 0 & 0 \\ 0 & 1 & 0 \end{pmatrix} & \begin{matrix} \delta_5 \\ \delta_6 \\ \delta_7 \\ \delta_8 \end{matrix} \end{matrix} \tag{4.35}$$

$$[B_3] = \begin{matrix} \Delta_1 & \Delta_2 & \Delta_3 \\ \begin{pmatrix} 0 & 0 & 1 \\ 0 & 1 & 0 \\ 0 & 0 & 0 \\ 0 & 0 & 0 \end{pmatrix} & \begin{matrix} \delta_9 \\ \delta_{10} \\ \delta_{11} \\ \delta_{12} \end{matrix} \end{matrix} \tag{4.36}$$

Using these transformation matrices and carrying out the operations indicated in (4.32), the stiffness matrices in (4.30) and (4.31) become

$$[K_1] = \frac{EI}{l^3} \begin{pmatrix} 4 & 0 & -6 \\ 0 & 0 & 0 \\ -6 & 0 & 12 \end{pmatrix} - \frac{P}{l} \begin{pmatrix} \frac{2}{15} & 0 & -\frac{1}{10} \\ 0 & 0 & 0 \\ -\frac{1}{10} & 0 & \frac{6}{5} \end{pmatrix} \qquad (4.37)$$

$$[K_2] = \frac{EI}{l^3} \begin{pmatrix} 4 & 2 & 0 \\ 2 & 4 & 0 \\ 0 & 0 & 0 \end{pmatrix} \qquad (4.38)$$

$$[K_3] = \frac{EI}{l^3} \begin{pmatrix} 0 & 0 & 0 \\ 0 & 4 & -6 \\ 0 & -6 & 12 \end{pmatrix} - \frac{P}{l} \begin{pmatrix} 0 & 0 & 0 \\ 0 & \frac{2}{15} & -\frac{1}{10} \\ 0 & -\frac{1}{10} & \frac{6}{5} \end{pmatrix} \qquad (4.39)$$

The structure stiffness matrix obtained by combining the transformed element stiffness matrices is

$$K = \frac{EI}{l^3} \begin{pmatrix} 8 & 2 & -6 \\ 2 & 8 & -6 \\ -6 & -6 & 24 \end{pmatrix} - \frac{P}{l} \begin{pmatrix} \frac{2}{15} & 0 & -\frac{1}{10} \\ 0 & \frac{2}{15} & -\frac{1}{10} \\ -\frac{1}{10} & -\frac{1}{10} & \frac{12}{5} \end{pmatrix} \qquad (4.40)$$

If we let

$$\lambda = \frac{Pl^2}{30EI} \qquad (4.41)$$

the structure stiffness matrix reduces to

$$K = \frac{EI}{l^3} \begin{pmatrix} 8 - 4\lambda & 2 & -6 + 3\lambda \\ 2 & 8 - 4\lambda & -6 + 3\lambda \\ -6 + 3\lambda & -6 + 3\lambda & 24 - 72\lambda \end{pmatrix} \qquad (4.42)$$

At the critical load the determinant of the stiffness matrix must vanish. Expanding the determinant of the matrix in (4.42) and setting the resulting expression equal to zero gives

$$1080\lambda^3 - 4596\lambda^2 + 5136\lambda - 1008 = 0 \qquad (4.43)$$

The smallest root of this equation is $\lambda_1 = 0.25$ from which

$$P_{cr} = \frac{7.5EI}{l^2}$$

This result is very close to the exact value of $7.34EI/l^2$ obtained in Article 4.3 for the critical load in the sidesway mode.

4.6 EFFECT OF PRIMARY BENDING AND PLASTICITY ON FRAME BEHAVIOR

In the preceding articles the stability of frames was investigated assuming that neither primary bending nor inelastic behavior existed in the frame prior to buckling. Since one or both of these conditions are often not fulfilled in an actual frame, we want to briefly consider how the presence of primary bending and plasticity affects the behavior of a frame.

Effect of Primary Bending on Elastic Buckling Load

If a frame is loaded as shown in Fig. 4-6a, no bending is present in any of its members prior to buckling, and the frame remains undeformed until the critical load is reached (curve 1, Fig. 4-6c). By comparison, if a frame is loaded as indicated in Fig. 4-6b, primary bending is present in each member from the onset of loading, and the frame deforms in accordance with curve 2 in Fig. 4-6c. Frames of the latter type, in which primary bending is present prior to buckling, have been studied by Masur, Chang, and Donnell (Ref. 4.2), Lu (Ref. 4.3), and Marcus (Ref. 4.4). In each of these investigations the same conclusion is reached: primary bending does not significantly lower the critical load of a frame as long as stresses remain elastic. The only exception to these findings occurs when the beam is exceptionally long in comparison with the columns. In that instance, the presence of primary bending reduces the symmetric buckling load of the frame. However, frames with relatively long beams are rarely encountered, and for the majority of cases it therefore appears safe to conclude that the effect of primary bending can be neglected in determining the elastic buckling load of a frame. In all this, it is important to underline the fact that primary bending is negligible only in the determination of the critical loading of framed members and not in their design. When carrying out the design, the member must be treated as a beam column, and both axial compression and bending must be considered.

Inelastic Buckling Load

The maximum load that a frame can support is equal to the elastically determined critical load only if the stress does not exceed the proportional

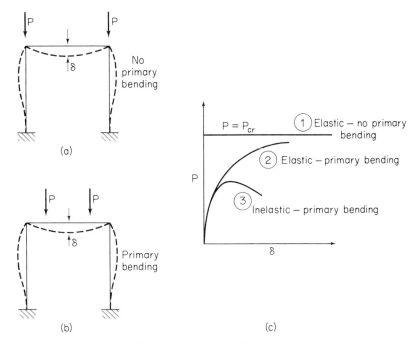

Fig. 4-6 Behavior of frames.

limit at any point in the frame prior to buckling. If the proportional limit is exceeded before instability occurs, the frame will fail at a load that is smaller than the elastic critical load (curve 3 in Fig. 4-6c). A rough estimate of the collapse load for inelastically stressed frames can be obtained if an interaction equation similar to the beam-column design formula is used.

The ultimate load of a frame can never exceed either the elastically determined critical load or the plastic mechanism load. If instability were the only factor leading to collapse, failure would occur at the critical load. On the other hand, if collapse were solely due to plasticity effects, the frame would fail when it became a mechanism as a result of the formation of plastic hinges. Actually, however, both instability and plasticity are present, and collapse occurs due to an interaction of the two at a load that is lower than either the critical load or the plastic mechanism load. It has been proposed by Horne and Merchant (Ref. 4.5) that the following empirical relation, known as the Rankine equation, be used to predict this failure load:

$$\frac{P_f}{P_e} + \frac{P_f}{P_p} = 1.0 \qquad (4.44)$$

where P_f = failure load

P_e = elastically determined critical load
P_p = plastic mechanism load

It has been shown that the results obtained using Eq. (4.44) are usually conservative and reasonably accurate. A more precise value of the collapse load than the one given by Eq. (4.44) can unfortunately be obtained only by carrying out a lengthy and complex analysis for which a computer is an absolute necessity. Examples of such an analysis have been presented by Moses (Ref. 4.6), Alvarez and Birnstiel (Ref. 4.7), and Galambos (Ref. 4.8).

4.7 DESIGN OF FRAMED COLUMNS

A framed compression member may be loaded axially, in which case it is designed as a column or, as is more likely, it is subject to both bending and axial loading and must be designed as a beam column using an interaction equation. In either case, the critical load of the member is required. One way of determining the critical load is to carry out a stability analysis of the entire frame. Such an analysis gives the magnitude of the external loads at the instant when the frame becomes unstable, from which the loads in individual compression members at buckling can readily be determined. However, an analysis of the entire frame is often too involved for routine design, and approximate methods involving relatively simple calculations are desirable.

One very simple but quite crude method of obtaining the critical load of a framed column is to estimate the degree of restraint existing at the ends of the member by interpolating between the idealized boundary conditions shown in Fig. 4-7. Both the rotational and translational restraint at the ends of the member must be considered. To estimate the degree of rotational restraint existing at the end of a member requires that one consider both the stiffness of the adjacent members and the rigidity of the connections. Whether or not the ends of the member translate laterally relative to each other depends on whether or not the frame is braced against sidesway.

A second method for estimating the critical load of a framed column, considerably more accurate than the previous procedure, was developed by Julian and Lawrence (Ref. 4.9). This method involves an exact analysis. However, only the member in question and the beams and columns that frame directly into it are considered. The influence of members in the frame not directly connected to the column being investigated is neglected. Thus the critical load of column AB in the frame in Fig. 4-8a is obtained by analyzing the subassemblage of members shown as dotted lines in the figure. The value of this method is greatly enhanced by the fact that the critical load can be obtained graphically. The nomograph shown in Fig. 4-8b allows one to determine directly the effective length of a framed column, given the

Buckled shape	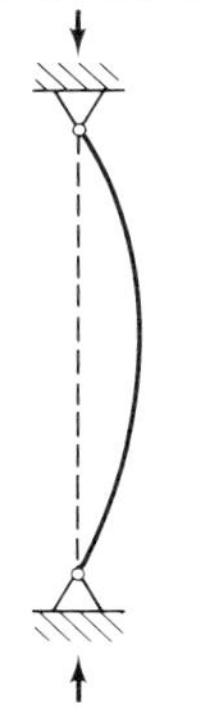			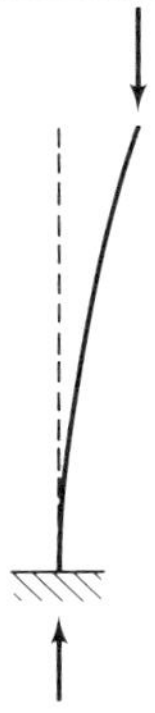	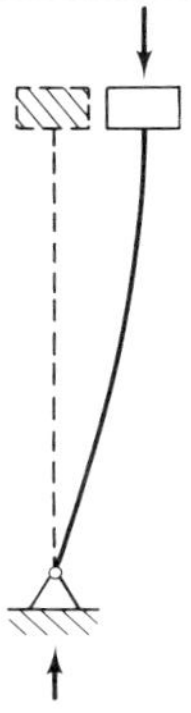	
Lower end conditions — Rotation	Free	Fixed	Fixed	Fixed	Free	Fixed
Lower end conditions — Translation	Fixed	Fixed	Fixed	Fixed	Fixed	Fixed
Upper end conditions — Rotation	Free	Fixed	Fixed	Free	Fixed	Free
Upper end conditions — Translation	Fixed	Fixed	Free	Free	Free	Fixed
Effective length λ	L	$0.5L$	L	$2L$	$2L$	$0.7L$
Critical load $\dfrac{\pi^2 EI}{\lambda^2}$	$\dfrac{\pi^2 EI}{L^2}$	$\dfrac{4\pi^2 EI}{L^2}$	$\dfrac{\pi^2 EI}{L^2}$	$\dfrac{\pi^2 EI}{4L^2}$	$\dfrac{\pi^2 EI}{4L^2}$	$\dfrac{2.02 EI}{L^2}$

Fig. 4-7 Idealized boundary conditions.

191

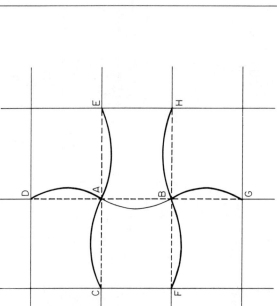

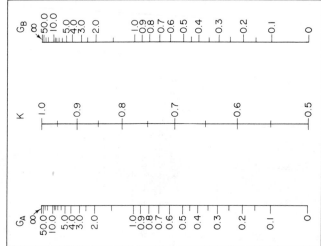

Sidesway prevented

(a) Framed column and subassemblage of adjacent members assumed to resist its deformation

(b) Jackson and Moreland nomograph for effective length of framed columns

Fig. 4-8 Julian and Lawrence method for estimating effective length of framed column. (Adapted from Ref. 4.9.)

stiffnesses of the adjacent members. The latter are accounted for by means of the parameters

$$G_A = \frac{I_{AB}/L_{AB} + I_{AD}/L_{AD}}{I_{CA}/L_{CA} + I_{AE}/L_{AE}} \tag{4.45}$$

$$G_B = \frac{I_{AB}/L_{AB} + I_{BG}/L_{BG}}{I_{FB}/L_{FB} + I_{BH}/L_{BH}} \tag{4.46}$$

in which I and L are the moment of inertia and unbraced length of the members lying in the plane of buckling of the column being considered. The nomograph shown in the figure is for a laterally braced frame. A similar graph for a laterally unbraced frame can also be constructed.

References

4.1   B. J. HARTZ, "Matrix Formulation of Structural Stability Problems," *Journal of the Structural Division, ASCE*, Vol. 91, No. ST6, 1965.

4.2   E. F. MASUR, I. C. CHANG, and L. H. DONNELL, "Stability of Frames in the Presence of Primary Bending Moments," *Journal of the Engineering Mechanics Division, ASCE*, Vol. 87, No. EM4, 1961.

4.3   L. W. LU, "Stability of Frames Under Primary Bending Moments," *Journal of the Structural Division, ASCE*, Vol. 89, No. ST3, 1963.

4.4   A. MARCUS, "A Stiffness Matrix Study of the Elastic Stability of Beams and Portal Frames" (Ph.D. Thesis, University of Massachusetts, 1969).

4.5   M. R. HORNE and W. MERCHANT, *The Stability of Frames* (New York: Pergamon Press, 1965), p. 138.

4.6   F. MOSES, "Stability of Inelastic Frames" (Ph.D. Thesis, Cornell University, 1963).

4.7   R. J. ALVAREZ and C. BIRNSTIEL, "Inelastic Analysis of Multistory Multibay Frames," *Journal of the Structural Division, ASCE*, Vol. 95, No. ST11, 1969.

4.8   T. V. GALAMBOS, *Structural Members and Frames* (Englewood Cliffs, N.J.: Prentice-Hall, Inc., 1968).

4.9   O. G. JULIAN and L. S. LAWRENCE, "Notes on J and L Nomograms for Determination of Effective Lengths," unpublished (1959).

Problems

4.1   Using the energy method, determine the critical loads and the corresponding mode shapes for the two-degree-of-freedom frame model shown in Fig. P4-1. Each member in the frame consists of two rigid bars connected to each other at the middle of the member by a pin and a rotational spring of stiffness $C = M/\theta$, where M is the moment at the spring and θ is the angle between the bars. The columns are pin connected at their bases and rigidly connected to the beam. $(P_1 = C/L, b = 0; P_2 = 3C/L, a = b)$

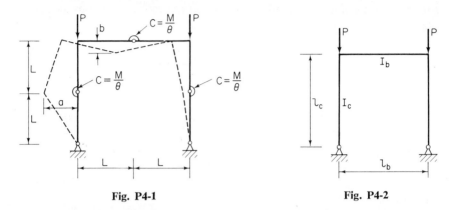

Fig. P4-1   Fig. P4-2

4.2 Using reasoning similar to that employed in Article 4.2, determine the limiting values for the symmetric and sidesway buckling loads of the frame in Fig. P4-2.

4.3 Letting $l_c = l_b = l$ and $I_c = I_b = I$, determine the critical load of the frame in Fig. P4-2 for
(a) the sidesway mode,
(b) the symmetric mode.
Find the critical load by setting up and solving the governing differential equations.

4.4 Using the matrix method, determine the critical load of the framed column in Fig. P4-3. Let each member consist of a single element.

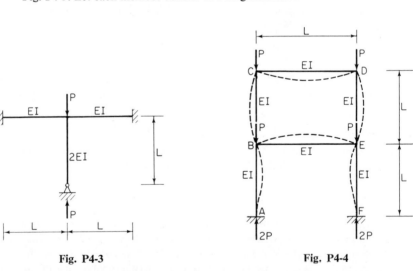

Fig. P4-3   Fig. P4-4

4.5 Using the nomograph given in Article 4.7, determine an approximate value for the critical load of member *CB* in the frame in Fig. P4-4. Compare this result with the solution obtained in Article 4.4 and discuss your findings.

5

TORSIONAL
BUCKLING

5.1 INTRODUCTION

Up to now we have considered only flexural buckling, in which the member
deforms by bending in the plane of one of the principal axes. However,
columns as well as beams also buckle by twisting or by a combination of
bending and twisting. These modes of failure occur when the torsional
stiffness of the member is very small or if bending and twisting are coupled so
that one necessarily produces the other. Thin-walled open sections usually
have a very low torsional rigidity and are therefore especially pronc to
torsional buckling. Combined bending and twisting occurs in axially loaded
members, such as angles and channels, whose shear center axis and centroidal
axis do not coincide. It also takes place in transversely loaded beams when the
compression flange becomes unstable and wants to buckle laterally at the
same time that the tension flange is stable and wants to remain straight.

In this chapter we shall consider both torsional buckling of axially loaded
columns and lateral torsional buckling of transversely loaded beams. However, before turning to these problems we shall review some fundamental
relationships of torsional behavior in general.

5.2 TORSIONAL LOAD–DEFORMATION CHARACTERISTICS OF STRUCTURAL MEMBERS

When torsion is applied to a structural member, the cross sections of that member may warp in addition to twisting. If the member is allowed to warp freely, then the applied torque is resisted solely by St. Venant shearing stresses. This type of behavior is referred to as pure or uniform torsion. On the other hand, if the member is restrained from warping freely, the applied torque is resisted by a combination of St. Venant shearing stresses and warping torsion. This behavior is called nonuniform torsion.

St. Venant Torsion

If a bar of constant circular cross section is twisted by a torsional moment, as shown in Fig. 5-1, the external torque at any section is resisted by circumferential shear stresses, whose magnitude varies as their distance from the centroid of the section. These shear stresses are due to the resistance of adjacent cross sections to rotate relative to one another. In such a member, the angle of twist, β, is related to the torque, T, by the expression

$$T = GJ \frac{d\beta}{dz} \tag{5.1}$$

in which G is the shearing modulus of elasticity, J is the torsional constant, and z is the direction along the axis of the member. The product GJ is the torsional rigidity of the section, analogous to EI, the bending stiffness.

Whereas bars of circular cross section, like the one in Fig. 5-1, twist

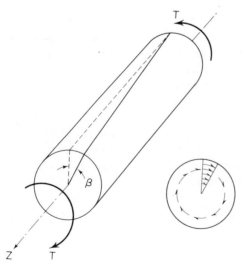

Fig. 5-1 Twisting of circular section.

without warping, most noncircular shapes warp when they are twisted. When a torque is applied to a member whose cross section is noncircular (Fig. 5-2), transverse sections that were plane prior to twisting warp in the axial direction so that they are no longer plane during twisting. However, as long as the warping of the member is permitted to take place freely, the applied torque will still be resisted by shearing stresses similar to those present in the circular bar, and Eq. (5.1) is still applicable. For a thin-walled open section made of rectangular elements, the shear stresses in each element are parallel to the middle line of the cross section, and their magnitude is proportional to the distance from that line (see Fig. 5-2). The torsional constant, J, for such a

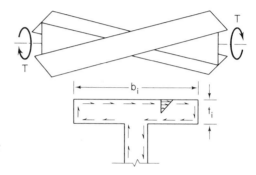

Fig. 5-2 Twisting of noncircular sections free to warp.

section can be approximated by (Ref. 5.1)

$$J = \tfrac{1}{3} \sum_i b_i(t_i)^3 \tag{5.2}$$

in which b_i and t_i are the length and thickness, respectively, of any element of the section. The type of resistance to twisting consisting solely of shear and described by Eq. (5.1) is called *St. Venant* or *uniform torsion*.

Nonuniform Torsion

If the longitudinal displacements that produce warping are allowed to take place freely, then longitudinal fibers do not change length, and no longitudinal stresses are induced as a result of warping (see Fig. 5-2). However, certain support or loading conditions will prevent longitudinal displacements from taking place freely. For example, the built-in end of the cantilever beam in Fig. 5-3 is completely restrained against warping, while the unsupported end is allowed to warp freely. As a consequence, longitudinal fibers change in length, and axial stresses are induced in the member. Comparison of the beam in Fig. 5-3, in which warping is partially restrained, with the beam in Fig. 5-2, which is free to warp, indicates that a restraint of warping deformation results in a differential bending of the flanges. One flange bends to the right and one to the left.

The flange bending moments, which exist in the cantilever beam in Fig.

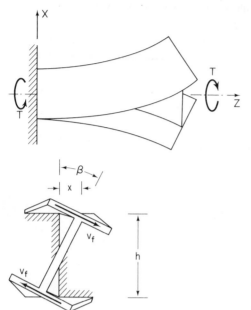

Fig. 5-3 Twisting of noncircular section restrained against free warping. (Adapted from Ref. 5.16.)

5-3, vary from zero at the free end of the member to a maximum at the fixed end. Hence at any intermediate section there exists a shear force in each flange equal to

$$V_f = -\frac{dM_f}{dz} \tag{5.3}$$

in which M_f is the flange bending moment and the minus sign indicates that M_f increases as z decreases. Since the flanges bend in opposite directions, the shear forces in the two flanges are oppositely directed and form a couple (see Fig. 5-3). This couple, which acts to resist the applied torque, is called *warping torsion*.

The axial stresses that produce warping torsion are brought about by the resistance of the member to free warping of its cross sections. By comparison, St. Venant torsion is due to the resistance of adjacent cross sections to rotate relative to one another.

A member that is not permitted to warp freely will resist an applied torque by a combination of St. Venant and warping torsion. Thus

$$T - T_{sv} + T_w \tag{5.4}$$

in which T_{sv} is St. Venant torsion and T_w is warping torsion. The type of behavior described by this equation is referred to as *nonuniform torsion*.

The part of the total resistance to twist due to St. Venant torsion is given by Eq. (5.1). Thus

$$T_{sv} = GJ \frac{d\beta}{dz} \tag{5.5}$$

A similar expression for the warping torsional resistance can be obtained if we consider the differential bending of the flanges that arises when the member is not permitted to warp freely.

For the I section in Fig. 5-3, the warping torsion is

$$T_w = V_f h \tag{5.6}$$

or, in view of Eq. (5.3),

$$T_w = -\frac{dM_f}{dz} h \tag{5.7}$$

Letting the lateral displacement of the flange centerline be given by x, as shown in Fig. 5-3, the bending moment in the upper flange is

$$M_f = EI_f \frac{d^2 x}{dz^2} \tag{5.8}$$

in which I_f is the moment of inertia of the flange about its strong axis. Since

$$x = \frac{\beta h}{2} \tag{5.9}$$

Eq. (5.8) becomes

$$M_f = \frac{EI_f h}{2} \frac{d^2 \beta}{dz^2} \tag{5.10}$$

Substitution of this expression into Eq. (5.7) gives

$$T_w = -\frac{EI_f h^2}{2} \frac{d^3 \beta}{dz^3} \tag{5.11}$$

The term $I_f h^2/2$ is a property of the cross section, called the *warping constant*. By introducing the notation

$$\Gamma = \frac{I_f h^2}{2} \tag{5.12}$$

Eq. (5.11) can be rewritten as

$$T_w = -E\Gamma \frac{d^3 \beta}{dz^3} \tag{5.13}$$

In this expression for the warping torsion, the term $E\Gamma$ is the warping rigidity of the section, analogous to GJ, the St. Venant torsional stiffness.

Although it was derived here specifically for a symmetrical I section, Eq. (5.13) is perfectly general and can be used for any open thin-walled section. However, the expression for the warping constant given by Eq. (5.12) applies only to an I section. Expressions for the warping constant of other open thin-walled sections can be found in Refs. 1.2, 1.12, and 5.17. A derivation of Eq. (5.13) more general than the one presented here and applicable to any section can be found in Ref. 1.2.

The differential equation for nonuniform torsion is obtained by combining the expressions in (5.5) and (5.13). Thus

$$T = GJ\frac{d\beta}{dz} - E\Gamma\frac{d^3\beta}{dz^3} \tag{5.14}$$

The first term represents the resistance of the section to twist and the second term the resistance to warping. As pointed out by McGuire (Ref. 3.8), it is important to keep in mind that the second term is caused not by the warping of the member but by its resistance to warping. The two terms together represent the internal resistance of the member to an applied torque.

5.3 STRAIN ENERGY OF TORSION

The strain energy stored in a twisted member can be broken down into two parts, that due to St. Venant torsion and that due to warping torsion.

St. Venant Torsion

The increment of strain energy stored in an element dz of a twisted member due to St. Venant torsion is equal to one half the product of the torque and the change in the angle of twist. Hence

$$dU_{sv} = \frac{1}{2}Td\beta \tag{5.15}$$

Since
$$d\beta = \frac{T}{GJ}dz \tag{5.16}$$

Eq. (5.15) becomes

$$dU_{sv} = \frac{1}{2}\frac{T^2}{GJ}dz \tag{5.17}$$

or if the expression in (5.1) is substituted for T, one obtains

$$dU_{sv} = \frac{1}{2}GJ\left(\frac{d\beta}{dz}\right)^2 dz \tag{5.18}$$

Integrating over the length gives the strain energy in the entire member due to St. Venant torsion. Thus

$$U_{sv} = \frac{1}{2} \int_0^l GJ \left(\frac{d\beta}{dz}\right)^2 dz \tag{5.19}$$

Warping Torsion

For an I beam, the strain energy stored in the member due to its resistance to warping is assumed to be equal to the bending energy of the flanges. As in ordinary beam theory, the shear energy associated with nonuniform bending is assumed to be negligible in comparison with the bending energy.

The bending energy stored in an element dz of one of the flanges of an I beam is equal to the product of one half the moment $EI_f(d^2x/dz^2)$ and the rotation $(d^2x/dz^2)\, dz$. Thus

$$dU_w = \frac{1}{2} EI_f \left(\frac{d^2x}{dz^2}\right)^2 dz \tag{5.20}$$

In view of Eqs. (5.9) and (5.12), this expression becomes

$$dU_w = \frac{1}{4} E\Gamma \left(\frac{d^2\beta}{dz^2}\right)^2 dz \tag{5.21}$$

Integrating over the length and multiplying by 2 to account for both flanges gives the strain energy due to warping resistance for the entire member. That is,

$$U_w = \frac{1}{2} \int_0^l E\Gamma \left(\frac{d^2\beta}{dz^2}\right)^2 dz \tag{5.22}$$

The total strain energy stored in a twisted member is obtained by adding the expressions in (5.19) and (5.22). It is equal to

$$U = \frac{1}{2} \int_0^l GJ \left(\frac{d\beta}{dz}\right)^2 dz + \frac{1}{2} \int_0^l E\Gamma \left(\frac{d^2\beta}{dz^2}\right)^2 dz \tag{5.23}$$

5.4   TORSIONAL AND TORSIONAL–FLEXURAL BUCKLING OF COLUMNS

In this article we shall determine the critical load of columns that buckle by twisting or by a combination of bending and twisting. Since open thin-walled sections are about the only sections that are susceptible to torsional or torsional–flexural buckling, the investigation is limited to these shapes. The study will also be restricted to elastic behavior, small deformations, and concentric loading.*

The problem of torsional buckling in columns has been studied extensively by many, including Goodier (Ref. 5.4), Timoshenko and Gere (Ref. 1.2), and Hoff (Refs. 1.3 and 5.5). In these investigations the critical load is determined either by integrating the governing differential equations or by making use of an energy principle. The analysis presented here uses the Rayleigh–Ritz method to determine the critical load. The calculations follow the general outline of those given by Hoff (Ref. 1.3).

Let us consider the thin-walled open cross section of arbitrary shape given in Fig. 5-4. The deformation taking place during buckling is assumed to

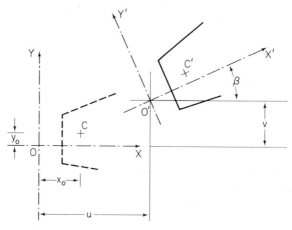

Fig. 5-4   Torsional–flexural buckling deformations. (Adapted from Ref. 5.5.)

consist of a combination of twisting and bending about two axes. For the purpose of expressing the strain energy in its simplest form, it is desirable to reduce the deformation to two pure translations and a pure rotation. This can be accomplished by using the shear center O as the origin of the coordinate system. The shear center is that point in the cross section through which lateral loads must pass to produce bending without twisting. It is also the center of rotation when a pure torque is applied to the section. The x and y directions are assumed to coincide with the principal axes of the section, and the z direction is taken along the longitudinal axis through the shear center. As indicated in Fig. 5-4, the coordinates of the centroid are denoted by x_0 and

*For information on inelastic buckling, postbuckling behavior, and eccentric loading, the reader is referred to a series of investigations recently undertaken at Cornell University (Refs. 5.2 and 5.3).

y_0. As a result of buckling, the cross section undergoes translations u and v in the x and y directions, respectively, and a rotation β about the z axis. The geometric shape of the cross section in the xy plane is assumed to remain constant throughout.

As far as the boundary conditions are concerned, it is assumed that the displacements in the x and y directions and the moments about these axes vanish at the ends of the member. That is,

$$u = v = 0 \quad \text{at } z = 0 \text{ and } l$$

$$\frac{d^2u}{dz^2} = \frac{d^2v}{dz^2} = 0 \quad \text{at } z = 0 \text{ and } l \tag{5.24}$$

The torsional conditions that correspond to these flexural conditions are zero rotation and zero warping restraint at the ends of the member. Thus

$$\beta = \frac{d^2\beta}{dz^2} = 0 \quad \text{at } z = 0 \text{ and } l \tag{5.25}$$

It is assumed that the warping restraint vanishes when the longitudinal stresses that accompany warping torsion vanish. The condition $d^2\beta/dz^2 = 0$ thus follows from Eq. (5.10).

The boundary conditions will be satisfied by assuming a deflected shape of the form

$$u = C_1 \sin \frac{\pi z}{l}$$

$$v = C_2 \sin \frac{\pi z}{l} \tag{5.26}$$

$$\beta = C_3 \sin \frac{\pi z}{l}$$

The strain energy stored in the member consists of four parts, the energies due to bending in the x and y directions, the energy of the St. Venant shear stresses, and the energy of the longitudinal stresses associated with warping torsion. Thus

$$U = \frac{1}{2} \int_0^l EI_y \left(\frac{d^2u}{dz^2}\right)^2 dz + \frac{1}{2} \int_0^l EI_x \left(\frac{d^2v}{dz^2}\right)^2 dz$$

$$+ \frac{1}{2} \int_0^l GJ \left(\frac{d\beta}{dz}\right)^2 dz + \frac{1}{2} \int_0^l E\Gamma \left(\frac{d^2\beta}{dz^2}\right)^2 dz \tag{5.27}$$

Substitution of the assumed deflection function into the strain energy expression gives

$$U = \frac{1}{2} \int_0^l EI_y C_1^2 \frac{\pi^4}{l^4} \sin^2 \frac{\pi z}{l} \, dz + \frac{1}{2} \int_0^l EI_x C_2^2 \frac{\pi^4}{l^4} \sin^2 \frac{\pi z}{l} \, dz$$

$$+ \frac{1}{2} \int_0^l GJC_3^2 \frac{\pi^2}{l^2} \cos^2 \frac{\pi z}{l} \, dz + \frac{1}{2} \int_0^l E\Gamma C_3^2 \frac{\pi^4}{l^4} \sin^2 \frac{\pi z}{l} \, dz \tag{5.28}$$

Making use of the definite integrals

$$\int_0^l \cos^2 \frac{\pi z}{l} \, dz = \int_0^l \sin^2 \frac{\pi z}{l} \, dz = \frac{l}{2}$$

Eq. (5.28) simplifies to

$$U = \frac{1}{4} \frac{\pi^2}{l} \left[C_1^2 \frac{EI_y \pi^2}{l^2} + C_2^2 \frac{EI_x \pi^2}{l^2} + C_3^2 \left(GJ + \frac{E\Gamma \pi^2}{l^2} \right) \right] \tag{5.29}$$

The potential energy of the external loads is equal to the negative product of the loads and the distances they move as the column deforms. Figure 5-5

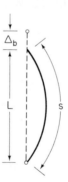

Fig. 5-5 Axial shortening of longitudinal fiber due to bending.

shows a longitudinal fiber whose ends approach one another by an amount Δ_b when the fiber bends. The distance Δ_b is equal to the difference between the arc length S and the chord length L of the fiber. If the cross-sectional area of the fiber is dA and the load it supports is $\sigma \, dA$, then the potential energy of the load acting on the fiber is $-\Delta_b \sigma \, dA$. The total potential energy for the entire member is obtained by integrating over the cross-sectional area. Thus

$$V = - \int_A \Delta_b \sigma \, dA \tag{5.30}$$

To determine Δ_b, consider fiber AB in Fig. 5-6, whose coordinates in the undeformed state are x and y. We shall direct our attention to an element dz

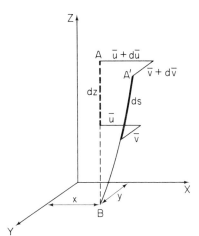

Fig. 5-6 Lateral deformations of longitudinal fiber due to bending. (Adapted from Ref. 1.5.)

of this fiber. After deformation has taken place the x and y displacements of the lower end of the element are $\bar{u}$ and $\bar{v}$, and the corresponding displacements at the upper end are $\bar{u} + d\bar{u}$ and $\bar{v} + d\bar{v}$. From the Pythagorean theorem, the length ds of the deformed element is

$$ds = (d\bar{u}^2 + d\bar{v}^2 + dz^2)^{1/2} = \left[\left(\frac{d\bar{u}}{dz}\right)^2 + \left(\frac{d\bar{v}}{dz}\right)^2 + 1 \right]^{1/2} dz \qquad (5.31)$$

It has previously been shown (Article 2.2) that the expression $(\eta + 1)^{1/2}$ can be replaced by $1 + \frac{1}{2}\eta$ if $\eta \ll 1$. In view of this relationship and because $d\bar{u}/dz$ and $d\bar{v}/dz$ are very small quantities, Eq. (5.31) reduces to

$$ds = \left[\frac{1}{2}\left(\frac{d\bar{u}}{dz}\right)^2 + \frac{1}{2}\left(\frac{d\bar{v}}{dz}\right)^2 + 1 \right] dz \qquad (5.32)$$

Integrating the left-hand side of this equation from 0 to S and the right-hand side from 0 to L gives

$$S = \int_0^L \left[\frac{1}{2}\left(\frac{d\bar{u}}{dz}\right)^2 + \frac{1}{2}\left(\frac{d\bar{v}}{dz}\right)^2 + 1 \right] dz \qquad (5.33)$$

from which

$$\Delta_b = S - L = \frac{1}{2} \int_0^L \left[\left(\frac{d\bar{u}}{dz}\right)^2 + \left(\frac{d\bar{v}}{dz}\right)^2 \right] dz \qquad (5.34)$$

The translations $\bar{u}$ and $\bar{v}$ of a fiber whose coordinates are x and y consist of the translation of the shear center, u and v, plus an additional translation due to the rotation of the fiber about the shear center. These latter translations, in the x and y directions, are denoted, as shown in Fig. 5-7, by $-a$ and b. From

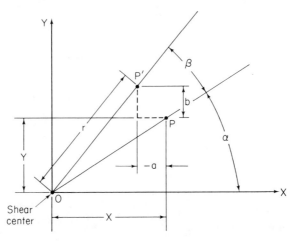

Fig. 5-7   Lateral translation of longitudinal fiber P due to rotation about shear center. (Adapted from Ref. 1.5.)

the geometry of the figure it is evident that

$$a = r\beta \sin \alpha$$
$$b = r\beta \cos \alpha$$
(5.35)

and since

$$r \sin \alpha = y, \qquad r \cos \alpha = x$$
(5.36)

one can also write

$$-a = -y\beta, \qquad b = x\beta$$
(5.37)

The total displacements of the fiber at (x, y) are therefore

$$\bar{u} = u - y\beta$$
$$\bar{v} = v + x\beta$$
(5.38)

and the expression for Δ_b given in (5.34) becomes

$$\Delta_b = \frac{1}{2} \int_0^L \left[\left(\frac{du}{dz}\right)^2 + \left(\frac{dv}{dz}\right)^2 + (x^2 + y^2)\left(\frac{d\beta}{dz}\right)^2 \right.$$
$$\left. - 2y\left(\frac{du}{dz}\right)\left(\frac{d\beta}{dz}\right) + 2x\left(\frac{dv}{dz}\right)\left(\frac{d\beta}{dz}\right) \right] dz$$
(5.39)

The potential energy of the external loads can now be obtained by substituting

(5.39) in Eq. (5.30). Thus

$$
V = -\frac{1}{2} \int_0^l \int_A \sigma \Bigg[\left(\frac{du}{dz}\right)^2 + \left(\frac{dv}{dz}\right)^2 + (x^2 + y^2)\left(\frac{d\beta}{dz}\right)^2
$$
$$
- 2y\left(\frac{du}{dz}\right)\left(\frac{d\beta}{dz}\right) + 2x\left(\frac{dv}{dz}\right)\left(\frac{d\beta}{dz}\right) \Bigg] dA\, dz
$$

(5.40)

To simplify this expression, we make use of the following relations:

$$
\int_A dA = A
$$
$$
\int_A y\, dA = y_0 A
$$
$$
\int_A x\, dA = x_0 A
$$
$$
\int_A (x^2 + y^2)\, dA = r_0^2 A
$$

(5.41)

in which x_0 and y_0 are the coordinates of the centroid and r_0 is the polar radius of gyration of the cross section with respect to the shear center.

Substitution of the relations in (5.41) in Eq. (5.40) gives

$$
V = -\frac{P}{2} \int_0^L \Bigg[\left(\frac{du}{dz}\right)^2 + \left(\frac{dv}{dz}\right)^2 + r_0^2\left(\frac{d\beta}{dz}\right)^2
$$
$$
- 2y_0\left(\frac{du}{dz}\right)\left(\frac{d\beta}{dz}\right) + 2x_0\left(\frac{dv}{dz}\right)\left(\frac{d\beta}{dz}\right) \Bigg] dz
$$

(5.42)

If the assumed expressions for u, v, and β, given by (5.26), are now introduced and the indicated integration carried out, one obtains

$$
V = -\frac{P\pi^2}{4l}(C_1^2 + C_2^2 + C_3^2 r_0^2 - 2C_1 C_3 y_0 + 2C_2 C_3 x_0)
$$

(5.43)

Combining this expression with the strain energy given in (5.29), we finally obtain the total potential energy of the system. Thus

$$
U + V = \frac{\pi^2}{4l}\Bigg\{ C_1^2\left(\frac{\pi^2 E I_y}{l^2} - P\right) + C_2^2\left(\frac{\pi^2 E I_x}{l^2} - P\right)
$$
$$
+ C_3^2 r_0^2\left[\frac{1}{r_0^2}\left(GJ + \frac{E\Gamma\pi^2}{l^2}\right) - P\right]
$$
$$
+ 2C_1 C_3 P y_0 - 2C_2 C_3 P x_0 \Bigg\}
$$

(5.44)

At this point it is useful to introduce the following notation:

$$P_x = \frac{\pi^2 EI_x}{l^2}$$

$$P_y = \frac{\pi^2 EI_y}{l^2} \tag{5.45}$$

$$P_\phi = \frac{1}{r_0^2}\left(GJ + \frac{E\Gamma\pi^2}{l^2}\right)$$

We are already familiar with the first two expressions. They are, of course, the flexural buckling loads about the x and y axes, respectively. The third term is as yet unfamiliar. However, it is seen to contain the St. Venant and warping stiffnesses, and it can therefore be expected to pertain to torsional buckling.

By means of expressions (5.45), Eq. (5.44) is reduced to the form

$$U + V = \frac{\pi^2}{4l}[C_1^2(P_y - P) + C_2^2(P_x - P)$$
$$+ C_3^2 r_0^2(P_\phi - P) + 2C_1 C_3 Py_0 - 2C_2 C_3 Px_0] \tag{5.46}$$

The critical load is defined as the load at which equilibrium is possible in a slightly deformed state. Hence it is the load for which the total potential energy of the system has a stationary value. Since $U + V$ is a function of three variables, it will have a stationary value when its derivative with respect to each of these three variables vanishes. Taking the derivative of the expression in (5.46) with respect to C_1, C_2, and C_3 and setting them each equal to zero gives

$$\frac{\partial(U + V)}{\partial C_1} = C_1(P_y - P) + C_3(Py_0) = 0$$

$$\frac{\partial(U + V)}{\partial C_2} = C_2(P_x - P) - C_3(Px_0) = 0 \tag{5.47}$$

$$\frac{\partial(U + V)}{\partial C_3} = C_1 Py_0 - C_2 Px_0 + C_3 r_0^2(P_\phi - P) = 0$$

This is a set of linear homogeneous equations. They have a solution $C_1 = C_2 = C_3 = 0$, indicating that equilibrium is possible at any load provided the member remains straight. There is also a nontrivial solution possible when the determinant of the equations vanishes. This latter solution is the one that interests us. It corresponds to equilibrium in a deformed configuration, and that is of course the type of equilibrium that exists only at the critical load. To determine the critical load, we therefore set the determinant of Eqs. (5.47) equal to zero. Thus

$$
\begin{vmatrix}
P_y - P & 0 & Py_0 \\
0 & P_x - P & -Px_0 \\
Py_0 & -Px_0 & r_0^2(P_\phi - P)
\end{vmatrix} = 0
\tag{5.48}
$$

Expansion of (5.48) gives

$$
(P_y - P)(P_x - P)(P_\phi - P) - (P_y - P)\frac{P^2 x_0^2}{r_0^2} - (P_x - P)\frac{P^2 y_0^2}{r_0^2} = 0
\tag{5.49}
$$

This is a cubic equation in P, whose roots are the critical loads of the member.

If the cross section has two axes of symmetry or if it is point symmetric, the shear center coincides with the centroid and $x_0 = y_0 = 0$. For this case Eq. (5.49) reduces to

$$
(P_y - P)(P_x - P)(P_\phi - P) = 0
\tag{5.50}
$$

It is obvious that the three roots of this equation are

$$
P = P_y = \frac{\pi^2 EI_y}{l^2}
$$

$$
P = P_x = \frac{\pi^2 EI_x}{l^2}
\tag{5.51}
$$

$$
P = P_\phi = \frac{1}{r_0^2}\left(GJ + \frac{\pi^2 E\Gamma}{l^2}\right)
$$

If each of the three roots is substituted into Eqs. (5.47), the following information regarding the mode shapes is obtained:

$$
\begin{aligned}
P = P_y: & \quad C_1 \neq 0, & C_2 = C_3 = 0 \\
P = P_x: & \quad C_2 \neq 0, & C_1 = C_3 = 0 \\
P = P_\phi: & \quad C_3 \neq 0, & C_1 = C_2 = 0
\end{aligned}
\tag{5.52}
$$

These results indicate that the loads P_y and P_x correspond to pure flexural buckling about the y and x axes, respectively, and that P_ϕ corresponds to pure torsional buckling.

It can thus be concluded that columns whose shear center and centroid coincide, such as I beams and Z sections, can buckle either by bending about one of the principal axes or by twisting about the shear center. Combined torsional–flexural buckling does not occur for these sections. Depending on the shape and dimensions of the cross section, one of the loads given by (5.51) will have the lowest value and will determine the mode of buckling of the members. For example, the flexural buckling load about the weak axis is almost always the lowest of the three possible buckling loads for hot-rolled wide-flange steel shapes. It is for this reason that the Euler load is used almost exclusively to design wide-flange shapes.

When the cross section has only one axis of symmetry, say the x axis, the shear center lies on that axis and $y_0 = 0$. For this case Eq. (5.49) reduces to

$$(P_y - P)\left[(P_x - P)(P_\phi - P) - \frac{P^2 x_0^2}{r_0^2}\right] = 0 \qquad (5.53)$$

This relation is satisfied either if

$$P = P_y = \frac{\pi^2 EI_y}{l^2} \qquad (5.54)$$

or if

$$(P_x - P)(P_\phi - P) - \frac{P^2 x_0^2}{r_0^2} = 0 \qquad (5.55)$$

The first expression corresponds to pure flexural buckling about the y axis. The second is a quadratic equation in P, whose roots both correspond to buckling by a combination of bending and twisting, that is, torsional–flexural buckling. The smaller of the two roots of Eq. (5.55) is

$$P_{TF} = \frac{1}{2k}[P_\phi + P_x - \sqrt{(P_\phi + P_x)^2 - 4kP_\phi P_x}] \qquad (5.56)$$

in which $k = [1 - (x_0/r_0)^2]$.

It is thus evident that a singly symmetric section, such as an angle, a channel, or a hat, can buckle either by bending in the plane of symmetry or by a combination of twisting and bending. Which of these two modes is critical depends on the shape and dimensions of the cross section.

The behavior of a singly symmetric section can be summarized as follows: An imperfect column that is centrally loaded tends to bend in one of the principal planes containing the centroidal axis. If this plane also contains the shear center axis (xz plane in our example), bending can take place without simultaneously inducing twist. However, if the plane of bending does not contain the shear center axis (YZ plane in our example), bending must necessarily be accompanied by twisting.

If the cross section of a member does not possess any symmetry at all, neither x_0 nor y_0 vanishes and Eq. (5.49) cannot be simplified. In this case bending about either principal axis is coupled with both twisting and bending about the other principal axis, and each of the three roots to Eq. (5.49) corresponds to torsional–flexural buckling. A nonsymmetric shape will thus always buckle in a torsional–flexural mode regardless of its shape or dimensions.

The critical load of such a section is the smallest root of Eq. (5.49). Since this equation is a cubic, its solution involves a large amount of numerical work. However, nonsymmetric sections are rarely used and their design does therefore not pose a serious problem.

It has been shown in this article that all centrally loaded columns possess three distinct buckling loads and that at least one of these corresponds to a torsional or torsional–flexural mode of failure. For the doubly symmetric hot-rolled steel sections commonly used in heavy construction, the flexural buckling load about the weak axis is almost always the lowest of the three possible buckling loads. Hence it is customary to neglect torsional buckling when designing such members and base the analysis solely on the Euler load. However, this is not the case for the thin-walled open sections without double symmetry, such as angles and channels which are commonly used in aerospace structures and other lightweight construction. For these shapes the torsional–flexural buckling load can be significantly below the Euler load, and torsional–flexural buckling must be considered in their design.

5.5 LATERAL BUCKLING OF BEAMS

A transversely loaded member that is bent about its major axis may buckle sideways if its compression flange is not laterally supported. The reason buckling occurs in a beam is that the compression flange, which is in effect a column on an elastic foundation, becomes unstable. At the critical loading there is a tendency for the compression flange to bend sideways and for the remainder of the cross section, which is stable, to restrain it from doing so. The net effect is that the entire section rotates and moves laterally, as shown in Fig. 5-8. Lateral buckling of a beam is thus a combination of twisting and lateral bending brought about by the instability of the compression flange.

The first theoretical studies of lateral buckling were made by Prandtl (Ref. 5.6) and Michell (Ref. 5.7) on beams with rectangular cross sections and by Timoshenko (Ref. 5.8) on I beams. Since then numerous investigations, including those by Winter (Ref. 5.9), Hill (Ref. 5.10), and Galambos (Ref. 5.11), have been conducted on both elastic and inelastic buckling of various shapes. In the following sections we shall consider a few of the basic aspects of lateral beam buckling uncovered in these investigations.

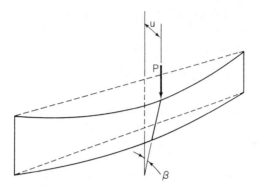

Fig. 5-8 Lateral buckling of beams.

5.6 LATERAL BUCKLING OF RECTANGULAR BEAMS IN PURE BENDING

Let us consider the rectangular beam in pure bending shown in Fig. 5-9a. It is assumed that the material obeys Hooke's law, that the deformations remain small, and that the geometry of the cross section does not change during buckling. The critical load will be determined by finding the smallest load at which neutral equilibrium is possible. To establish equilibrium in a deformed configuration, we shall satisfy the governing differential equations. These equations are derived using the procedure outlined by Timoshenko and Gere in Ref. 1.2.

A set of fixed coordinate axes x, y, and z, as shown in Fig. 5-9b, is chosen. In addition, a second set of coordinate axes x', y', and z', whose directions are taken relative to the deformed member, is also established. The x' and y' directions coincide with the principal axes of the cross section, and the z' axis is tangent to the centroidal axis of the member. Deformation of the member at any section can be broken down into three distinct motions, a lateral displacement u in the x direction, a vertical displacement v in the y direction, and a rotation β about the z axis. The rotation β is positive when clockwise, looking toward the origin, and u and v are positive when in the positive directions of the x and y axes. Thus the three displacements shown in Fig. 5-9b are all positive.

The ends of the member are assumed to be simply supported as far as bending about the x and y axes is concerned. Hence

$$u = v = \frac{d^2u}{dz^2} = \frac{d^2v}{dz^2} = 0 \quad \text{at } z = 0, l \tag{5.57}$$

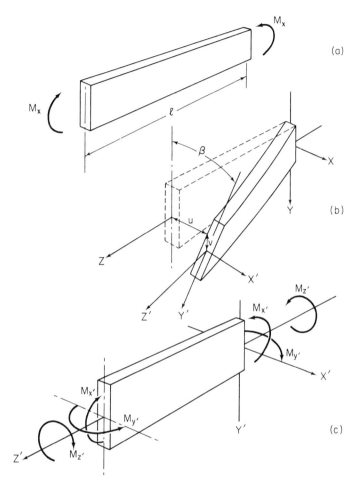

Fig. 5-9 Lateral buckling of simply supported rectangular beam in pure bending.

In addition, the ends of the member are prevented from rotating about the z axis but are free to warp. Thus

$$\beta = \frac{d^2\beta}{dz^2} = 0 \quad \text{at } z = 0, l \tag{5.58}$$

Assuming that the positive directions of the moments $M_{x'}$, $M_{y'}$, and $M_{z'}$, acting on an element of the deformed member, are as shown in Fig. 5.9c, and the positive directions of the displacements are as indicated previously, the differential equations of bending and twisting are

$$EI_x \frac{d^2v}{dz^2} = -M_{x'} \tag{5.59}$$

$$EI_y \frac{d^2u}{dz^2} = M_{y'} \tag{5.60}$$

$$GJ \frac{d\beta}{dz} = M_{z'} \tag{5.61}$$

The first two equations are the familiar equations of beam bending written about the x' and y' axes. The third equation is an analogous expression for twisting about the z' axis. Since the warping stiffness of a rectangular section is negligible, the twisting relation is obtained from Eq. (5.14) by dropping the warping term. The negative sign in Eq. (5.59) indicates that a positive moment $M_{x'}$ corresponds to a negative curvature d^2v/dz^2. By comparison, in Eqs. (5.60) and (5.61) positive moments $M_{y'}$ and $M_{z'}$ correspond, respectively, to a positive curvature d^2u/dz^2 and a positive slope $d\beta/dz$.

The quantities $M_{x'}$, $M_{y'}$, and $M_{z'}$ that appear in Eqs. (5.59), (5.60), and (5.61) are the components of the applied moment M_x about the x', y', and z' axes. To determine these components, it is necessary to know the angles that the x', y', and z' axes make with the x axis. As shown in Fig. 5-10a, the angle between the x' and x axes is equal to the rotation β, and the angle between the y' and x axes is $\beta + 90$. The moments about the x' and y' axes, denoted by vectors in the figure, are therefore given by

$$M_{x'} = M_x \cos \beta = M_x \tag{5.62}$$

$$M_{y'} = M_x \cos (\beta + 90) = -M_x \sin \beta = -M_x\beta \tag{5.63}$$

The z' axis is tangent to the deflection curve of the member. As indicated in Fig. 5-10b, the angle between the z' axis and the z axis is therefore equal to du/dz, and the angle between the z' axis and the x axis is $90 - (du/dz)$. Hence

$$M_{z'} = M_x \cos \left(90 - \frac{du}{dz}\right) = M_x \sin \frac{du}{dz} = M_x \frac{du}{dz} \tag{5.64}$$

In line with the assumption of small deformations, the cosines of small angles have been replaced by unity and the sines by the angles.

Substitution of the expressions in (5.62), (5.63), and (5.64) into Eqs. (5.59), (5.60), and (5.61) leads to the following differential equations:

$$EI_x \frac{d^2v}{dz^2} + M_x = 0 \tag{5.65}$$

$$EI_y \frac{d^2u}{dz^2} + M_x\beta = 0 \tag{5.66}$$

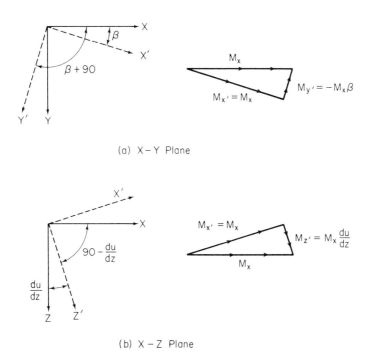

(a) X – Y Plane

(b) X – Z Plane

Fig. 5-10 Components of M_x along X', Y', and Z' axes. (Adapted from Ref. 4.8.)

$$GJ\frac{d\beta}{dz} - M_x\frac{du}{dz} = 0 \qquad (5.67)$$

The first of these three equations contains only the variable v, and this variable does not appear in either of the other two equations. Hence the first equation, which describes bending in the vertical plane, can be solved independently of the other two. The second and third equations, which describe lateral bending and twisting, are of course coupled and must be solved simultaneously. The buckling problem governed by Eqs. (5.66) and (5.67) is thus independent of the equilibrium problem that is described by Eq. (5.65). This situation is analogous to that existing in the Euler column where the bending that occurs during buckling is independent of the axial compression that precedes it. When the Euler column was considered in Chapter 1, it was tacitly assumed that axial shortening could be omitted when describing the buckling deformation of the member. A differential equation corresponding to axial compression was therefore never written. However, in analyzing the lateral buckling of beams in this chapter, the most general form of the deformation, containing all possible components, was employed, and the vertical bending equation as well as the buckling equations therefore appears in the analysis.

The variable u can be eliminated between Eqs. (5.66) and (5.67) if Eq. (5.67) is differentiated and the resulting expression is substituted for d^2u/dz^2 in Eq. (5.66). Thus one obtains

$$GJ\frac{d^2\beta}{dz^2} + \frac{M_x^2}{EI_y}\beta = 0 \tag{5.68}$$

or

$$\frac{d^2\beta}{dz^2} + k^2\beta = 0 \tag{5.69}$$

where $k^2 = M_x^2/GJEI_y$. The solution of Eq. (5.69) is

$$\beta = A\sin kz + B\cos kz \tag{5.70}$$

Substitution of the boundary condition $\beta = 0$ at $z = 0$ into Eq. (5.70) gives

$$B = 0$$

and from the condition $\beta = 0$ at $z = l$ one obtains

$$A\sin kl = 0 \tag{5.71}$$

For neutral equilibrium, the member must be in equilibrium in a deformed as well as in the undeformed configuration. Equilibrium in the undeformed configuration is possible at any load, since $A = 0$ satisfies Eq. (5.71) for any value of k. However, equilibrium in a deformed configuration is possible only when

$$\sin kl = 0$$

This gives

$$kl = \pi$$

from which

$$M_{cr} = \frac{\pi}{l}\sqrt{GJEI_y} \tag{5.72}$$

Equation (5.72) gives the critical moment for a simply supported rectangular beam subject to uniform bending. Since lateral buckling is a combination of twisting and bending about the y axis, it is not surprising that the critical moment is proportional to the torsional stiffness GJ and the bending stiffness EI_y.

The extreme fiber stress at which buckling occurs is obtained by dividing the critical moment by the section modulus. Thus

$$\sigma_{cr} = \frac{M_{cr}}{S_x}$$

or

$$\sigma_{cr} = \frac{\pi}{lS_x}\sqrt{GJEI_y} \tag{5.73}$$

For the rectangular cross section being considered,

$$J = \frac{hb^3}{3}, \qquad S_x = \frac{2I_x}{h}, \qquad I_x = \frac{bh^3}{12}$$

In view of these expressions, Eq. (5.73) becomes

$$\sigma_{cr} = \frac{\pi}{l} \sqrt{GE} \sqrt{\frac{hb^3}{3} \frac{I_y h^2}{4I_x} \frac{12}{bh^3}} = \frac{\pi \sqrt{GE}}{l/b} \sqrt{\frac{I_y}{I_x}} \tag{5.74}$$

This relation indicates that the critical stress is proportional to the ratio of the principal rigidities, I_y/I_x, and inversely proportional to the ratio of span to width. Hence lateral buckling will occur in beams that are relatively deep, narrow, and long.

5.7 BUCKLING OF I BEAMS BY ENERGY METHOD

In this article we shall consider the lateral buckling of an I beam. Following the general lines of an analysis presented by Winter (Ref. 5.9), the Rayleigh–Ritz method will be used to determine the critical load of the member.

Uniform Bending—Simple Supports

Let us consider the simply supported I beam, subject to a uniform bending moment M, shown in Fig. 5-11. The x and y coordinate axes are taken along the principal axes of the cross section, and the z axis coincides with the longitudinal centroidal axis of the member. The flexural and torsional boundary conditions corresponding to simple supports are

$$u = v = \frac{d^2u}{dz^2} = \frac{d^2v}{dz^2} = 0 \quad \text{at } z = 0, l$$

$$\beta = \frac{d^2\beta}{dz^2} = 0 \quad \text{at } z = 0, l \tag{5.75}$$

where u and v are the displacements in the x and y directions and β is the angle of twist about the z axis. The condition $d^2\beta/dz^2 = 0$ indicates that the section is free to warp at the supports.

At the critical moment, the member can be in equilibrium in a slightly buckled form. To determine the critical moment by the energy method, it is therefore necessary to find the moment for which the total potential energy of the buckled system has a stationary value. We have seen in the investigation of the rectangular beam (Article 5.6) that the final deformation of the member consisting of a vertical displacement v, a horizontal displacement u, and a rotation β is reached in two distinct stages. First, the member bends in the

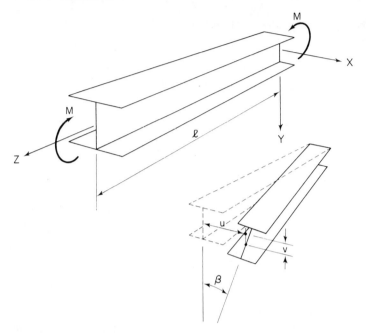

Fig. 5-11   Lateral buckling of a simply supported I beam in pure bending.

vertical plane, and then at the critical load it twists and bends laterally. It has also been shown that during the first stage of the deformation, when only vertical bending takes place, the member is in equilibrium for any and all values of the applied moment. Hence the part of the variation of the total potential energy that corresponds to vertical bending will be identically equal to zero and does not have to be included in the analysis. Omitting the vertical bending energy in the beam is analogous to omitting the energy of axial compression in the column.

The strain energy stored in the member as it buckles consists of two parts, the energy due to bending about the y axis and the energy due to twisting about the z axis. Thus the strain energy is

$$U = \frac{1}{2} EI_y \int_0^l \left(\frac{d^2 u}{dz^2}\right)^2 dz + \frac{1}{2} GJ \int_0^l \left(\frac{d\beta}{dz}\right)^2 dz + \frac{1}{2} E\Gamma \int_0^l \left(\frac{d^2 \beta}{dz^2}\right)^2 dz$$

$$(5.76)$$

The I beam, unlike the rectangular beam considered in Article 5-6, has a significant warping stiffness. The twisting energy therefore consists of two parts, that due to St. Venant torsion and that due to warping torsion. The torsional energy expressions used in Eq. (5.76) are derived in Article 5.3.

To the strain energy (5.76) must now be added the potential energy V of the external loads. For a beam subject to pure bending, the potential energy

V is equal to the negative product of the applied moments and the angles they move through as the member buckles. Thus

$$V = -2M\psi \tag{5.77}$$

where ψ is the angle of rotation about the x axis at each end of the beam. As shown in Fig. 5-12, buckling causes the ends of longitudinal fibers in

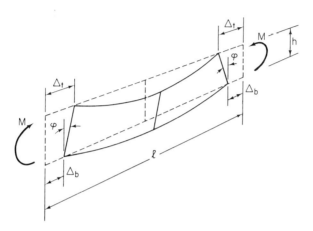

Fig. 5-12   End rotations due to lateral buckling. (Adapted from Ref. 5.9.)

the beam to approach one another. If the deformation consisted only of lateral bending, the ends of every fiber in the beam would move toward one another the same distance. However, lateral bending is accompanied by twisting, and the ends of the upper fibers therefore approach one another a greater distance than do the ends of the lower fibers. This gives rise to the rotation ψ of the end cross sections of the member. Letting the movement of the uppermost fiber at each end of the beam be given by Δ_t and the corresponding movement of the lowermost fiber by Δ_b, the angle ψ is

$$\psi = \frac{\Delta_t - \Delta_b}{h} \tag{5.78}$$

where h is the depth of the cross section. In view of Eq. (2.2),

$$\Delta_t = \frac{1}{4} \int_0^l \left(\frac{du_t}{dz}\right)^2 dz \tag{5.79}$$

and

$$\Delta_b = \frac{1}{4} \int_0^l \left(\frac{du_b}{dz}\right)^2 dz \tag{5.80}$$

The quantities u_t and u_b appearing in these expressions are the lateral displace-

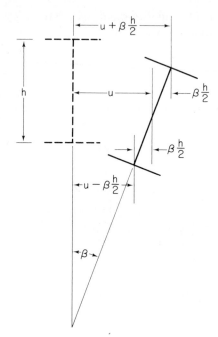

Fig. 5-13 Lateral deflection of flanges due to twist.

ments of the top and bottom of the web, respectively. From Fig. 5-13 these displacements are seen to be

$$u_t = u + \beta \frac{h}{2} \tag{5.81}$$

and

$$u_b = u - \beta \frac{h}{2} \tag{5.82}$$

Thus

$$\Delta_t = \frac{1}{4} \int_0^l \frac{d}{dz} \left(u + \beta \frac{h}{2} \right)^2 dz \tag{5.83}$$

and

$$\Delta_b = \frac{1}{4} \int_0^l \frac{d}{dz} \left(u - \beta \frac{h}{2} \right)^2 dz \tag{5.84}$$

Substituting these expressions in Eq. (5.78) and simplifying leads to

$$\psi = \frac{1}{2} \int_0^l \frac{du}{dz} \frac{d\beta}{dz} dz \tag{5.85}$$

Thus the potential energy of the external loads given by Eq. (5.77) becomes

$$V = -M \int_0^l \frac{du}{dz} \frac{d\beta}{dz} dz \tag{5.86}$$

Finally, combining the expressions in (5.76) and (5.86), one obtains for the total potential energy of the system

$$U + V = \frac{1}{2}EI_y \int_0^l \left(\frac{d^2u}{dz^2}\right)^2 dz + \frac{1}{2}GJ \int_0^l \left(\frac{d\beta}{dz}\right)^2 dz$$
$$+ \frac{1}{2}E\Gamma \int_0^l \left(\frac{d^2\beta}{dz^2}\right)^2 dz - M \int_0^l \frac{du}{dz}\frac{d\beta}{dz} dz \tag{5.87}$$

It is now necessary to assume suitable expressions for the buckling deformations u and β. The boundary conditions given in Eqs. (5.75) will be satisfied if u and β are approximated by

$$u = A \sin\frac{\pi z}{l} \tag{5.88}$$

$$\beta = B \sin\frac{\pi z}{l} \tag{5.89}$$

If these shapes are substituted in Eq. (5.87), one obtains the total energy of the system expressed as a function of the two variables A and B. One can then determine the critical moment by solving the two equations that result if the variation of $U + V$ is made to vanish with respect to both A and B. An alternative approach is to express A in terms of B, using Eq. (5.66), and thus reduce the total energy expression to a function of the single variable B. This alternative procedure involves less computations than the foregoing method and will therefore be followed here. The first procedure must of course be followed if a relation between u and β is not available.

From Eq. (5.66)

$$\beta = -\frac{EI_y}{M}\frac{d^2u}{dz^2} \tag{5.90}$$

Substitution of the expressions in (5.88) and (5.89) into this relation gives

$$A = B\frac{l^2}{\pi^2}\frac{M}{EI_y} \tag{5.91}$$

The assumed function for u can now be written in the form

$$u = \frac{Bl^2}{\pi^2}\frac{M}{EI_y} \sin\frac{\pi z}{l} \tag{5.92}$$

Using (5.89) and (5.92), the total potential energy becomes

$$U + V = \frac{1}{2}\frac{B^2M^2}{EI_y} \int_0^l \sin^2\frac{\pi z}{l} dz + \frac{1}{2}GJB^2\frac{\pi^2}{l^2} \int_0^l \cos^2\frac{\pi z}{l} dz$$
$$+ \frac{1}{2}E\Gamma B^2\frac{\pi^4}{l^4} \int_0^l \sin^2\frac{\pi z}{l} dz - \frac{M^2B^2}{EI_y} \int_0^l \cos^2\frac{\pi z}{l} dz \tag{5.93}$$

and since

$$\int_0^l \sin^2 \frac{\pi z}{l} \, dz = \int_0^l \cos^2 \frac{\pi z}{l} \, dz = \frac{l}{2}$$

Eq. (5.93) reduces to

$$U + V = \frac{1}{4} \left[\frac{GJB^2 \pi^2}{l} + \frac{E\Gamma B^2 \pi^4}{l^3} - \frac{M^2 B^2 l}{EI_y} \right] \tag{5.94}$$

The critical moment is reached when neutral equilibrium is possible, and the requirement for neutral equilibrium is that the derivative of $U + V$ with respect to B vanish. Hence

$$\frac{d(U + V)}{dB} = \frac{B}{2} \left[\frac{GJ\pi^2}{l} + \frac{E\Gamma\pi^4}{l^3} - \frac{M^2 l}{EI_y} \right] = 0 \tag{5.95}$$

If equilibrium is to correspond to a deformed configuration, B cannot be zero. Instead, the term inside the brackets must vanish. Thus

$$\frac{GJ\pi^2}{l} + \frac{E\Gamma\pi^4}{l^3} - \frac{M^2 l}{EI_y} = 0$$

from which

$$M_{cr} = \frac{\pi}{l} \sqrt{EI_y \left(GJ + E\Gamma \frac{\pi^2}{l^2} \right)} \tag{5.96}$$

Equation (5.96) gives the critical moment for a simply supported I beam subject to pure bending. As was the case for the rectangular beam analyzed in Article 5.6, the critical moment of the I beam is proportional to the lateral bending stiffness and the torsional stiffness of the member. The only difference between the two cases is that the torsional stiffness of the I beam includes warping rigidity as well as St. Venant stiffness, whereas only St. Venant stiffness is present in the torsional stiffness of the rectangular beam.

Uniform Bending—Fixed Ends

In the preceding analysis, the ends of the member were assumed to be restrained against twisting and lateral translation, but free to warp and free to rotate about the principal axes. These conditions were said to be analogous to those existing at hinged supports in simple flexure. We shall now consider a member whose ends are free to rotate about the horizontal axis, but fully restrained against all other displacements. The analytical formulation of these boundary conditions is

$$\begin{aligned} v = v'' = 0 & \quad \text{at } z = 0, l \\ u = u' = 0 & \quad \text{at } z = 0, l \\ \beta = \beta' = 0 & \quad \text{at } z = 0, l \end{aligned} \tag{5.97}$$

We have attempted to choose end restraints here that are as similar as possible to full fixety in ordinary bending. As far as the displacements u and β that occur during buckling are concerned, these boundary conditions do represent complete fixety at the supports. In order to apply concentrated moments at the ends of the member, it is, however, necessary to permit the ends of the beam to rotate about the horizontal axis.

The boundary conditions of (5.97), as well as the hinged conditions considered previously, may not appear at first sight to be very realistic. However, these conditions, like the corresponding conditions in simple flexure, are studied not because of their similarity to support conditions in actual structures, but because they provide a set of limits between which most actual restraints lie and because homogeneous boundary conditions can be handled with relative ease.

The conditions in (5.97) will be satisfied if u and β are approximated by

$$u = A\left(1 - \cos\frac{2\pi z}{l}\right)$$

$$\beta = B\left(1 - \cos\frac{2\pi z}{l}\right)$$

(5.98)

Substitution of these shapes into the energy expression given by Eq. (5.87) leads to

$$
\begin{aligned}
U + V = {} & \frac{1}{2}EI_y\frac{16A^2\pi^4}{l^4}\int_0^l \cos^2\left(\frac{2\pi z}{l}\right) dz \\
& + \frac{1}{2}GJ\frac{4B^2\pi^2}{l^2}\int_0^l \sin^2\left(\frac{2\pi z}{l}\right) dz \\
& + \frac{1}{2}E\Gamma\frac{16B^2\pi^4}{l^4}\int_0^l \cos^2\left(\frac{2\pi z}{l}\right) dz \\
& - M\frac{4AB\pi^2}{l^2}\int_0^l \sin^2\left(\frac{2\pi z}{l}\right) dz
\end{aligned}
$$

(5.99)

Since $\displaystyle\int_0^l \sin^2\left(\frac{2\pi z}{l}\right) dz = \int_0^l \cos^2\left(\frac{2\pi z}{l}\right) dz = \frac{l}{2}$

Eq. (5.99) can be reduced to

$$U + V = \frac{\pi^2}{l}\left(4EI_y\frac{A^2\pi^2}{l^2} + GJB^2 + 4E\Gamma B^2\frac{\pi^2}{l^2} - 2MAB\right)$$

(5.100)

To determine the critical moment, we again find the value of M for which equilibrium in a deformed configuration is possible. For equilibrium

$$\frac{\partial(U+V)}{\partial A} = \frac{\pi^2}{l}\left[8EI_y A\frac{\pi^2}{l^2} - 2MB\right] = 0$$

$$\frac{\partial(U+V)}{\partial B} = \frac{\pi^2}{l}\left[2GJB + 8E\Gamma B\frac{\pi^2}{l^2} - 2MA\right] = 0$$

(5.101)

or

$$\left(4EI_y\frac{\pi^2}{l^2}\right)A - (M)B = 0$$

$$-(M)A + \left(GJ + 4E\Gamma\frac{\pi^2}{l^2}\right)B = 0$$

(5.102)

If equilibrium is to correspond to a deformed configuration, the determinant of Eqs. (5.102) must vanish. Hence

$$4EI_y\frac{\pi^2}{l^2}\left(GJ + 4E\Gamma\frac{\pi^2}{l^2}\right) - M^2 = 0$$

from which

$$M_{cr} = \frac{2\pi}{l}\sqrt{EI_y\left(GJ + 4E\Gamma\frac{\pi^2}{l^2}\right)}$$

(5.103)

Comparing this expression for the critical moment of a fixed beam with the one for a hinged beam, given by Eq. (5.96), it is evident that the critical moment of the fixed beam can be anywhere from two to four times as large as the critical moment of the hinged beam. If the warping stiffness is negligible compared to the St. Venant stiffness, the strength of the fixed beam is twice that of the hinged beam. However, if the St. Venant stiffness is negligible compared to the warping stiffness, the strength is increased fourfold in going from hinged to fixed-end conditions. The reason the beam behaves in this manner is that the lateral bending strength and warping strength depend on the length of the member, whereas the St. Venant torsional strength does not. The warping and lateral bending strength are thus affected by changes in the boundary conditions, whereas the St. Venant torsional strength is not.

Concentrated Load—Simple Supports

Let us now return to the simply supported beam considered at the beginning of the article, and determine its critical moment if the member is bent by a concentrated load at midspan, as shown in Fig. 5-14a, instead of being subject to uniform bending. It is assumed that the concentrated load is applied at the centroid of the cross section and that the load remains vertical as the beam buckles. As before, the x and y directions coincide with the principal axes of the cross section, the z axis is taken along the centroidal axis of the member, and the origin is at the right-hand support.

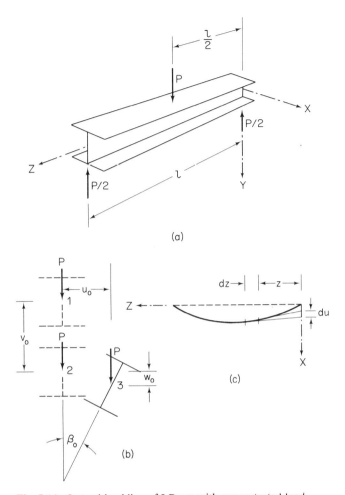

Fig. 5-14   Lateral buckling of I Beam with concentrated load.

The strain energy stored in the member during buckling has the same form it had in the preceding computations. It is therefore given by Eq. (5.76). A new relation must, however, be determined for the potential energy of the external loads. This expression will consist of the negative product of the force P that is applied to the member at midspan and the vertical distance that P moves through during buckling. The manner in which P moves as the member deforms is indicated in Fig. 5-14b. Prior to buckling, as the member bends in the vertical plane, P moves from 1 to 2. Then, as buckling occurs, P moves from 2 to 3. The movement from 2 to 3, which is the only one we are concerned with in calculating the energy of buckling, consists of a horizontal displacement u_0 and a vertical motion w_0. The subscripts 0 denote the fact that the displacements being considered are at midspan. In calculating the strain energy, only that part of the total energy caused by u, the horizontal displacement, was included. The part due to w, being very small, was neglected. However, of the two components u and w that make up the buckling displacement, only w contributes to the potential energy of the applied load, and even though it is small, it therefore cannot be neglected in this case.

To determine w_0, let us consider an element dz of the beam located a distance z from the right support, as shown in Fig. 5-14c. Due to lateral bending, there is a horizontal deviation du at the right support between the tangents drawn to the two ends of this element. The value of the deviation is, according to the moment-area theorem, given by

$$du = \frac{M_{y'}}{EI_y} z \, dz$$

For small deformations, the increment in the vertical displacement dw that corresponds to du is

$$dw = \beta \, du = \frac{M_{y'}}{EI_y} \beta z \, dz$$

Thus the vertical displacement w_0 at midheight is

$$w_0 = \int_0^{l/2} dw = \int_0^{l/2} \frac{M_{y'}}{EI_y} \beta z \, dz \tag{5.104}$$

In accordance with Eq. (5.63) and the sign conventions adopted in Article 5.6,

$$M_{y'} = -M_x \beta = \frac{Pz}{2} \beta \tag{5.105}$$

Hence

$$w_0 = \int_0^{l/2} \frac{Pz^2 \beta^2 \, dz}{2EI_y} \tag{5.106}$$

and the potential energy of P is

$$V = -Pw_0 = -\int_0^{l/2} \frac{P^2 z^2 \beta^2}{2EI_y} \, dz \tag{5.107}$$

Combining the expressions in (5.76) and (5.107), one obtains for the total potential energy of the system

$$U + V = \int_0^l \frac{EI_y}{2} \left(\frac{d^2u}{dz^2}\right)^2 dz + \int_0^l \frac{GJ}{2} \left(\frac{d\beta}{dz}\right)^2 dz$$
$$+ \int_0^l \frac{E\Gamma}{2} \left(\frac{d^2\beta}{dz^2}\right)^2 dz - \int_0^{l/2} \frac{P^2 z^2 \beta^2}{2EI_y} \, dz \tag{5.108}$$

As before, it is desirable to express u in terms of β and thus reduce the number of variables in the problem. Substitution of $M_{y'}$ as given by (5.105) into Eq. (5.60) leads to

$$EI_y \frac{d^2u}{dz^2} = \frac{Pz\beta}{2}$$

or
$$\frac{d^2u}{dz^2} = \frac{Pz\beta}{2EI_y} \tag{5.109}$$

Making use of this relationship to rewrite the first term in Eq. (5.108) in terms of β, one obtains

$$U + V = -\int_0^{l/2} \frac{P^2 z^2 \beta^2}{4EI_y} \, dz + \int_0^l \frac{GJ}{2} \left(\frac{d\beta}{dz}\right)^2 dz + \int_0^l \frac{E\Gamma}{2} \left(\frac{d^2\beta}{dz^2}\right)^2 dz \tag{5.110}$$

We now assume that β can be approximated by

$$\beta = B \sin \frac{\pi z}{l} \tag{5.111}$$

and substitute this shape into Eq. (5.110). Thus

$$\begin{aligned}
U + V = &-\frac{P^2 B^2}{4EI_y} \int_0^{l/2} z^2 \sin^2 \frac{\pi z}{l} \, dz \\
&+ \frac{GJB^2\pi^2}{2l^2} \int_0^l \cos^2 \frac{\pi z}{l} \, dz \\
&+ \frac{E\Gamma B^2 \pi^4}{2l^4} \int_0^l \sin^2 \frac{\pi z}{l} \, dz
\end{aligned} \tag{5.112}$$

Using the definite integrals

$$\begin{aligned}
\int_0^{l/2} z^2 \sin^2 \frac{\pi z}{l} \, dz &= \frac{l^3}{8\pi^2}\left(\frac{\pi^2}{6} + 1\right) \\
\int_0^l \sin^2 \frac{\pi z}{l} \, dz &= \int_0^l \cos^2 \frac{\pi z}{l} \, dz = \frac{l}{2}
\end{aligned} \tag{5.113}$$

Eq. (5.112) becomes

$$U + V = -\frac{P^2 B^2 l^3}{32EI_y\pi^2}\left(\frac{\pi^2}{6} + 1\right) + \frac{GJB^2\pi^2}{4l} + \frac{E\Gamma B^2 \pi^4}{4l^3} \tag{5.114}$$

At the critical load the first variation of $U + V$ must vanish. Hence

$$\frac{d(U + V)}{dB} = \frac{B}{2}\left[\frac{P^2 l^3}{8EI_y\pi^2}\left(\frac{\pi^2}{6} + 1\right) + \frac{GJ\pi^2}{l} + \frac{E\Gamma\pi^4}{l^3}\right] = 0$$

from which

$$P_{cr} = \frac{4\pi^2}{l^2}\sqrt{\frac{3}{\pi^2 + 6}EI_y\left(GJ + E\Gamma\frac{\pi^2}{l^2}\right)} \tag{5.115}$$

Comparison between the critical load of (5.115) and the critical moment given by Eq. (5.96) indicates that both are functions of the same beam properties. In fact, the two expressions differ by only a constant.

5.8 LATERAL BUCKLING OF CANTILEVER BEAM BY FINITE DIFFERENCES

We shall now consider the buckling of a cantilever beam bent by a concentrated load acting at the free end, as shown in Fig. 5-15a. The beam has a rectangular cross section, and the applied load is assumed to act at the centroid of the cross section. It is also assumed that the load remains vertical during buckling. To obtain the critical load, we shall derive the governing differential equations in much the same manner as was done in Article 5.6 and then solve them using the finite-difference method. The calculations follow the general outline of those given by Salvadori (Ref. 2.4).

As before, we make use of a fixed x, y, and z coordinate system and a set of axes x', y', and z' that move with the member as it deforms. Positive directions for the displacements u, v, and β and for the bending and twisting moments are shown in Figs. 5-15b and c.

As a result of buckling, the free end of the member deflects an amount δ in the x direction. This induces a moment $M_z = P\delta$ at the fixed end. There is of course also a vertical reaction P and a moment $M_x = -Pl$ at the fixed end. At a section a distance z from the fixed end the moments are

$$M_x = -Pl + Pz = -P(l - z) \tag{5.116}$$

$$M_y = 0 \tag{5.117}$$

$$M_z = P\delta - Pu = P(\delta - u) \tag{5.118}$$

Since it is convenient to write the equations of equilibrium in the x', y', z' system, it is necessary to obtain the components of the moments in (5.116) and (5.118) about the x', y', and z' axes. The angles between the axes of the two systems are shown in Fig. 5-16. Also shown in the figure are vectorial representations of the moments M_x and M_z and their components about the x', y', and z' axes. Replacing the cosines of small angles by unity and the sines of small angles by the angles themselves, one obtains

$$M_{x'} = M_x - M_z\frac{du}{dz} = -P(l - z) - P(\delta - u)\frac{du}{dz} \tag{5.119}$$

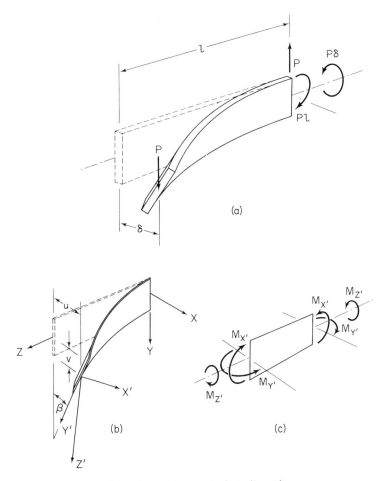

Fig. 5-15   Lateral buckling of cantilever beam.

$$M_{y'} = -M_x(\beta) - M_z\frac{dv}{dz} = P(l - z)(\beta) - P(\delta - u)\frac{dv}{dz} \qquad (5.120)$$

$$M_{z'} = M_x\frac{du}{dz} + M_z = -P(l - z)\frac{du}{dz} + P(\delta - u) \qquad (5.121)$$

Neglecting terms that contain deformations to a higher order than one, these relations reduce to

$$M_{x'} = -P(l - z) \qquad (5.122)$$

$$M_{y'} = P(l - z)\beta \qquad (5.123)$$

$$M_{z'} = -P(l - z)\frac{du}{dz} + P(\delta - u) \qquad (5.124)$$

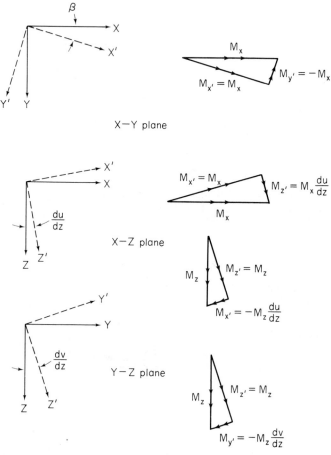

Fig. 5-16   Components of M_x and M_z along X', Y', and Z' axes. (Adapted from Ref. 4.8.)

For the positive directions of moments and deformations assumed in Fig. 5-15, the equations of bending and twisting about the x', y', and z' axes are

$$EI_x \frac{d^2v}{dz^2} = -M_{x'} \tag{5.125}$$

$$EI_y \frac{d^2u}{dz^2} = M_{y'} \tag{5.126}$$

$$GJ \frac{d\beta}{dz} = M_z \tag{5.127}$$

Substitution of the moments in (5.122) through (5.124) into Eqs. (5.125),

(5.126), and (5.127) leads to

$$EI_x\frac{d^2v}{dz^2} - P(l - z) = 0 \tag{5.128}$$

$$EI_y\frac{d^2u}{dz^2} - P(l - z)\beta = 0 \tag{5.129}$$

$$GJ\frac{d\beta}{dz} + P(l - z)\frac{du}{dz} - P(\delta - u) = 0 \tag{5.130}$$

As was the case in Article 5.6, Eqs. (5.129) and (5.130), which govern the buckling displacements u and β, are independent of Eq. (5.128), which describes the vertical bending of the beam that takes place before the member becomes unstable.

Before attempting to solve Eqs. (5.129) and (5.130), it is convenient to eliminate u by differentiating (5.130) and combining the resulting expression with (5.129). Thus one obtains

$$GJ\frac{d^2\beta}{dz^2} + \frac{P^2(l - z)^2}{EI_y}\beta = 0$$

or

$$\frac{d^2\beta}{dz^2} + \lambda^2\left(1 - \frac{z}{l}\right)^2\beta = 0 \tag{5.131}$$

where

$$\lambda^2 = \frac{P^2l^2}{GJEI_y} \tag{5.132}$$

Equation (5.131) is linear, but it does not have constant coefficients. Its solution is therefore considerably more complicated than, for example, that of Eq. (5.69). By making several changes of variables, Eq. (5.131) can be transformed into a Bessel equation whose solution is known. This procedure is followed by Timoshenko and Gere (Ref. 1.2) and will not be reproduced here. Instead, the finite-difference method will be used to obtain an approximate solution.

To obtain the finite-difference formulation of the problem, the member is divided into two equal segments of length $h = l/2$ (Fig. 5-17). The ends of the

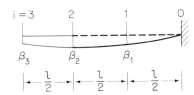

Fig. 5-17 Cantilever beam divided into two segments.

segments thus formed are denoted by $i = 0$, 1, and 2. The point $i = 0$ is at the fixed end and $i = 2$ is at the free end of the member. An additional segment extending from $i = 2$ to $i = 3$ is formed by prolonging the axis of the member a distance $l/2$ beyond the free end. It is necessary to imagine the member to be extended in this manner, because the second difference ratio of β at $i = 2$ involves the value of β at points on either side of $i = 2$.

The difference equation at any point $z = i$ is obtained by substituting the difference ratio for the second derivative, given by (2.78), for the second derivative in Eq. (5.131). Thus

$$\frac{\beta_{i+h} - 2\beta_i + \beta_{i-h}}{h^2} + \lambda^2\left(1 - \frac{z_i}{l}\right)^2 \beta_i = 0 \tag{5.133}$$

Writing this equation at $i = 1$ gives

$$\beta_2 - 2\beta_1 + \beta_0 + \lambda^2\left(1 - \frac{1}{2}\right)^2 \frac{l^2}{4}\beta_1 = 0$$

and at $i = 2$ one obtains

$$\beta_3 - 2\beta_2 + \beta_1 + \lambda^2(0)\frac{l^2}{4}\beta_2 = 0$$

Combining terms, these equations become

$$\beta_0 + \left(\frac{\lambda^2 l^2}{16} - 2\right)\beta_1 + \beta_2 = 0 \tag{5.134}$$

$$\beta_1 - 2\beta_2 + \beta_3 = 0 \tag{5.135}$$

At the fixed end of the member the angle of twist is zero. Hence

$$\beta_0 = 0 \tag{5.136}$$

A second boundary condition is obtained from the requirement that the twisting moment must vanish at the free end of the member. Thus

$$M_z = GJ\frac{d\beta}{dz} = 0 \quad \text{at } z = l$$

or

$$\frac{d\beta}{dz} = 0 \quad \text{at } z = l$$

which requires that

$$\beta_3 = \beta_1 \tag{5.137}$$

In view of (5.136) and (5.137), Eqs. (5.134) and (5.135) reduce to

$$\left(\frac{\lambda^2 l^2}{16} - 2\right)\beta_1 + \beta_2 = 0$$

$$2\beta_1 - 2\beta_2 = 0$$

To obtain the nontrivial solution to these equations, from which the critical load is determined, we set their determinant equal to zero. Thus

$$\begin{vmatrix} \dfrac{\lambda^2 l^2}{16} - 2 & 1 \\[2ex] 2 & -2 \end{vmatrix} = 0$$

or

$$-2\left(\frac{\lambda^2 l^2}{16} - 2\right) - 2 = 0$$

Taking the positive root of the equation gives

$$\lambda = \frac{4}{l}$$

from which

$$P_{cr} = \frac{4}{l^2}\sqrt{GJEI_y} \tag{5.138}$$

The exact value of the critical load, calculated by Timoshenko and Gere (Ref. 1.2) is $(4.013/l^2)\sqrt{GJEI_y}$.

5.9 DESIGN SIMPLIFICATIONS FOR LATERAL BUCKLING

In the preceding articles we determined the critical loading for several different beams. A simply supported I beam subject to uniform bending was shown to buckle when the applied moment reaches the value

$$M_{cr} = \frac{\pi}{l}\sqrt{EI_y\left(GJ + \frac{E\Gamma\pi^2}{l^2}\right)} \tag{5.139}$$

It was also found that the same beam, bent by a concentrated load at midspan, buckles when the load is equal to

$$P_{cr} = \frac{4\pi^2}{l^2}\sqrt{\frac{3}{\pi^2 + 6}EI_y\left(GJ + \frac{E\Gamma\pi^2}{l^2}\right)} \tag{5.140}$$

The similarity of these two expressions leads one to suspect that a single design formula valid for both loading conditions may exist. Such a relation can in fact be obtained if one substitutes the criterion of a critical internal bending moment for that of a critical applied loading. Accordingly, the critical moment for uniform bending is given by Eq. (5.139) and that for a concentrated load at midspan is

$$M_{cr} = \frac{Pl}{4} = 1.36\frac{\pi}{l}\sqrt{EI_y\left(GJ + \frac{E\Gamma\pi^2}{l^2}\right)} \tag{5.141}$$

It is now evident that a suitable design relationship is

$$M_{cr} = C_1 \frac{\pi}{l} \sqrt{EI_y \left(GJ + \frac{E\Gamma\pi^2}{l^2} \right)}$$

(5.142)

where the loading coefficient C_1 is equal to 1.0 for uniform bending and 1.36 for a concentrated load at midspan.

The results of numerous theoretical studies have shown that Eq. (5.142) is also valid for other loading conditions beside the two considered here. For example, the constant C_1 in Eq. (5.142) has been found to be equal to 1.13 for a uniformly distributed load and 1.04 for concentrated loads at the third points. These values of C_1, as well as others, corresponding to various different loading conditions, are listed in a survey article by Clark and Hill (Ref. 5.12). Included in the article is a bibliography of the investigations from which these data were taken.

Having demonstrated that the expression for the critical moment of a simply supported I beam subject to uniform bending can be made valid for other loading conditions by means of the factor C_1, we shall now show that this equation can be made applicable to different boundary conditions as well. In Article 5.7 the critical moment was determined for a uniformly bent I beam with fully restrained ends. The result of that analysis, given by Eq. (5.103), can be rewritten in the form

$$M_{cr} = \frac{\pi}{0.5l} \sqrt{EI_y \left[GJ + \frac{E\Gamma\pi^2}{(0.5l)^2} \right]}$$

(5.143)

Comparison of this relation with the corresponding one for hinged ends, Eq. (5.139), indicates that full fixety at the supports can be accounted for by an effective-length concept similar to the one used in columns. Thus the design relation given by Eq. (5.142) can be rewritten in the form

$$M_{cr} = C_1 \frac{\pi}{kl} \sqrt{EI_y \left[GJ + \frac{E\Gamma\pi^2}{(kl)^2} \right]}$$

(5.144)

where k is an effective-length factor that is equal to 1 for simply supported ends and equal to $\frac{1}{2}$ for fully fixed ends. Boundary conditions other than hinged-hinged and fixed-fixed can also be accounted for by using the effective-length concept. Based on results obtained by Vlasov (Ref. 5.13), Galambos (Ref. 4.8) lists values of the effective-length factor for several such end conditions.

For design purposes, Eq. (5.144) is sometimes simplified by omitting either one or the other of the two terms under the radical sign. For example, it is reasonable to neglect the warping term in comparison with the St.

Venant torsion term when dealing with members that have long unbraced spans, the reason being that the warping term decreases as the span increases, whereas the St. Venant torsion term does not. For thin-walled members just the opposite is true. The St. Venant torsion term, which varies as the cube of the thickness, is usually much smaller than the warping term and is therefore neglected.

Many hot-rolled wide-flange structural-steel beams fall into the first of the above two categories. The critical stress in pure bending for these members can accordingly be approximated by

$$\sigma_{cr} = \frac{M_{cr}}{S_x} = \frac{\pi}{S_x l}\sqrt{EI_y GJ} \tag{5.145}$$

The expression for σ_{cr} can further be simplified if the area of the web is neglected when calculating the section properties of the member. Thus

$$S_x = btd$$

$$I_y = \frac{tb^3}{6}$$

$$J = \frac{2bt^3}{3}$$

$$G = \frac{E}{2(1+\mu)} = 11.5 \times 10^3 \text{ ksi}$$

and Eq. (5.145) reduces to

$$\sigma_{cr} = \frac{20 \times 10^3}{ld/bt}$$

where b and t are the width and thickness of the flange and d is the depth of the section. Dividing this relation by a safety factor of 1.65, one obtains the allowable stress given in the 1969 AISC specifications for elastic lateral buckling (Ref. 1.17). That is,

$$\sigma_{all} = \frac{12 \times 10^3}{ld/bt} \tag{5.146}$$

A corresponding design expression for light-gage I beams is obtained by neglecting the St. Venant torsion term. Thus

$$\sigma_{cr} = \frac{2M_{cr}}{I_x d} = \frac{2\pi}{I_x dl}\sqrt{\frac{EI_y E\Gamma\pi^2}{l^2}} \tag{5.147}$$

In view of Eq. (5.12), the warping constant of an I section is given by $I_y d^2/8$.

The critical stress can accordingly be written as

$$\sigma_{cr} = \frac{E\pi^2}{4(l/d)^2} \frac{I_y}{I_x}$$

or

$$\sigma_{cr} = \frac{74 \times 10^3}{(l/d)^2} \left(\frac{r_y}{r_x}\right)^2$$

where r_x and r_y are the radii of gyration about the x and y axes. The AISI specification uses a safety factor of 1.85 and assumes that $d/r_x = 2.5$ is a representative value for light-gage I sections (Ref. 5.18). Thus

$$\sigma_{all} = \frac{247 \times 10^3}{(l/r_y)^2} \tag{5.148}$$

Since stress was assumed to be proportional to strain throughout this chapter, the critical moment given by Eq. (5.144) is valid only as long as the maximum stress at buckling is below the proportional limit of the material. As with columns, this will be the case for long members, but not for short ones. For short beams, the maximum stress reaches the proportional limit prior to buckling, and as soon as this occurs, the stiffness of the member begins to decrease. As a consequence, the stiffness of short members at buckling is considerably smaller than it would have been had no yielding taken place, and the actual inelastic critical moment is less than the one based on elastic behavior. A design curve for beams, indicating that the inelastic critical moment becomes a smaller and smaller fraction of the elastic one as the length decreases, could be obtained for beams just as it was for columns in Article 1.18. The calculation of the inelastic critical moment is, however, fairly complex and will not be considered here. The reader interested in the subject is referred to the following work done in this area (Refs. 5.11, 5.14, and 5.15).

References

5.1   F. B. SEELY and J. O. SMITH, *Advanced Mechanics of Materials*, 2nd ed. (New York: John Wiley & Sons, Inc., 1967).

5.2   A. CHAJES, P. J. FANG and G. WINTER, "Torsional-Flexural Buckling Elastic and Inelastic of Cold-Formed Thin-Walled Columns," *Cornell Engineering Research Bulletin, No. 66-1*, Ithaca, N.Y., 1966.

5.3   T. B. PEKÖZ, "Torsional-Flexural Buckling of Thin-Walled Sections Under Eccentric Load," *Cornell Engineering Research Bulletin, No. 69-1*, Ithaca, N. Y., 1969.

5.4   J. N. GOODIER, "The Buckling of Compressed Bars by Torsion and Flexure," *Cornell University Experimental Station Bulletin, No. 27*, Ithaca, N. Y., 1941.

5.5   N. J. HOFF, "A Strain Energy Derivation of the Torsional-Flexural Buckling Loads of Straight Columns of Thin-Walled Open Sections," *Quarterly of Applied Mathematics*, Vol. 1, No. 4, 1944.

5.6   L. PRANDTL, "Kipperscheinungen" (Dissertation, Munich, 1899).

5.7   A. G. M. MICHELL, "Elastic Stability of Long Beams Under Transverse Forces," *Philosophic Magazine*, Vol. 48, 1899.

5.8   S. TIMOSHENKO, "Einige Stabilitäts-probleme der Elasticitäts-theorie," *Zeitschrift für Mathematik und Physik*, Vol. 58, 1910.

5.9   G. WINTER, "Lateral Stability of Unsymmetrical I-Beams and Trusses in Bending," *Transactions, ASCE*, Vol. 108, 1943.

5.10 H. N. HILL, "Lateral Buckling of Channels and Z-Beams," *Transactions, ASCE*, Vol. 119, 1954.

5.11 T. V. GALAMBOS, "Inelastic Lateral Buckling of Beams," *Journal of the Structural Division, ASCE*, Vol. 89, No. ST5, 1963.

5.12 J. W. CLARK and H. N. HILL, "Lateral Buckling of Beams," *Transactions ASCE*, Vol. 127, 1962.

5.13 V. Z. VLASOV, *Thin-Walled Elastic Beams*, 2nd ed. (Washington, D.C.: National Science Foundation, 1961).

5.14 W. H. WITTRICK, "Lateral Instability of Rectangular Beams of Strain-Hardening Material Under Uniform Bending," *Journal of the Aeronautical Sciences*, Vol. 19, No. 12, 1952.

5.15 B. G. NEAL, "The Lateral Instability of Yielded Mild Steel Beams of Rectangular Cross Section," *Philosophic Transactions of the Royal Society*, Vol. 242, Jan. 1960.

5.16 S. P. TIMOSHENKO, *Strength of Materials*, Part II, 3rd ed. (New York: Van Nostrand Reinhold Company, 1956).

5.17 AISI, *Supplementary Information on the 1968 Edition of the Specifications for the Design of Cold-Formed Steel Structural Members* (New York: American Iron and Steel Institute, 1971).

5.18 AISI, *Design of Light Gage Cold-formed Stainless Steel Structural Members*, 1968 ed. (New York: American Iron and Steel Institute, 1968).

Problems

5.1   Determine the critical loading for a simply supported I beam subjected to a uniformly distributed load w. For this loading condition the constant C_1 in Eq. (5.142) has been found to be equal to 1.13. How does this compare with the results obtained here?

5.2   Using the finite-difference method, determine the critical moment of a simply supported rectangular beam subjected to uniform bending. Obtain solutions with the member divided into three and four segments, and extrapolate these results using Richardson's method.

6
BUCKLING
OF PLATES

6.1 INTRODUCTION

In the preceding chapters we dealt with the buckling of one-dimensional members such as beams and columns. The analysis of these members is relatively simple because bending can be assumed to take place in one plane only. By comparison, the buckling of a plate, which is the subject of this chapter, involves bending in two planes and is therefore fairly involved. From a mathematical point of view, the main difference between columns and plates is that quantities such as deflections and bending moments which are functions of a single independent variable in columns become functions of two independent variables in plates. Consequently, the behavior of plates is described by partial differential equations, whereas ordinary differential equations suffice for describing the behavior of columns.

A significant difference between columns and plates is also apparent if one compares their buckling characteristics. For a column, buckling terminates the ability of the member to resist axial load, and the critical load is thus the failure load of the member. The same is, however, not true for plates. These structural elements can, subsequent to reaching the critical load, continue to resist increasing axial force, and they do not fail until a load considerably in excess of the critical load is reached. The critical load of a plate is therefore not its failure load. Instead, one must determine the load-carrying capacity of a plate by considering its postbuckling behavior.

The theory of plate stability developed in this chapter is applicable to two distinct groups of plates. One includes the relatively small plate elements of which structural shapes such as I beams, channels, and angles are composed. When such an element buckles, only that element and not the entire member becomes deformed. Buckling of a plate element of a member is usually referred to as *local buckling*. The other category of plates to which the material in this chapter applies is ordinary flat panels, such as may be found in any structure having large flat surfaces.

Small-Deflection Theory of Thin Plates

Let us consider the plate of uniform thickness h shown in Fig. 6-1a. The

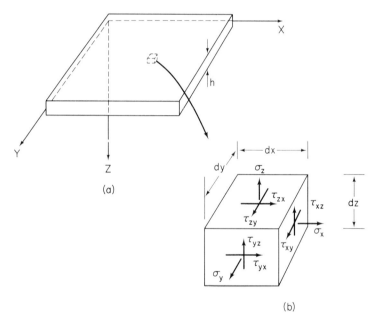

Fig. 6-1 Plate coordinates and stresses.

x and y coordinate axes are directed along the edges of the plate and the z axis is directed vertically downward. The xy plane midway between the two faces of the plate is called the middle surface. Figure 6-1b depicts a differential element of the plate. On each side of the element there can exist a normal stress σ and two shearing stresses τ. It is customary to designate planes in a physical body by the direction of their normal. The normal stress acting on a plane then carries the same designation as the plane. The designation of a shear stress consists of two parts; the first denotes the plane on which it acts and the second the direction of the stress.

Plates can be separated into three categories: thick plates, thin plates, and membranes. If the thickness of a plate is sizeable compared to the other dimensions, transverse shear deformations tend to be of the same order of magnitude as bending deflections and must be considered. Such plates are called *thick plates*. By comparison, plates are considered *thin plates* if their thickness is small compared to the other dimensions and transverse shear deformations are negligible compared to bending deflections. A third group, known as *membranes*, consists of plates whose thickness is so small that the bending stiffness tends to vanish, and transverse loads must be resisted almost entirely by membrane action. Of these three types, only thin plates will be considered in this chapter.

It is customary to make the following two assumptions regarding the behavior of thin plates:

1. The shear strains γ_{xz} and γ_{yz} are negligible, and lines normal to the middle surface prior to bending remain straight and normal to the middle surface during bending.
2. The normal stress σ_z and the corresponding strain ϵ_z are negligible, and therefore the transverse deflection at any point (x, y, z) is equal to the transverse deflection of the corresponding point $(x, y, 0)$ along the middle surface.

In addition to limiting the analysis to thin plates, the following idealizations are made.

3. The transverse deflections of the plates are small compared to the thickness of the plate. Thus middle-surface stretching caused by bending can be neglected; that is, membrane action resulting from flexure is negligible compared to the flexure.
4. The material of the plate is homogeneous, isotropic, and obeys Hooke's law.

As a consequence of assumptions 1 and 2, the plate can be treated as a two-dimensional stress problem, and assumptions 3 and 4 make it possible to describe the behavior of the plate by linear differential equations with constant coefficients.

6.2 DIFFERENTIAL EQUATION OF PLATE BUCKLING: LINEAR THEORY

To determine the critical in-plane loading of a flat plate by the concept of neutral equilibrium, it is necessary to have the equation of equilibrium for the plate in a slightly bent configuration. This equation will be derived here for a loading condition consisting of constant biaxial compression forces and

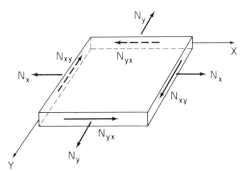

Fig. 6-2 Applied middle-surface forces—positive when acting as indicated. (Adapted from Ref. 6.1.)

constant in-plane shears, as shown in Fig. 6-2. The forces are considered to be positive when acting in the directions indicated. As is customary in plate theory, the unit of force used is load per unit length; that is, N_x is equal to the axial stress σ_x multiplied by the thickness h.

An element of a laterally bent plate is acted on by two sets of forces, in-plane forces equal to the externally applied loads and moments and shears that result from the transverse bending of the plate. In developing the equation of equilibrium it is convenient to consider these two sets of forces separately and then to combine the results.*

Equilibrium of In-Plane Forces

A differential element of a laterally bent plate is shown in Fig. 6-3. The sides of the element are of length dx and dy, and its thickness is equal to that of the plate, h. Acting on the element are the in-plane forces N_x, N_y, N_{xy}, and N_{yx}. Since middle-surface strains caused by bending are neglected, the in-plane forces are solely due to the applied constant in-plane loads and do not vary with x or y. The lateral deflection w does, however, vary with x and y, giving rise to the slopes and curvatures indicated in the figure.

For small lateral deflections, the cosines of the angles between the forces and the horizontal are approximately equal to unity, and the sines of the angles can be replaced by the angles. The sum of the moments about the x and y axes and the sum of the forces along these axes are thus all identically equal to zero. In the z direction the components of the N_x forces are equal to

$$N_x\left(\frac{\partial w}{\partial x} + \frac{\partial^2 w}{\partial x^2}dx\right)dy - N_x\frac{\partial w}{\partial x}dy$$

or simply

$$N_x\frac{\partial^2 w}{\partial x^2}dx\,dy \tag{6.1}$$

*The derivation of the plate equation presented here follows the general outline of the derivation given by Gerard (Ref. 6.1).

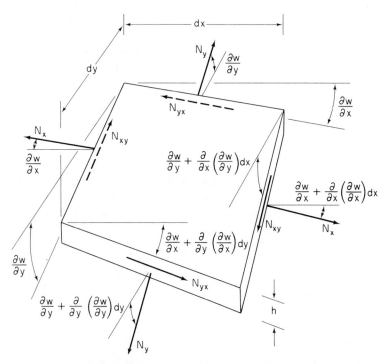

Fig. 6-3 In-plane forces on plate element—small deflections. (Adapted from Ref. 6.1.)

Similarly, the z direction components of the remaining forces acting on the element are

$$\left(N_y\frac{\partial^2 w}{\partial y^2} + N_{xy}\frac{\partial^2 w}{\partial x\,\partial y} + N_{yx}\frac{\partial^2 w}{\partial x\,\partial y}\right) dx\,dy \qquad (6.2)$$

In determining the z components of the shear forces, the curvature of the edges on which they act is neglected. It is permissible to do this because the terms that would result from including the curvature are of higher order than the remaining terms in the expression.

Noting that $N_{xy} = N_{yx}$ for moment equilibrium about the z axis, and adding the terms in (6.1) and (6.2), one obtains for the resultant of the middle-surface forces in the z direction

$$\left(N_x\frac{\partial^2 w}{\partial x^2} + N_y\frac{\partial^2 w}{\partial y^2} + 2N_{xy}\frac{\partial^2 w}{\partial x\,\partial y}\right) dx\,dy \qquad (6.3)$$

Equilibrium of Bending Moments, Twisting Moments, and Shears

In addition to the in-plane forces shown in Fig. 6-3, a differential element of a slightly bent plate will have acting on it the moments and shears shown in Fig. 6-4. All forces and moments are considered positive when acting in

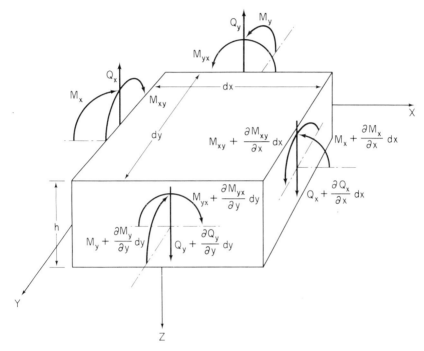

Fig. 6-4 Bending moments, twisting moments, and shears on plate element. (Adapted from Ref. 6.1.)

the direction indicated. Components of the shear forces in the x and y directions are negligible. In the z direction the components of the shear forces are

$$\left(\frac{\partial Q_x}{\partial x} + \frac{\partial Q_y}{\partial y}\right) dx\, dy \tag{6.4}$$

Addition of these terms to the z components of the middle-surface forces, given by (6.3), leads to the equation of equilibrium in the z direction:

$$\frac{\partial Q_x}{\partial x} + \frac{\partial Q_y}{\partial y} + N_x\frac{\partial^2 w}{\partial x^2} + N_y\frac{\partial^2 w}{\partial y^2} + 2N_{xy}\frac{\partial^2 w}{\partial x\, \partial y} = 0 \tag{6.5}$$

The condition that the sum of the moments about the x axis must vanish gives

$$\frac{\partial M_y}{\partial y}dy\,dx - \frac{\partial M_{xy}}{\partial x}dx\,dy - \frac{\partial Q_x}{\partial x}\frac{dx\,dy\,dy}{2} - Q_y\,dx\,dy - \frac{\partial Q_y}{\partial y}dx\,dy\,dy = 0$$

If the higher-order terms are neglected, this relation reduces to

$$\frac{\partial M_y}{\partial y} - \frac{\partial M_{xy}}{\partial x} - Q_y = 0 \qquad (6.6)$$

Similarly, moment equilibrium about the y axis leads to

$$\frac{\partial M_x}{\partial x} - \frac{\partial M_{yx}}{\partial y} - Q_x = 0 \qquad (6.7)$$

Equations (6.5), (6.6), and (6.7) are three equilibrium equations of plate buckling. As is often the case, it is possible to combine these equations and thus eliminate some of the variables in the problem. Differentiation of (6.6) and (6.7) gives

$$\frac{\partial Q_y}{\partial y} = \frac{\partial^2 M_y}{\partial y^2} - \frac{\partial^2 M_{xy}}{\partial x\,\partial y} \qquad (6.8)$$

and

$$\frac{\partial Q_x}{\partial x} = \frac{\partial^2 M_x}{\partial x^2} - \frac{\partial^2 M_{yx}}{\partial x\,\partial y} \qquad (6.9)$$

If one now substitutes the expressions in (6.8) and (6.9) into Eq. (6.5), one obtains a single equation of equilibrium from which the shear forces have been eliminated. Thus

$$\frac{\partial^2 M_x}{\partial x^2} - 2\frac{\partial^2 M_{xy}}{\partial x\,\partial y} + \frac{\partial^2 M_y}{\partial y^2} + N_x\frac{\partial^2 w}{\partial x^2} + N_y\frac{\partial^2 w}{\partial y^2} + 2N_{xy}\frac{\partial^2 w}{\partial x\,\partial y} = 0 \qquad (6.10)$$

Equation (6.10) contains four unknown functions, M_x, M_y, M_{xy}, and w. To obtain a solution, it is obviously necessary to have three relations, in addition to (6.10), among these variables. Since it is not possible to write any more equations of equilibrium, the additional relations will have to be obtained by considering the deformation of the plate.

Moment–Displacement Relations

Equations that express the moments in terms of the displacements will be obtained by relating the moments to the stresses, the stresses to the strains, and finally the strains to the displacements. The moments M_x, M_y, and M_{xy} are due to normal and shear stresses whose magnitude is proportional to the distance of the stress from the neutral surface (Fig. 6-5). Consequently,

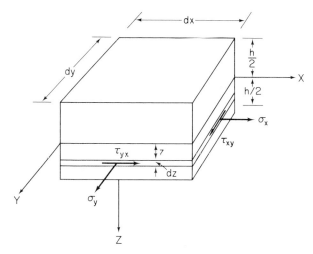

Fig. 6-5 Normal and shear stresses corresponding to bending and twisting moments. (Adapted from Ref. 6.1.)

$$M_x = \int_{-h/2}^{h/2} \sigma_x z \, dz \tag{6.11}$$

$$M_y = \int_{-h/2}^{h/2} \sigma_y z \, dz \tag{6.12}$$

$$M_{xy} = -\int_{-h/2}^{h/2} \tau_{xy} z \, dz \tag{6.13}$$

The negative sign in Eq. (6.13) indicates that M_{xy} is negative when z and τ_{xy} are positive. By comparison, M_x and M_y in Eqs. (6.11) and (6.12) are positive when z and the normal stress are positive. The moments and stresses are positive when in the directions indicated in Figs. 6-4 and 6-5.

As a result of assuming elastic behavior and negligible stresses in the z direction, the stress–strain relations for the plate are

$$\epsilon_x = \frac{1}{E}(\sigma_x - \mu\sigma_y) \tag{6.14}$$

$$\epsilon_y = \frac{1}{E}(\sigma_y - \mu\sigma_x) \tag{6.15}$$

$$\gamma_{xy} = \frac{1}{G}(\tau_{xy}) = \frac{2(1+\mu)}{E}\tau_{xy} \tag{6.16}$$

Solving for the stresses in terms of the strains, one obtains

$$\sigma_x = \frac{E}{1-\mu^2}(\epsilon_x + \mu\epsilon_y) \tag{6.17}$$

$$\sigma_y = \frac{E}{1 - \mu^2}(\epsilon_y + \mu\epsilon_x) \tag{6.18}$$

$$\tau_{xy} = \frac{E}{2(1 + \mu)}\gamma_{xy} \tag{6.19}$$

These expressions are equally valid for relating bending stresses to bending strains, which is what we are doing, or for relating total stresses due to in-plane forces as well as bending to the corresponding total strains.

To obtain a set of bending strain–displacement relations, we denote the x, y, and z components of the bending displacement of a point in the plate by u_b, v_b, and w. The subscripts are used to differentiate the bending displacements from the total displacements. At any point in the plate, the total displacement consists of two parts: that due to in-plane forces, which is constant over the thickness, and that due to bending, which varies from zero at the middle surface to a maximum at the outer surfaces. Thus

$$u = u_0 + u_b \tag{6.20}$$

$$v = v_0 + v_b \tag{6.21}$$

where u and v are the total displacements made up of the displacements u_0 and v_0 of the middle surface plus the displacements u_b and v_b relative to the middle surface due to bending. Since ϵ_z is neglected, w is constant over the thickness, and no expression is required for w.

During bending of the plate, a thin lamina *abcd* located a distance z above the middle surface undergoes the displacement and distortion shown in Fig.

6-6a. From the definition of strain it is evident that the strain of fiber *ab* in the x direction is given by

$$\epsilon_x = \frac{a'b' - ab}{ab} = \frac{dx - u_b + u_b + (\partial u_b/\partial x)\,dx - dx}{dx}$$

or simply

$$\epsilon_x = \frac{\partial u_b}{\partial x} \tag{6.22}$$

and the strain of fiber *ad* in the y direction by

$$\epsilon_y = \frac{\partial v_b}{\partial y} \tag{6.23}$$

The shear strain is equal to the change in the angle *dab*. This is given by

$$\gamma_{xy} = \frac{\partial u_b}{\partial y} + \frac{\partial v_b}{\partial x} \tag{6.24}$$

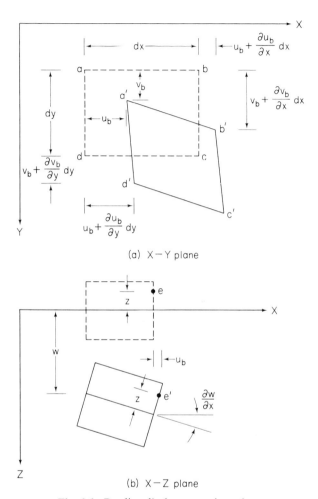

(a) X−Y plane

(b) X−Z plane

Fig. 6-6   Bending displacements in a plate.

During bending, plane sections are assumed to remain plane. The displacement u_b of point e located at a distance z above the middle surface (Fig. 6-6b) is therefore given by

$$u_b = -z\frac{\partial w}{\partial x} \tag{6.25}$$

Similarly, in the y direction

$$v_b = -z\frac{\partial w}{\partial y} \tag{6.26}$$

The negative sign indicates that a negative z and a positive slope correspond to a positive displacement. Substitution of the expressions for the displacements given by (6.25) and (6.26) into Eqs. (6.22), (6.23), and (6.24) leads to

$$\epsilon_x = -z\frac{\partial^2 w}{\partial x^2} \tag{6.27}$$

$$\epsilon_y = -z\frac{\partial^2 w}{\partial y^2} \tag{6.28}$$

$$\gamma_{xy} = -2z\frac{\partial^2 w}{\partial x\, \partial y} \tag{6.29}$$

These expressions are the bending strain–displacement relations for the plate. Their substitution into Eqs. (6.17), (6.18), and (6.19) gives

$$\sigma_x = -\frac{Ez}{1-\mu^2}\left(\frac{\partial^2 w}{\partial x^2} + \mu\frac{\partial^2 w}{\partial y^2}\right) \tag{6.30}$$

$$\sigma_y = -\frac{Ez}{1-\mu^2}\left(\frac{\partial^2 w}{\partial y^2} + \mu\frac{\partial^2 w}{\partial x^2}\right) \tag{6.31}$$

$$\tau_{xy} = -\frac{Ez}{1+\mu}\frac{\partial^2 w}{\partial x\, \partial y} \tag{6.32}$$

Finally, by substituting (6.30), (6.31), and (6.32) into Eqs. (6.11), (6.12), and (6.13) and carrying out the indicated integrations, the following moment–curvature relations are obtained:

$$M_x = -D\left(\frac{\partial^2 w}{\partial x^2} + \mu\frac{\partial^2 w}{\partial y^2}\right) \tag{6.33}$$

$$M_y = -D\left(\frac{\partial^2 w}{\partial y^2} + \mu\frac{\partial^2 w}{\partial x^2}\right) \tag{6.34}$$

$$M_{xy} = D(1-\mu)\frac{\partial^2 w}{\partial x\, \partial y} \tag{6.35}$$

in which

$$D = \frac{Eh^3}{12(1-\mu^2)} \tag{6.36}$$

The quantity D is the flexural rigidity per unit width of plate. It corresponds to the bending stiffness EI of a beam. Equations (6.33), (6.34), and (6.35) are the plate moment–curvature relations analogous to the beam equation $M = -EI(d^2y/dx^2)$. Comparison of the beam rigidity with that of the plate indicates that a strip of plate is stiffer than a beam of similar width and depth by a factor of $1/(1-\mu^2)$. The difference in stiffness exists because the beam is free to deform laterally, whereas the plate strip is constrained from deforming in this manner by the adjacent material.

Differential Equation of Plate Buckling

Substitution of Eqs. (6.33), (6.34), and (6.35) into Eq. (6.10) gives

$$D\left(\frac{\partial^4 w}{\partial x^4} + 2\frac{\partial^4 w}{\partial x^2 \partial y^2} + \frac{\partial^4 w}{\partial y^4}\right) = N_x\frac{\partial^2 w}{\partial x^2} + N_y\frac{\partial^2 w}{\partial y^2} + 2N_{xy}\frac{\partial^2 w}{\partial x\,\partial y} \qquad (6.37)$$

This is the differential equation of plate buckling under the action of in-plane forces N_x, N_y, and N_{xy}. Setting $N_y = N_{xy} = 0$, the critical load for uniaxial compression can be determined. In a similar manner the critical load under pure shear or due to a combination of compression and shear can be found.

At the beginning of the section it was pointed out that a primary difference between plates and beams was the existence of two independent variables in the former as opposed to a single independent variable in the latter. Thus removal of the y-dependent deformation terms from Eq. (6.37) results, as is to be expected, in a relation that is very similar to Eq. (1.34), the column buckling equation.

6.3   CRITICAL LOAD OF A PLATE UNIFORMLY COMPRESSED IN ONE DIRECTION

Let us consider a simply supported rectangular plate with sides a and b units long, as shown in Fig. 6-7. The plate is acted on by a compression force, N_x,

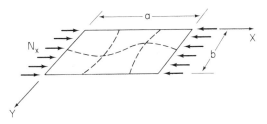

Fig. 6-7   Simply supported plate uniformly compressed in x-direction.

per unit length, distributed uniformly along the edges $x = 0$ and $x = a$. It is assumed that the edges of the plate are free to move in the plane of the plate and that no in-plane forces in addition to the applied load can therefore develop as the plate is axially compressed. Letting $N_y = N_{xy} = 0$, and noting that N_x is negative, Eq. (6.37), the differential equation of plate bending, reduces to

$$D\left(\frac{\partial^4 w}{\partial x^4} + 2\frac{\partial^4 w}{\partial x^2 \partial y^2} + \frac{\partial^4 w}{\partial y^4}\right) + N_x\frac{\partial^2 w}{\partial x^2} = 0 \qquad (6.38)$$

Since all four edges of the plate are simply supported, the lateral deflection as well as the bending moment vanishes along each edge. Taking the coordinate axes as shown in the figure, the boundary conditions are

$$w = \frac{\partial^2 w}{\partial x^2} + \mu \frac{\partial^2 w}{\partial y^2} = 0 \quad \text{at } x = 0, a \tag{6.39}$$

$$w = \frac{\partial^2 w}{\partial y^2} + \mu \frac{\partial^2 w}{\partial x^2} = 0 \quad \text{at } y = 0, b \tag{6.40}$$

In view of the condition of zero lateral deflection along each of the four boundaries,

$$\frac{\partial^2 w}{\partial y^2} = 0 \quad \text{at } x = 0, a$$

$$\frac{\partial^2 w}{\partial x^2} = 0 \quad \text{at } y = 0, b$$

Making use of these relations, the boundary conditions in (6.39) and (6.40) can be reduced to

$$w = \frac{\partial^2 w}{\partial x^2} = 0 \quad \text{at } x = 0, a \tag{6.41}$$

$$w = \frac{\partial^2 w}{\partial y^2} = 0 \quad \text{at } y = 0, b \tag{6.42}$$

Since the bending of the plate is limited to small deformations, only bending strains need be considered. The in-plane strains caused by flexure are assumed to be negligible. In view of this fact only the boundary conditions dealing with transverse deformations are required. The in-plane boundary conditions were needed to determine whether or not in-plane forces other than the applied ones would be induced during the axial compression of the plate. They are, however, not required from here on, when we shall be dealing only with the bending of the plate.

To determine the critical loading of a system by means of the concept of neutral equilibrium requires that one obtain the nontrivial solution of the governing linear differential equation. In the case of a plate this equation is a partial differential equation, and since we have not considered this type of equation heretofore, a few introductory words regarding its solution are in order.

The main difference between an ordinary and a partial differential equation is that the former can be satisfied by only one function, whereas there exist numerous functions that can satisfy the latter. As a consequence, the general solution of a partial differential equation is more difficult to obtain than that of an ordinary differential equation and of less practical value. Whereas the general solution of an ordinary differential equation gives the

dependent variable to within one or more arbitrary constants, the general
solution of a partial differential equation only describes the dependent
variable in general terms and does not give its specific form. For these
reasons it is not worthwhile to obtain the general solution of a partial differential equation. Instead, it is customary to solve the equation by the use of a
series.

Let us assume that the solution to Eq. (6.38) is of the form

$$w = \sum_{m=1}^{\infty} \sum_{n=1}^{\infty} A_{mn} \sin \frac{m\pi x}{a} \sin \frac{n\pi y}{b} \quad \begin{array}{l} m = 1, 2, 3 \ldots \\ n = 1, 2, 3 \ldots \end{array} \tag{6.43}$$

in which m and n are the number of half-waves that the plate buckles into in
the x and y directions, respectively. The assumed solution already satisfies the
boundary conditions, and there remains only the task of ensuring that it also
satisfies the differential equation. Substitution of the appropriate derivatives
of w into Eq. (6.38) leads to

$$\sum_{m=1}^{\infty} \sum_{n=1}^{\infty} A_{mn} \left[\frac{m^4\pi^4}{a^4} + 2\frac{m^2n^2\pi^4}{a^2b^2} + \frac{n^4\pi^4}{b^4} - \frac{N_x}{D}\frac{m^2\pi^2}{a^2} \right] \sin \frac{m\pi x}{a} \sin \frac{n\pi y}{b} = 0 \tag{6.44}$$

The left-hand side of (6.44) consists of the sum of an infinite number of
independent functions. The only way such a sum can vanish is if the coefficient of every one of the terms is equal to zero. Thus

$$A_{mn} \left[\pi^4 \left(\frac{m^2}{a^2} + \frac{n^2}{b^2} \right)^2 - \frac{N_x}{D}\frac{m^2\pi^2}{a^2} \right] = 0 \tag{6.45}$$

This expression can be satisfied in one of two ways, either $A_{mn} = 0$ or the
term in the brackets vanishes. If $A_{mn} = 0$, N_x can have any value. This is the
trivial solution of equilibrium at all loads, provided the plate remains perfectly
straight. The nontrivial solution that leads to the critical load is obtained by
setting the expression in the brackets equal to zero. Thus

$$N_x = \frac{Da^2\pi^2}{m^2} \left(\frac{m^2}{a^2} + \frac{n^2}{b^2} \right)^2$$

or

$$N_x = \frac{D\pi^2}{b^2} \left(\frac{mb}{a} + \frac{n^2a}{mb} \right)^2 \tag{6.46}$$

According to (6.46), N_x depends on the dimensions and the physical
properties of the plate and on m and n, the number of half-waves that the
plate buckles into. Since the critical value of N_x is the smallest value that
satisfies Eq. (6.46), the values of m and n that minimize (6.46) must be
determined. It is obvious that N_x increases as n increases and that $n = 1$

therefore results in a minimum value of N_x; that is, the plate buckles in a single half-wave in the y direction. The number of half-waves in the x direction that correspond to a minimum value of N_x is found by minimizing Eq. (6.46) with respect to m. Thus

$$\frac{d(N_x)}{dm} = \frac{2D\pi^2}{b^2}\left(\frac{mb}{a} + \frac{a}{mb}\right)\left(\frac{b}{a} - \frac{a}{bm^2}\right) = 0$$

from which

$$m = \frac{a}{b} \tag{6.47}$$

Substitution of this result into (6.46) leads to

$$(N_x)_{cr} = \frac{4D\pi^2}{b^2} \tag{6.48}$$

Since a simply supported plate must buckle into a whole number of half-waves, a/b, which according to (6.47) is equal to m, must be an integer. The critical load given by Eq. (6.48) is thus valid only when a/b is a whole number. For plates in this category, the buckling pattern consists of a single half-wave in the y direction and a/b half-waves in the x direction. In other words, the plate buckles into a/b square waves.

The more general case, where a/b is not an integer, will now be considered. Equation (6.46) can be rewritten in the form

$$N_x = \frac{kD\pi^2}{b^2} \tag{6.49}$$

where

$$k = \left(\frac{mb}{a} + \frac{n^2a}{mb}\right)^2 \tag{6.50}$$

The factor k depends on the aspect ratio a/b and on m and n, the number of half-waves that the plate buckles into. As before, $n = 1$ leads to the smallest value of N_x; that is, the plate buckles in a single half-wave in the y direction. To determine the buckling pattern in the x direction, one must consider how k varies with a/b for different values of m. Letting $m = 1$ in Eq. (6.50), the variation of k with a/b given by the curve labeled $m = 1$ in Fig. 6-8 is obtained. In a similar manner, by letting m in Eq. (6.50) take on successively higher values, the curves for $m = 2, 3, 4 \ldots$ are obtained. It is evident from these curves that there exist an unlimited number of values for k, corresponding to any given a/b, that satisfy Eq. (6.50). Of these we are interested in only the smallest one, because this is the value of k that will minimize N_x in Eq. (6.49). The solid line in Fig. 6-8 obtained by connecting the lower branches of the various curves gives the critical value of k as a function of a/b. In addition,

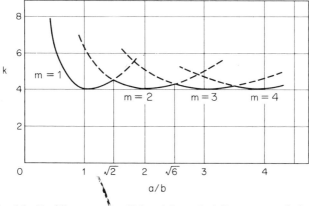

Fig. 6-8 Buckling stress coefficient k for uniaxially compressed plate.

the solid line indicates the number of half-waves into which the plate buckles, corresponding to a given a/b. For example, the buckling stress coefficient k is obtained from the curve for $m = 1$ for all plates with $a/b < \sqrt{2}$. These plates therefore buckle into a single half-wave in the x direction. For plates with a/b between $\sqrt{2}$ and $\sqrt{6}$, k is taken from the curve for $m = 2$, and these plates accordingly buckle into two half-waves in the longitudinal direction.

As long as a/b is relatively small, k varies considerably with the aspect ratio, and a curve like the one given in Fig. 6-8 is required to obtain the correct value of k. However, for $a/b > 4$ the variation of k from 4.0 is almost negligible, and $k = 4.0$ is therefore a satisfactory approximation for plates with $a/b > 4$.

Having determined the critical load of a uniaxially loaded plate, it is worthwhile to compare it to the critical load of a column. This is best accomplished by replacing D in Eq. (6.49) with $E/12(1 - \mu^2)$ and N_x with $\sigma_x t$. Thus one obtains

$$\sigma_x = \frac{k\pi^2 E}{12(1 - \mu^2)} \frac{1}{(b/t)^2} \tag{6.51}$$

The equivalent expression for the column is

$$\sigma_{cr} = \frac{C\pi^2 E}{(l/r)^2} \tag{6.52}$$

in which C is a constant that depends on the boundary conditions.

Comparison of Eqs. (6.51) and (6.52) indicates that the critical stress of both the plate and the column are directly proportional to the stiffness of the material, E, and inversely proportional to the square of a ratio of two lengths. The plate stress varies inversely as the flat width ratio squared, $(b/t)^2$, and the column stress is inversely proportional to the slenderness ratio squared, $(l/r)^2$. The critical stress of the column thus depends on its length, whereas that of the plate depends on the width of the plate and is independent of the length.

The investigation of the stability of a simply supported, axially compressed plate considered in this article dates back to 1891 when Bryan (Ref. 6.2) presented one of the first solutions to the problem. At the beginning of the twentieth century, plate buckling was again considered by Timoshenko, who not only investigated the simply supported case, but various other boundary conditions as well. Many of the solutions he obtained are given in his textbook on stability (Ref. 1.2).

6.4 STRAIN ENERGY OF BENDING IN A PLATE

In Chapter 2 the energy method was used to determine the critical load of a column. To apply the same method to plates, it is necessary to obtain an expression for the strain energy in a bent plate. Since the strain energy stored in a deformed body is equal to the work done by the external forces, the strain energy in an element of a bent plate can be obtained by determining the work due to the stresses acting on the element. For thin plates it is assumed that σ_z, γ_{xz}, and γ_{yz} are negligible. Consequently, only the stresses shown acting on the differential element in Fig. 6-9 need be considered. The total strain

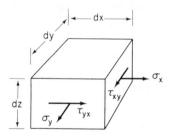

Fig. 6-9 Stresses on plate element.

energy due to these stresses will be obtained by applying the stresses one at a time and adding the energy thus produced.

At first let the element be acted on only by the stress σ_x. The energy stored in the element due to this stress is equal to one half the force $\sigma_x \, dz \, dy$ multiplied by the distance, $(\sigma_x/E)dx$, through which the force moves. Thus

$$dU_1 = \frac{1}{2E}\sigma_x^2 \, dx \, dy \, dz \qquad (6.53)$$

Now let the stress σ_y be applied to the element on which σ_x is already acting at its full value. Due to σ_y, deformations occur in the x and y directions, and work is done by both the new stress σ_y and the existing stress σ_x. In the y direction the force $\sigma_y\ dx\ dz$ and the deformation $(\sigma_y/E)dy$ increase simultaneously from zero to their final value. This results in an increase of strain energy equal to

$$dU_2 = \frac{1}{2E}\sigma_y^2\ dx\ dy\ dz \tag{6.54}$$

In the x direction the force $\sigma_x\ dy\ dz$ remains constant while the deformation changes by an amount $-\mu\sigma_y/E$. The resulting strain energy is

$$dU_3 = -\frac{\mu}{E}\sigma_x\sigma_y\ dx\ dy\ dz \tag{6.55}$$

To obtain the total strain energy due to σ_x and σ_y, we add dU_2 and dU_3 to dU_1. Thus

$$dU_4 = \frac{1}{2E}(\sigma_x^2 + \sigma_y^2 - 2\mu\sigma_x\sigma_y)\ dx\ dy\ dz \tag{6.56}$$

Assuming that normal stress produces no shear strain, and vice versa, it is possible to obtain the strain energy due to shear independent of the energy caused by axial stress. Due to the shear stress there exists a force $\tau_{xy}\ dx\ dz$ and a displacement in the direction of the force of $\gamma_{xy}\ dy$. Since both force and displacement increase simultaneously from zero to their final value, the strain energy is equal to

$$dU_5 = \frac{1}{2}(\tau_{xy}\ dx\ dz)(\gamma_{xy}\ dy) = \frac{1+\mu}{E}\tau_{xy}^2\ dx\ dy\ dz \tag{6.57}$$

The total strain energy stored in an element of a bent plate is the sum of dU_4 and dU_5. Hence

$$dU = \frac{1}{2E}[\sigma_x^2 + \sigma_y^2 - 2\mu\sigma_x\sigma_y + 2(1+\mu)\tau_{xy}^2]\ dx\ dy\ dz \tag{6.58}$$

For an entire plate, whose length and width are a and b, respectively, and whose thickness is h, the strain energy is

$$U = \int_{-h/2}^{h/2}\int_0^b\int_0^a \frac{1}{2E}[\sigma_x^2 + \sigma_y^2 - 2\mu\sigma_x\sigma_y + 2(1+\mu)\tau_{xy}^2]\ dx\ dy\ dz \tag{6.59}$$

As a consequence of neglecting σ_z, γ_{xz}, and γ_{yz}, this expression is limited to thin plates. However, it is not limited to small deformations. As a matter of fact, Eq. (6.59) will give the strain energy due to either bending or membrane action or a combination of the two, depending on what stresses are used.

At present it is desired to obtain an expression for the strain energy due to bending only. Twisting that accompanies bending in a plate is here considered to be part of bending. Substitution of (6.30), (6.31), and (6.32), which relate the bending stresses to the lateral displacements, into Eq. (6.59) leads to

$$U = \frac{E}{2(1-\mu^2)^2} \int_{-h/2}^{h/2} z^2 \int_0^b \int_0^a \left\{ (1-\mu^2)\left[\left(\frac{\partial^2 w}{\partial x^2}\right)^2 + \left(\frac{\partial^2 w}{\partial y^2}\right)^2 \right. \right.$$
$$\left. \left. + 2\mu\frac{\partial^2 w}{\partial x^2}\frac{\partial^2 w}{\partial y^2} + 2(1-\mu)\left(\frac{\partial^2 w}{\partial x \partial y}\right)^2 \right] \right\} dx \, dy \, dz \tag{6.60}$$

which, after integrating with respect to z and combining like terms, reduces to

$$U = \frac{D}{2} \int_0^b \int_0^a \left[\left(\frac{\partial^2 w}{\partial x^2}\right)^2 + \left(\frac{\partial^2 w}{\partial y^2}\right)^2 + 2\mu\frac{\partial^2 w}{\partial x^2}\frac{\partial^2 w}{\partial y^2} \right.$$
$$\left. + 2(1-\mu)\left(\frac{\partial^2 w}{\partial x \partial y}\right)^2 \right] dx \, dy \tag{6.61}$$

Equation (6.61) gives the strain energy due to bending in a thin plate.

6.5 CRITICAL LOAD OF A UNIAXIALLY COMPRESSED PLATE, FIXED ALONG ALL EDGES, BY THE ENERGY METHOD

To illustrate the use of the energy method in plate analysis, the critical compression load of a square plate fixed along all four edges will be determined. The plate, shown in Fig. 6-10, has sides of length a and is compressed

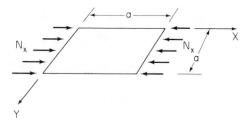

Fig. 6-10 Fixed plate uniformly compressed in x-direction.

by a uniformly distributed force N_x acting along two opposite edges. Taking the coordinate axes as shown in the figure, the boundary conditions are

$$w = \frac{\partial w}{\partial x} = 0 \quad \text{at } x = 0, a \tag{6.62}$$

$$w = \frac{\partial w}{\partial y} = 0 \quad \text{at } y = 0, a \tag{6.63}$$

In accordance with these conditions the plate is prevented from moving in the z direction or rotating at the boundaries. The edges of the plate are, however, free to move in the xy plane.

Boundary conditions (6.62) and (6.63) are satisfied if w is assumed to be of the form

$$w = A\left(1 - \cos\frac{2\pi x}{a}\right)\left(1 - \cos\frac{2\pi y}{a}\right) \tag{6.64}$$

The total potential energy of the system consists of two parts, the strain energy due to bending and the potential energy of the external loads. The former, derived in Article 6.4, is given by

$$U = \frac{D}{2}\int_0^a\int_0^a\left[\left(\frac{\partial^2 w}{\partial x^2}\right)^2 + \left(\frac{\partial^2 w}{\partial y^2}\right)^2 + 2\mu\frac{\partial^2 w}{\partial x^2}\frac{\partial^2 w}{\partial y^2} \right.$$
$$\left. + 2(1-\mu)\left(\frac{\partial^2 w}{\partial x\,\partial y}\right)^2\right]dx\,dy \tag{6.65}$$

To evaluate this expression, the following derivatives of w are needed:

$$\frac{\partial w}{\partial x} = \frac{2\pi A}{a}\left(\sin\frac{2\pi x}{a}\right)\left(1 - \cos\frac{2\pi y}{a}\right)$$

$$\frac{\partial w}{\partial y} = \frac{2\pi A}{a}\left(\sin\frac{2\pi y}{a}\right)\left(1 - \cos\frac{2\pi x}{a}\right)$$

$$\frac{\partial^2 w}{\partial x^2} = \frac{4\pi^2 A}{a^2}\left(\cos\frac{2\pi x}{a}\right)\left(1 - \cos\frac{2\pi y}{a}\right) \tag{6.66}$$

$$\frac{\partial^2 w}{\partial y^2} = \frac{4\pi^2 A}{a^2}\left(\cos\frac{2\pi y}{a}\right)\left(1 - \cos\frac{2\pi x}{a}\right)$$

$$\frac{\partial^2 w}{\partial x\,\partial y} = \frac{4\pi^2 A}{a^2}\left(\sin\frac{2\pi x}{a}\right)\left(\sin\frac{2\pi y}{a}\right)$$

Substitution of these expressions into (6.65) leads to

$$U = \frac{D}{2}\frac{16\pi^4 A^2}{a^4}\int_0^a\int_0^a\left[\left(\cos^2\frac{2\pi x}{a}\right)\left(1 - 2\cos\frac{2\pi y}{a} + \cos^2\frac{2\pi y}{a}\right)\right.$$
$$+ \left(\cos^2\frac{2\pi y}{a}\right)\left(1 - 2\cos\frac{2\pi x}{a} + \cos^2\frac{2\pi x}{a}\right)$$
$$+ 2\mu\left(\cos\frac{2\pi x}{a} - \cos^2\frac{2\pi x}{a}\right)\left(\cos\frac{2\pi y}{a} - \cos^2\frac{2\pi y}{a}\right)$$
$$\left. + 2(1-\mu)\left(\sin^2\frac{2\pi x}{a}\right)\left(\sin^2\frac{2\pi y}{a}\right)\right]dx\,dy \tag{6.67}$$

Making use of the following definite integrals,

$$\int_0^a \sin^2 \frac{2\pi x}{a}\, dx = \frac{a}{2}$$

$$\int_0^a \cos^2 \frac{2\pi x}{a}\, dx = \frac{a}{2} \qquad (6.68)$$

$$\int_0^a \cos \frac{2\pi x}{a}\, dx = 0$$

the expression for the strain energy reduces to

$$U = \frac{8D\pi^4 A^2}{a^4}\left[\frac{a}{2}\left(a + \frac{a}{2}\right) + \frac{a}{2}\left(a + \frac{a}{2}\right) + 2\mu\left(\frac{a^2}{4}\right) + 2(1 - \mu)\frac{a^2}{4}\right]$$

from which

$$U = \frac{16D\pi^4 A^2}{a^2} \qquad (6.69)$$

To determine the potential energy of the external loads, the plate is considered to be made up of a series of longitudinal strips, as shown in Fig. 6-11. For any strip the potential energy is equal to the negative product of the

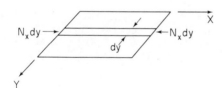

$N_x dy \rightarrow$ $\leftarrow N_x dy$ X

dy

Y

Fig. 6-11

force $N_x\, dy$ and the shortening of the strip in the x direction due to bending. That is,

$$dV = -(N_x\, dy)\left[\frac{1}{2}\int_0^a \left(\frac{\partial w}{\partial x}\right)^2 dx\right]$$

The total potential energy for the entire plate is obtained by adding the potential energies for all the individual strips. Thus

$$V = -\int_0^a \frac{N_x}{2}\int_0^a \left(\frac{\partial w}{\partial x}\right)^2 dx\, dy \qquad (6.70)$$

Substitution of the expression for $\partial w/\partial x$ from (6.66) into this relation leads to

$$V = -\left(\frac{N_x}{2}\right)\left(\frac{4\pi^2 A^2}{a^2}\right)\int_0^a\int_0^a \left(\sin^2 \frac{2\pi x}{a}\right)\left(1 - 2\cos \frac{2\pi y}{a}\right.$$
$$\left. + \cos^2 \frac{2\pi y}{a}\right) dx\, dy \qquad (6.71)$$

which can, in view of (6.68), be reduced to

$$V = -\frac{2N_x\pi^2A^2}{a^2}\left[\frac{a}{2}\left(a + \frac{a}{2}\right)\right]$$

or
$$V = -\frac{3N_x\pi^2A^2}{2} \tag{6.72}$$

The total potential energy of the system is obtained by adding the expressions in (6.69) and (6.72). Thus

$$U + V = \frac{16D\pi^4A^2}{a^2} - \frac{3N_x\pi^2A^2}{2} \tag{6.73}$$

In accordance with the concept of neutral equilibrium and the principle of stationary energy, the critical loading can be determined by finding the slightly bent configuration for which the total potential energy has a stationary value. Hence

$$\frac{d(U + V)}{dA} = \frac{32D\pi^4A}{a^2} - 3N_x\pi^2A = 0$$

from which

$$N_x = \frac{32D\pi^2}{3a^2} = \frac{10.67D\pi^2}{a^2} \tag{6.74}$$

Using an infinite series for w, Levy (Ref. 6.3) obtained an exact solution to the same problem. His critical load is

$$N_x = \frac{10.07D\pi^2}{a^2} \tag{6.75}$$

6.6 CRITICAL LOAD OF A PLATE IN SHEAR BY GALERKIN METHOD

For buckling to take place, it is not necessary that a member be loaded in axial compression. All that is necessary is that compression stresses exist in some part of the member. Thus we have seen that instability can occur in transversely loaded beams due to the compression stresses that are present in the compression flange of the member. Another structural member that is not loaded in axial compression, but may nevertheless become unstable, is a plate loaded in shear. In this case, compression exists on planes that make a 45-degree angle with the loaded edges, and when these stresses become sufficiently large, buckling will take place.

Let us consider the simply supported square plate shown in Fig. 6-12. The plate is loaded by uniform shearing forces N_{xy} applied along the four edges. To determine the critical loading of the plate, we make use of the Galerkin

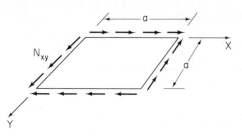

Fig. 6-12 Simply supported plate in pure shear.

method outlined in Article 2.8. As is the case when using the energy method, one must first choose an expression for the deflected shape of the member that satisfies the boundary conditions. Thus we let

$$w = A_1 \sin \frac{\pi x}{a} \sin \frac{\pi y}{a} + A_2 \sin \frac{2\pi x}{a} \sin \frac{2\pi y}{a} \tag{6.76}$$

Next, the Galerkin equation, whose general form is given by (2.72), must be written. For a plate subject to pure shear, whose deflection is assumed to be given by (6.76), the Galerkin equation is of the form

$$\int_0^a \int_0^a Q(w) g_i(x) \, dx \, dy, \qquad i = 1, 2 \tag{6.77}$$

where
$$Q(w) = \frac{\partial^4 w}{\partial x^4} + 2\frac{\partial^4 w}{\partial x^2 \partial y^2} + \frac{\partial^4 w}{\partial y^4} + 2N_{xy}\frac{\partial^2 w}{\partial x \, \partial y} \tag{6.78}$$

$$g_1(x) = \sin \frac{\pi x}{a} \sin \frac{\pi y}{a} \tag{6.79}$$

$$g_2(x) = \sin \frac{2\pi x}{a} \sin \frac{2\pi y}{a} \tag{6.80}$$

Since there are two terms in the assumed deflection function, two Galerkin equations must be written. Substituting the appropriate derivatives of w into $Q(w)$, these equations take the form

$$\int_0^a \int_0^a \left[\frac{4A_1\pi^4}{a^4} \sin^2 \frac{\pi x}{a} \sin^2 \frac{\pi y}{a} + \frac{64A_2\pi^4}{a^4} \sin \frac{2\pi x}{a} \sin \frac{\pi x}{a} \sin \frac{2\pi y}{a} \sin \frac{\pi y}{a} \right.$$
$$+ \frac{2N_{xy}}{D}\left(\frac{A_1\pi^2}{a^2} \cos \frac{\pi x}{a} \sin \frac{\pi x}{a} \cos \frac{\pi y}{a} \sin \frac{\pi y}{a} \right. \tag{6.81}$$
$$\left. \left. + \frac{4A_2\pi^2}{a^2} \cos \frac{2\pi x}{a} \sin \frac{\pi x}{a} \cos \frac{2\pi y}{a} \sin \frac{\pi y}{a} \right) \right] dx \, dy$$

$$\int_0^a \int_0^a \left[\frac{4A_1\pi^4}{a^4} \sin \frac{\pi x}{a} \sin \frac{2\pi x}{a} \sin \frac{\pi y}{a} \sin \frac{2\pi y}{a} + \frac{64A_2\pi^4}{a^4} \sin^2 \frac{2\pi x}{a} \sin^2 \frac{2\pi y}{a} \right.$$
$$+ \frac{2N_{xy}}{D}\left(\frac{A_1\pi^2}{a^2} \cos \frac{\pi x}{a} \sin \frac{2\pi x}{a} \cos \frac{\pi y}{a} \sin \frac{2\pi y}{a} \right. \tag{6.82}$$
$$\left. \left. + \frac{4A_2\pi^2}{a^2} \cos \frac{2\pi x}{a} \sin \frac{2\pi x}{a} \cos \frac{2\pi y}{a} \sin \frac{2\pi y}{a} \right) \right] dx \, dy$$

The definite integrals appearing in Eqs. (6.81) and (6.82) have the following values:

$$\int_0^a \sin^2 \frac{m\pi x}{a} \, dx = \frac{a}{2}$$

$$\int_0^a \sin \frac{m\pi x}{a} \sin \frac{n\pi x}{a} \, dx = 0$$

$$\int_0^a \cos \frac{m\pi x}{a} \sin \frac{m\pi x}{a} \, dx = 0 \qquad (6.83)$$

$$\int_0^a \cos \frac{2\pi x}{a} \sin \frac{\pi x}{a} \, dx = -\frac{2a}{3\pi}$$

$$\int_0^a \sin \frac{2\pi x}{a} \cos \frac{\pi x}{a} \, dx = \frac{4a}{3\pi}$$

Hence the equations can be reduced to

$$\frac{4A_1\pi^4}{a^4}\left(\frac{a}{2}\right)^2 + \frac{2N_{xy}}{D}\frac{4A_2\pi^2}{a^2}\left(-\frac{2a}{3\pi}\right)^2 = 0$$

$$\frac{64A_2\pi^4}{a^4}\left(\frac{a}{2}\right)^2 + \frac{2N_{xy}}{D}\frac{A_1\pi^2}{a^2}\left(\frac{4a}{3\pi}\right)^2 = 0$$

or

$$\frac{\pi^4}{a^2}A_1 + \frac{32N_{xy}}{9D}A_2 = 0 \qquad (6.84)$$

$$\frac{32N_{xy}}{9D}A_1 + \frac{16\pi^4}{a^2}A_2 = 0 \qquad (6.85)$$

To determine the critical load, we set the determinant of Eqs. (6.84) and (6.85) equal to zero. That is,

$$\begin{vmatrix} \dfrac{\pi^4}{a^2} & \dfrac{32N_{xy}}{9D} \\[2mm] \dfrac{32N_{xy}}{9D} & \dfrac{16\pi^4}{a^2} \end{vmatrix} = 0 \qquad (6.86)$$

Expanding (6.86) leads to

$$N_{xy_{cr}} = 11.1\frac{\pi^2}{a^2}D \qquad (6.87)$$

Using a more precise analysis than the one presented here, Stein and Neff (Ref. 6.4) obtained for the critical load

$$N_{xy_{cr}} = 9.34\frac{\pi^2}{a^2}D \qquad (6.88)$$

6.7 FINITE-DIFFERENCE METHOD
APPLIED TO PLATE BUCKLING

In Article 2.10 the finite-difference technique was used to approximate the buckling load of a column. The same method is also applicable to plate-buckling problems. To extend the finite-difference method from one-dimensional to two-dimensional problems, it is necessary for us to obtain expressions for difference ratios corresponding to partial derivatives. Specifically, we are interested in the partial derivatives that appear in the plate equation.

Difference Ratios for Partial Derivatives

Consider a plate represented by a network of discrete points as shown in Fig. 6-13. The points are evenly spaced a distance h apart in both the x and y

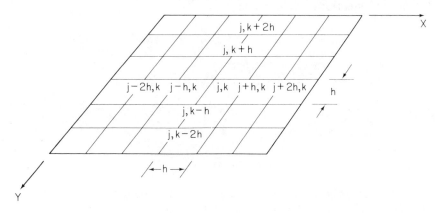

Fig. 6-13 Finite-difference mesh in two dimensions.

directions. According to Eqs. (2.78) and (2.80), the second and fourth differences with respect to x of a function $w(x, y)$ at point (j, k) are

$$\left(\frac{\partial^2 w}{\partial x^2}\right)_{j,k} = \frac{w_{j+h,k} - 2w_{j,k} + w_{j-h,k}}{h^2} \tag{6.89}$$

and $$\left(\frac{\partial^4 w}{\partial x^4}\right)_{j,k} = \frac{w_{j+2h,k} - 4w_{j+h,k} + 6w_{j,k} - 4w_{j-h,k} + w_{j-2h,k}}{h^4} \tag{6.90}$$

Similarly, the second and fourth differences with respect to y are

$$\left(\frac{\partial^2 w}{\partial y^2}\right)_{j,k} = \frac{w_{j,k+h} - 2w_{j,k} + w_{j,k-h}}{h^2} \tag{6.91}$$

and $$\left(\frac{\partial^4 w}{\partial y^4}\right)_{j,k} = \frac{w_{j,k+2h} - 4w_{j,k+h} + 6w_{j,k} - 4w_{j,k-h} + w_{j,k-2h}}{h^4} \tag{6.92}$$

The fourth mixed difference with respect to x and y is obtained by applying the operator for the second difference in the x direction [Eq. (6.89)] to the second difference in the y direction [Eq. (6.91)]. Thus

$$\frac{\partial^4 w}{\partial x^2 \partial y^2} = \frac{\partial^2}{\partial x^2}\frac{\partial^2 w}{\partial y^2} \cong \frac{1}{h^2}\left[\left(\frac{\partial^2 w}{\partial y^2}\right)_{j+h,k} - 2\left(\frac{\partial^2 w}{\partial y^2}\right)_{j,k} + \left(\frac{\partial^2 w}{\partial y^2}\right)_{j-h,k}\right]$$

$$\cong \frac{1}{h^4}[(w_{j+h,k+h} - 2w_{j+h,k} + w_{j+h,k-h}) - 2(w_{j,k+h} - 2w_{j,k}$$

$$+ w_{j,k-h}) + (w_{j-h,k+h} - 2w_{j-h,k} + w_{j-h,k-h})] \qquad (6.93)$$

Critical Load of a Biaxially Compressed Plate

To illustrate the analysis of a plate by means of the finite-difference technique, let us calculate the critical load of the biaxially compressed plate shown in Fig. 6-14. The plate is assumed to be square and the edges of the

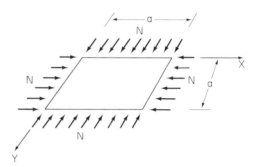

Fig. 6-14 Simply supported plate uniformly compressed in x and y directions.

plate are taken as simply supported. Acting on each edge is a uniformly distributed compression force of magnitude $N_x = N_y = N$. Taking the coordinate axes as indicated in the figure, the differential equation of bending is

$$\frac{\partial^4 w}{\partial x^4} + 2\frac{\partial^4 w}{\partial x^2 \partial y^2} + \frac{\partial^4 w}{\partial y^4} + \frac{N}{D}\left(\frac{\partial^2 w}{\partial x^2} + \frac{\partial^2 w}{\partial y^2}\right) = 0 \qquad (6.94)$$

This equation is obtained from the general equation of plate bending under the action of in-plane forces [Eq. (6.37)] by dropping the nonexistent shear forces N_{xy} and changing the sign of the axial forces. The boundary conditions for a simply supported plate were shown in Article 6.3 to be

$$w = \frac{\partial^2 w}{\partial x^2} = 0 \quad \text{at } x = 0, a$$

$$w = \frac{\partial^2 w}{\partial y^2} = 0 \quad \text{at } y = 0, a$$

To formulate the governing difference relations, each side of the plate is divided into n equal sections of size $h = a/n$. To obtain the difference equation corresponding to Eq. (6.94) at any point of the network of nodal points thus formed, one substitutes the difference ratios in (6.90), (6.92), and (6.93) for the derivatives in Eq. (6.94). Thus at a point (j, k) the difference equation is

$$
\begin{aligned}
20w_{j,k} &- 8(w_{j+h,k} + w_{j-h,k} + w_{j,k+h} + w_{j,k-h}) \\
&+ 2(w_{j+h,k+h} + w_{j+h,k-h} + w_{j-h,k+h} + w_{j-h,k-h}) \\
&+ (w_{j+2h,k} + w_{j,k-2h} + w_{j-2h,k} + w_{j,k+2h}) \\
&+ \frac{Nh^2}{D}(w_{j+h,k} + w_{j-h,k} + w_{j,k+h} + w_{j,k-h} - 4w_{j,k}) = 0
\end{aligned}
\tag{6.95}
$$

Using computational molecules, this equation can be represented pictorially as shown in Fig. 6-15. The first molecule corresponds to the biharmonic

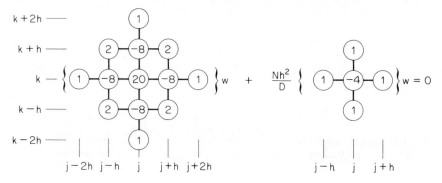

Fig. 6-15 Plate equation in molecule form.

operator ∇^4 and the second molecule to the sum of the second differences in the x and y directions.

The values of w at each of the $n \times n$ interior nodal points are the $n \times n$ unknowns in the problem. However, it is evident from the molecule in Fig. 6-15 that the difference equation at an interior point adjacent to a boundary involves the value of w at the boundary and the value of w at a fictitious point outside the boundary. For example, if $x = j - h$ represents a boundary, then the difference equation at (j, k) involves the value of $w_{j-h,k}$ along the boundary and of $w_{j-2h,k}$ outside the boundary. To obtain the values of $w_{j-h,k}$ and $w_{j-2h,k}$, one uses the given boundary conditions. From the condition of zero deflection along the edge $x = j - h$

$$
w_{j-h,k} = 0
\tag{6.96}
$$

and from the condition of zero curvature in the x direction at the same edge

$$
\frac{w_{j-2h,k} - 2w_{j-h,k} + w_{j,k}}{h^2} = 0
\tag{6.96a}
$$

Substitution of (6.96) into (6.96a) gives

$$w_{j-2h,k} = -w_{j,k} \qquad (6.96b)$$

Thus we see that for a simply supported edge the deflection at a point immediately outside the boundary is the negative of the deflection at the corresponding point inside the boundary.

First Approximation n = 2

As a first attempt, let the plate be subdivided into four equal squares, as shown in Fig. 6-16a. This network results in a single interior point whose lateral deflection is denoted by w_1. The deflection is zero along the boundary and equal to $-w_1$ at the exterior points opposite the centers of the four edges.

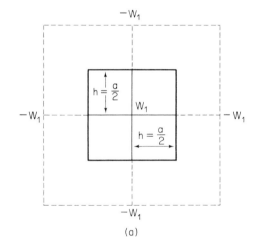

(a)

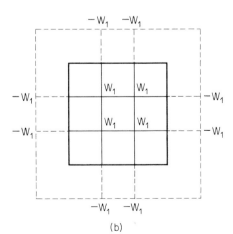

Fig. 6-16 Plate subdivided into (a) four sections and (b) nine sections.

(b)

Writing Eq. (6.95) at the interior point gives

$$w_1\left(16 - \frac{Na^2}{D}\right) = 0$$

from which

$$N_{cr} = \frac{16D}{a^2}$$

This approximation differs from the exact solution $2\pi^2 D/a^2$, given by Timoshenko and Gere (Ref. 1.2), by about 20%.

Second Approximation n = 3

If the plate is subdivided into nine equal squares, the nodal deflection pattern depicted in Fig. 6-16b results. Due to symmetry, the same deflection exists at all four interior points, and only one independent equation can be written. This equation is

$$w_1\left(4 - \frac{2Na^2}{9D}\right) = 0$$

from which

$$N_{cr} = \frac{18D}{a^2}$$

Comparison of this solution with the exact value of the critical load $2\pi^2 D/a^2$ indicates that the error is now 10%. A decrease in the mesh size from $h = a/2$ to $h = a/3$ has thus halved the size of the error.

6.8 PLATE BUCKLING BY FINITE ELEMENTS

The matrix method, developed in Articles 2.14 and 4.5 for determining the critical loading of columns and frames, is equally well suited for the solution of plate-buckling problems. As was done in the case of columns and frames, the plate to be investigated is subdivided into a number of discrete elements, and the element stiffness matrix relating element nodal forces to deformations is constructed. The stiffness matrix for the entire plate is then formed by combining the individual element stiffness matrices. Finally, the critical load is calculated by requiring the determinant of the structure stiffness matrix to vanish.

Element Stiffness Matrix

Let us consider a plate divided into a number of rectangular elements, as shown in Fig. 6-17a. The individual elements are assumed to be connected to one another only at the corners. A typical element, like the one in Fig. 6-17b,

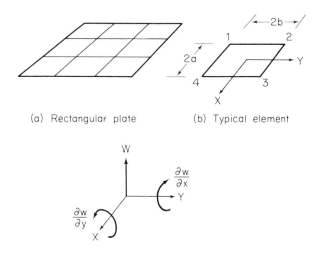

(a) Rectangular plate   (b) Typical element

(c) Nodal displacements

Fig. 6-17   Finite-element analysis of rectangular plate.

therefore has four nodal points at each of which we define three displacements. These include a vertical deflection w and rotations about the x and y axes $\partial w/\partial y$ and $\partial w/\partial x$ (Fig. 6-17c). Thus the element displacements at the first node are

$$[\delta_1] = \begin{bmatrix} \dfrac{\partial w_1}{\partial x} \\ \dfrac{\partial w_1}{\partial y} \\ w_1 \end{bmatrix} \tag{6.97}$$

and the element displacements for the nth element are

$$[\delta_n] = \begin{bmatrix} \delta_1 \\ \delta_2 \\ \delta_3 \\ \delta_4 \end{bmatrix} \tag{6.97a}$$

Corresponding to these displacements, there exist element forces at node 1,

$$[q_1] = \begin{bmatrix} M_{x1} \\ M_{y1} \\ Q_1 \end{bmatrix} \tag{6.97b}$$

and forces for the entire nth element,

$$[q_n] = \begin{bmatrix} q_1 \\ q_2 \\ q_3 \\ q_4 \end{bmatrix} \tag{6.97c}$$

These forces and deformations are related to each other by

$$[q_n] = [k_n][\delta_n]$$

in which the 12×12 matrix $[k_n]$ is the stiffness matrix for the nth element.

Using the energy method, in a manner similar to that employed in Article 2.14 for columns, the plate element stiffness matrix will now be developed. Let the moments and torques acting on a differential element of the plate, dx by dy, be denoted by

$$[M] = \begin{bmatrix} M_x \\ M_y \\ M_{xy} \end{bmatrix} \tag{6.97d}$$

and the corresponding curvatures and twists by

$$[\phi] = \begin{bmatrix} \dfrac{\partial^2 w}{\partial x^2} \\ \dfrac{\partial^2 w}{\partial y^2} \\ 2\dfrac{\partial^2 w}{\partial x\,\partial y} \end{bmatrix} \tag{6.97e}$$

The strain energy of bending for the differential element can then be written as

$$dU = \tfrac{1}{2}[M]^T[\phi]\, dx\, dy$$

and the bending strain energy of an entire plate element, of size $2a \times 2b$, as

$$U = \tfrac{1}{2}\int_{-b}^{b}\int_{-a}^{a} [M]^T[\phi]\, dx\, dy$$

In view of the moment–curvature relations for a plate, given by Eqs. (6.33), (6.34), and (6.35), $[M]$ can be expressed as

$$[M] = [D][\phi]$$

in which $[D]$, a matrix consisting of material constants, is given by

$$[D] = \begin{bmatrix} D & \mu D & 0 \\ \mu D & D & 0 \\ 0 & 0 & \dfrac{D}{2}(1-\mu) \end{bmatrix} \tag{6.97f}$$

Thus the strain energy becomes

$$U = \tfrac{1}{2}\int_{-b}^{b}\int_{-a}^{a} [\phi]^{T}[D][\phi]\,dx\,dy$$

The external work for the nth element consists of two parts, one due to the nodal forces $[q_n]$ and another due to the in-plane forces $[N]$. The first of these is given by

$$W_1 = \tfrac{1}{2}[q_n]^{T}[\delta_n] = \tfrac{1}{2}[\delta_n]^{T}[k_n][\delta_n]$$

and the second by

$$W_2 = \tfrac{1}{2}\int_{-b}^{b}\int_{-a}^{a} [\alpha]^{T}[N][\alpha]\,dx\,dy$$

in which

$$[\alpha] = \begin{bmatrix} \dfrac{\partial w}{\partial x} \\[2mm] \dfrac{\partial w}{\partial y} \end{bmatrix} \tag{6.97g}$$

and

$$[N] = \begin{bmatrix} N_x & N_{xy} \\ N_{xy} & N_y \end{bmatrix} \tag{6.97h}$$

Thus the total external work for the nth element is

$$W = \tfrac{1}{2}[\delta_n]^{T}[k_n][\delta_n] + \tfrac{1}{2}\int_{-b}^{b}\int_{-a}^{a} [\alpha]^{T}[N][\alpha]\,dx\,dy$$

Equating the strain energy for the nth element to the external work and rearranging terms, one obtains

$$[\delta_n]^{T}[k_n][\delta_n] = \int_{-b}^{b}\int_{-a}^{a} [\phi]^{T}[D][\phi]\,dx\,dy - \int_{-b}^{b}\int_{-a}^{a} [\alpha]^{T}[N][\alpha]\,dx\,dy \tag{6.98}$$

To evaluate $[k_n]$ in this expression, we assume that the deflection w at any point on the element can be approximated by a 12-term polynomial.

Thus

$$w = A_1 + A_2x + A_3y + A_4x^2 + A_5xy + A_6y^2 + A_7x^3$$
$$+A_8x^2y + A_9xy^2 + A_{10}y^3 + A_{11}x^3y + A_{12}xy^3 \tag{6.99}$$

Using the boundary conditions at the four corners of the nth element, the constants in (6.99) can be expressed in terms of the nodal displacements $[\delta_n]$, and w can be rewritten in the form

$$w = [A][\delta_n] \tag{6.99a}$$

The 12×12 matrix $[A]$ relates the deflection w at any point on the element to the nodal displacements of the element. Differentiation of Eq. (6.99a) makes it possible to obtain relations for $[\alpha]$ and $[\phi]$ in terms of $[\delta_n]$. Differentiating once we obtain

$$[\alpha] = [B][\delta_n]$$

and differentiating a second time leads to

$$[\phi] = [C][\delta_n]$$

in which $[\alpha]$ and $[\phi]$ are defined in (6.97g) and (6.97e), and $[B]$ and $[C]$ are obtained by differentiating $[A]$.

Substitution of the preceding expressions into Eq. (6.98) leads to

$$[\delta_n]^T[k_n][\delta_n] = [\delta_n]^T \left\{ \int_{-b}^{b} \int_{-a}^{a} [C]^T[D][C]\, dx\, dy \right.$$
$$\left. - \int_{-b}^{b} \int_{-a}^{a} [B]^T[N][B]\, dx\, dy \right\} \ [\delta_n]$$

from which

$$[k_n] = \int_{-b}^{b} \int_{-a}^{a} [C]^T[D][C]\, dx\, dy - \int_{-b}^{b} \int_{-a}^{a} [B]^T[N][B]\, dx\, dy \tag{6.100}$$

or $$[k_n] = [k'_n] - [k''_n] \tag{6.100a}$$

As was the case with columns, the plate stiffness matrix consists of two parts. The first, $[k'_n]$, is the stiffness matrix for pure flexure and the second, $[k''_n]$, is the initial stress stiffness matrix, which accounts for the influence of in-plane forces on the flexural stiffness.

To obtain the numerical values of the coefficients in $[k'_n]$ and $[k''_n]$, it is necessary to evaluate the matrices $[A]$, $[B]$, and $[C]$ and then carry out the integrations indicated by Eq. (6.100). Since this procedure involves a considerable amount of numerical work, it is not included here. However, the final forms of both $[k'_n]$ and $[k''_n]$ are given in Tables 6-1, 6-2, and 6-3. In

Table 6-1 Permutation matrix for $[k'_n]$ and $[k''_n]$

$$
\begin{Bmatrix}
Q_1 \\[2pt]
\dfrac{M_{x1}}{a} \\[4pt]
\dfrac{M_{y1}}{b} \\[4pt]
Q_2 \\[2pt]
\dfrac{M_{x2}}{a} \\[4pt]
\dfrac{M_{y2}}{b} \\[4pt]
Q_3 \\[2pt]
\dfrac{M_{x3}}{a} \\[4pt]
\dfrac{M_{y3}}{b} \\[4pt]
Q_4 \\[2pt]
\dfrac{M_{x4}}{a} \\[4pt]
\dfrac{M_{y4}}{b}
\end{Bmatrix}
=
\begin{Bmatrix}
w_1 \\[2pt]
a\dfrac{\partial w_1}{\partial x} \\[4pt]
b\dfrac{\partial w_1}{\partial y} \\[4pt]
w_2 \\[2pt]
a\dfrac{\partial w_2}{\partial x} \\[4pt]
b\dfrac{\partial w_2}{\partial y} \\[4pt]
w_3 \\[2pt]
a\dfrac{\partial w_3}{\partial x} \\[4pt]
b\dfrac{\partial w_3}{\partial y} \\[4pt]
w_4 \\[2pt]
a\dfrac{\partial w_4}{\partial x} \\[4pt]
b\dfrac{\partial w_4}{\partial y}
\end{Bmatrix}
$$

where the permutation matrix (Symmetric) is:

	w_1	$a\frac{\partial w_1}{\partial x}$	$b\frac{\partial w_1}{\partial y}$	w_2	$a\frac{\partial w_2}{\partial x}$	$b\frac{\partial w_2}{\partial y}$	w_3	$a\frac{\partial w_3}{\partial x}$	$b\frac{\partial w_3}{\partial y}$	w_4	$a\frac{\partial w_4}{\partial x}$	$b\frac{\partial w_4}{\partial y}$
Q_1	k_{11}											
$\frac{M_{x1}}{a}$	k_{21}	k_{22}										
$\frac{M_{y1}}{b}$	k_{31}	k_{32}	k_{33}									
Q_2	k_{41}	k_{42}	k_{43}	k_{11}								
$\frac{M_{x2}}{a}$	k_{51}	k_{52}	k_{53}	k_{21}	k_{22}							
$\frac{M_{y2}}{b}$	k_{61}	k_{62}	k_{63}	$-k_{31}$	$-k_{32}$	k_{33}						
Q_3	k_{71}	k_{72}	k_{73}	$k_{10,1}$	$k_{10,2}$	$-k_{10,3}$	k_{11}					
$\frac{M_{x3}}{a}$	k_{81}	k_{82}	k_{83}	$k_{11,1}$	$k_{11,2}$	$-k_{11,3}$	$-k_{21}$	k_{22}				
$\frac{M_{y3}}{b}$	k_{91}	k_{92}	k_{93}	$-k_{12,1}$	$-k_{12,2}$	$k_{12,3}$	$-k_{31}$	k_{32}	k_{33}			
Q_4	$k_{10,1}$	$k_{10,2}$	$k_{10,3}$	k_{71}	k_{72}	$-k_{73}$	k_{41}	$-k_{42}$	$-k_{43}$	k_{11}		
$\frac{M_{x4}}{a}$	$k_{11,1}$	$k_{11,2}$	$k_{11,3}$	k_{81}	k_{82}	$-k_{83}$	k_{51}	$-k_{52}$	$-k_{53}$	$-k_{21}$	k_{22}	
$\frac{M_{y4}}{b}$	$k_{12,1}$	$k_{12,2}$	$k_{12,3}$	$-k_{91}$	$-k_{92}$	k_{93}	$-k_{61}$	k_{62}	k_{63}	k_{31}	$-k_{32}$	k_{33}

Table 6-2 Stiffness coefficients for node 1 for $[k_n']$

$$
\begin{bmatrix}
k_{11} & & \\
k_{21} & k_{22} & \\
k_{31} & k_{32} & k_{33} \\
k_{41} & k_{42} & k_{43} \\
k_{51} & k_{52} & k_{53} \\
k_{61} & k_{62} & k_{63} \\
k_{71} & k_{72} & k_{73} \\
k_{81} & k_{82} & k_{83} \\
k_{91} & k_{92} & k_{93} \\
k_{10,1} & k_{10,2} & k_{10,3} \\
k_{11,1} & k_{11,2} & k_{11,3} \\
k_{12,1} & k_{12,2} & k_{12,3}
\end{bmatrix}
= \frac{bD}{6a^3}
\begin{bmatrix}
6 & 6 & 0 \\
6 & 8 & 0 \\
0 & 0 & 0 \\
3 & 3 & 0 \\
3 & 4 & 0 \\
0 & 0 & 0 \\
-3 & -3 & 0 \\
3 & 2 & 0 \\
0 & 0 & 0 \\
-6 & -6 & 0 \\
6 & 4 & 0 \\
0 & 0 & 0
\end{bmatrix}
+ \frac{aD}{6b^3}
\begin{bmatrix}
6 & 0 & 8 \\
0 & 0 & -6 \\
6 & 0 & 0 \\
-6 & 0 & 4 \\
0 & 0 & -3 \\
6 & 0 & 0 \\
-3 & 0 & 0 \\
0 & 0 & 2 \\
3 & 0 & 3 \\
3 & 0 & 0 \\
0 & 0 & 0 \\
3 & 0 & 4
\end{bmatrix}
+ \frac{\mu D}{2ab}
\begin{bmatrix}
1 & 1 & 0 \\
1 & 0 & 0 \\
1 & 2 & 0 \\
-1 & -1 & 0 \\
-1 & 0 & 0 \\
0 & 0 & 0 \\
1 & 1 & 0 \\
0 & 0 & 0 \\
0 & 0 & 0 \\
-1 & 0 & -1 \\
0 & 0 & 0 \\
-1 & 0 & 0
\end{bmatrix}
+ \frac{(1-\mu)D}{30ab}
\begin{bmatrix}
21 & 3 & 8 \\
3 & 8 & -3 \\
3 & 0 & 0 \\
-21 & -3 & -2 \\
-3 & -8 & 3 \\
3 & 0 & 0 \\
21 & 3 & 3 \\
-3 & 2 & 0 \\
-3 & 0 & 2 \\
-21 & -3 & -3 \\
3 & -2 & 0 \\
-3 & 0 & -8
\end{bmatrix}
$$

Table 6-3 Stiffness coefficients for node 1 for $[k_n'']$ for axial compression in x direction

$$
\begin{bmatrix}
k_{11} & & \\
k_{21} & k_{22} & \\
k_{31} & k_{32} & k_{33} \\
k_{41} & k_{42} & k_{43} \\
k_{51} & k_{52} & k_{53} \\
k_{61} & k_{62} & k_{63} \\
k_{71} & k_{72} & k_{73} \\
k_{81} & k_{82} & k_{83} \\
k_{91} & k_{92} & k_{93} \\
k_{10,1} & k_{10,2} & k_{10,3} \\
k_{11,1} & k_{11,2} & k_{11,3} \\
k_{12,1} & k_{12,2} & k_{12,3}
\end{bmatrix}
= \frac{-N_x}{630}\frac{b}{a}
\begin{bmatrix}
276 & & \\
42 & 112 & \\
66 & 0 & 24 \\
102 & 21 & 39 \\
21 & 56 & 0 \\
-39 & 0 & -18 \\
-102 & -21 & -39 \\
21 & -14 & 0 \\
39 & 0 & 18 \\
-276 & -42 & -66 \\
42 & -28 & 0 \\
-66 & 0 & -24
\end{bmatrix}
$$

presenting these matrices, use is made of the fact that for both $[k_n']$ and $[k_n'']$ the stiffness coefficients for nodes 2, 3, and 4 can be obtained from those of node 1 by the proper permutations and sign changes. Table 6-1 gives the permutations and sign changes for obtaining the coefficients for nodes 2, 3, and 4 from those of node 1, and Tables 6-2 and 6-3 give the values of the coefficients for node 1 for $[k_n']$ and $[k_n'']$, respectively. The data presented in these tables are taken from Refs. 6.14 and 6.15. Table 6-3 gives the coefficients for node 1 of $[k_n'']$ when a uniform compression N_x is acting. Similar data for N_y and N_{xy} can be found in Ref. 6.14.

Calculation of the Critical Load

As an illustration of the procedure for calculating the critical load of a plate, let us consider the buckling of a simply supported square plate under uniform edge compression in the x direction. The plate is subdivided into 16 elements, with the nodal points numbered as indicated in Fig. 6-18. Due to symmetry, only a quarter of the plate, that is, four elements, need be considered.

To obtain the structure stiffness matrix for the quadrant of the plate being considered, we combine the corresponding four element stiffness matrices in the manner described in Article 2.14. Accordingly, any influence coefficient in the structure stiffness matrix is obtained by adding all the influence coefficients from the four element stiffness matrices that carry the same subscripts as the desired structure stiffness coefficient. The structure stiffness matrix obtained in this manner is a 27×27 matrix.

The next step is to reduce the size of the stiffness matrix in accordance with the boundary conditions

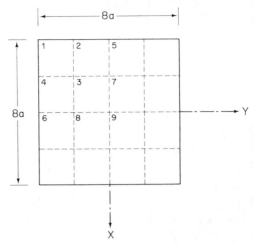

Fig. 6-18   Nodal point designations.

$$w_1 = w_2 = w_4 = w_5 = w_6 = 0$$

$$\frac{\partial w_1}{\partial x} = \frac{\partial w_1}{\partial y} = \frac{\partial w_2}{\partial y} = \frac{\partial w_4}{\partial x} = \frac{\partial w_5}{\partial y} = 0$$

$$\frac{\partial w_6}{\partial x} = \frac{\partial w_7}{\partial y} = \frac{\partial w_8}{\partial x} = \frac{\partial w_9}{\partial x} = \frac{\partial w_9}{\partial y} = 0$$

Deleting the rows and columns corresponding to these conditions, the stiffness matrix reduces to the form given in Table 6-4 (Ref. 6.16).

   To determine the critical loading, it is necessary to obtain the nontrivial solution of the equations

$$\{[K'] - N_x[K'']\}[\Delta] = 0 \qquad (6.101)$$

in which $[K']$ and $N_x[K'']$ are the flexural and initial stress stiffness matrices given in Table 6-4 and $[\Delta]$ consists of the structure nodal deflections. If the order of the system of equations in (6.101) is relatively small, say three or less, the critical load can be obtained by setting the determinant of the equations equal to zero and solving for the smallest root of the resulting polynomial equation. However, when one is dealing with a large number of equations, as we are, it is usually best to obtain the critical load by iteration. Prior to carrying out the iteration, it may be desirable to put Eq. (6.101) into the more commonly encountered form where the eigenvalue appears only along the main diagonal. This is accomplished by premultiplying the equation by $[K'']^{-1}$. Thus Eq. (6.101) becomes

$$\{[K'']^{-1}[K'] - N_x[I]\}[\Delta] = 0 \qquad (6.101\text{a})$$

in which $[I]$ is the identity matrix.

Table 6-4a Flexural stiffness matrix $[K']$

$$= \frac{D}{a^2}$$

	$a\frac{\partial w_2}{\partial x}$	w_3	$a\frac{\partial w_3}{\partial x}$	$a\frac{\partial w_3}{\partial y}$	$a\frac{\partial w_4}{\partial y}$	$a\frac{\partial w_5}{\partial x}$	$a\frac{\partial w_6}{\partial y}$	w_7	$a\frac{\partial w_7}{\partial x}$	w_8	$a\frac{\partial w_8}{\partial y}$	w_9
$\frac{M_{x2}}{a}$	3.04											
Q_3	−2.14	10.56										
$\frac{M_{x3}}{a}$	1.24	0	6.08									
$\frac{M_{y3}}{a}$	0	0	0	6.08								
$\frac{M_{y4}}{a}$	0	−2.14	0	1.24	3.04							
$\frac{M_{x5}}{a}$	0.48	−0.43	0.38	0	0	1.52						
$\frac{M_{y6}}{a}$	0	−0.43	0	0.38	0.48	0	1.52					
Q_7	−0.43	−2.28	0	−2.14	0	−1.07	0	5.28				
$\frac{M_{x7}}{a}$	0.38	0	0.96	0	0	0.62	0	0	3.04			
Q_8	0	−2.28	−2.14	0	−0.43	0	−1.07	−0.36	−0.43	5.28		
$\frac{M_{y8}}{a}$	0	0	0	0.96	0.38	0	0.62	−0.43	0	0	3.04	
Q_9	0	−0.36	−0.43	−0.43	0	0	0	−1.14	−1.07	−1.14	−1.07	2.64

Symmetric

Table 6-4b Initial stress matrix $N_x[K'']$

$$\frac{N_x}{630}\begin{bmatrix}
224 & & & & & & & & & & & \\
-84 & 1104 & & & & \text{Symmetric} & & & & & & \\
-56 & 0 & 448 & & & & & & & & & \\
0 & 0 & 0 & 96 & & & & & & & & \\
0 & 78 & 0 & -36 & 48 & & & & & & & \\
56 & -21 & -14 & 0 & 0 & 112 & & & & & & \\
0 & -39 & 0 & 18 & -24 & 0 & 24 & & & & & \\
-21 & 204 & 0 & 78 & 0 & -42 & 0 & 552 & & & & \\
-14 & 0 & 112 & 0 & 0 & -28 & 0 & 0 & 224 & & & \\
0 & 552 & -84 & 0 & -39 & 0 & 39 & -102 & -21 & 552 & & \\
0 & 0 & 0 & -48 & 18 & 0 & -18 & -39 & 0 & 0 & 48 & \\
0 & -102 & -21 & -39 & 0 & 0 & 0 & -276 & -42 & 102 & 39 & 276
\end{bmatrix}$$

If the eigenvalues of the matrix in (6.101a) are found by iteration, the highest eigenvalue is obtained first. However, the critical load corresponds to the lowest eigenvalue. Hence it is convenient to invert the matrix in (6.101a), leading to

$$\left\{[K']^{-1}[K''] - \frac{1}{N_x}[I]\right\}[\Delta] = 0 \tag{6.101b}$$

Now iteration gives the highest value of $1/N_x$, or the lowest value of N_x, first.

An alternative procedure for determining the critical load is to assume ever-increasing values of N_x and to evaluate the determinant at each step. The critical load then corresponds to the value of N_x for which the determinant reduces to zero.

6.9 PLATE-BUCKLING COEFFICIENTS FOR VARIOUS CASES

If the results obtained in the previous articles are compared, it becomes evident that for each case studied the critical stress is of the form

$$F_{cr} = \frac{k\pi^2 E}{12(1 - \mu^2)}\left(\frac{t}{b}\right)^2 \tag{6.102}$$

where F_{cr} is either the critical normal stress or the critical shear stress and k is a numerical coefficient that depends on the specific case being considered. Furthermore, it can be shown that Eq. (6.102) is valid for other cases not studied here as well. In each instance, regardless of the plate geometry, the boundary conditions, or the type of loading, the critical stress has the same form. Only the numerical value of k varies from case to case.

The most important loading conditions for which Eq. (6.102) is valid are uniform compression, pure shear, and pure bending. Values of k for plates with several different boundary conditions and subjected to these loadings are shown in Fig. 6-19. The data presented in the figure are taken from Ref. 6.5. In addition to the cases contained in Fig. 6-19 numerous combinations of edge and loading conditions have been investigated over the years. For a

Loading condition	Edge conditions	Buckling stress coeff. k
Uniaxial compression ![plate diagram with b vertical, a horizontal, forces F] $a/b > 4.0$	Both loaded edges simply supported Unloaded edges 1. Both simply supported	4.0
	2. One fixed, one simply supported	5.42
	3. Both fixed	6.97
	4. One simply supported, one free	0.425
	5. One fixed, one free	1.28
Pure shear 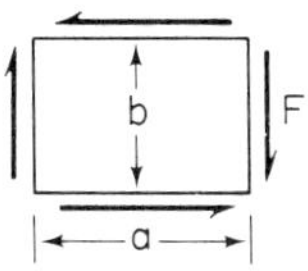 ![plate diagram with b vertical, a horizontal, shear forces F] $a/b > 1.0$	1. All edges simply supported	$5.34 + \dfrac{4.0}{(a/b)^2}$
	2. All edges fixed	$8.98 + \dfrac{5.6}{(a/b)^2}$
Pure bending 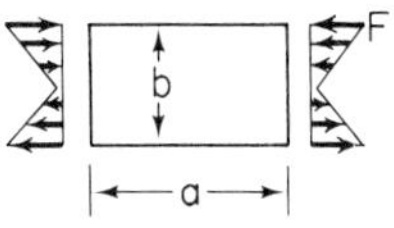 ![plate diagram with b vertical, a horizontal, bending forces F] $a/b > 1.0$	1. All edges simply supported	24
	2. Loaded edges simply supported Unloaded edges fixed	40

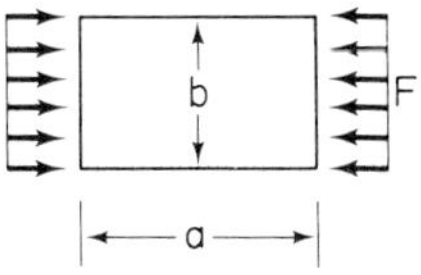

Fig. 6-19 Plate buckling stress coefficient k for various cases.

summary of many of these studies the reader is referred to an article by
Stowell, Heimerl, Libove, and Lundquist (Ref. 6.6).

6.10 INELASTIC BUCKLING OF PLATES

For plates as well as columns and beams, it is not unusual for the proportional
limit of the material to be exceeded prior to reaching the critical stress. If this
occurs, the elastic theory presented in the preceding articles must be replaced
by an analysis capable of dealing with the inelastic behavior that exists
between the proportional limit and the critical stress. As would be expected,
a theory of this type is extremely complex and beyond the scope of this book.
However, the conclusions that have been drawn from inelastic plate-buckling
studies are simple and straightforward and will be briefly considered here.
The reader interested in the theory itself is advised to consult Refs. 6.1, 6.5,
6.6, or 6.17.

Investigations of inelastic plate buckling indicate that Eq. (6.102), the
elastic buckling relationship, can be extended into the inelastic range,
provided Young's modulus is replaced by a reduced modulus. Thus the
inelastic critical stress for plates is usually given in the form

$$F_{cr} = \frac{k\pi^2\eta E}{12(1 - \mu^2)} \left(\frac{t}{b}\right)^2 \qquad (6.103)$$

where η is a plasticity reduction factor, or ηE a reduced modulus. Since
inelastic behavior always decreases the stiffness of a plate, $\eta < 1$, and the
inelastic critical stress given by (6.103) is always less than the corresponding
elastic stress given by (6.102).

The results obtained from inelastic plate studies indicate that the factor η
is a function of the shape of the stress–strain curve, the type of loading, the
length-to-width ratio of the plate, and the boundary conditions. No generally
applicable expression, like the tangent modulus in columns, therefore exists
for the reduced modulus of a plate. If a long rectangular plate is uniaxially
compressed and simply supported along both unloaded edges, Gerard (Ref.
6.1) shows the plasticity reduction factor to be

$$\eta = \frac{E_s}{E} \left(\frac{1}{2} + \frac{1}{2}\sqrt{\frac{1}{4} + \frac{3}{4}\frac{E_t}{E}}\right)$$

in which E_s is the secant modulus and E_t is the tangent modulus of the
material. For the same plate, if only one edge is simply supported and the
other is free,

$$\eta = \frac{E_s}{E}$$

Values of η for several other cases are tabulated in Ref. 6.6.

The preceding expressions for η were obtained using a fairly rigorous theory, and they lead to critical loads that agree well with test results. However, these expressions are not very suitable for routine calculations. A relation for η considerably more suited for design purposes than the foregoing ones has been derived by Bleich (Ref. 1.12). Using an approximate theory, he obtained the simple expression

$$\eta = \sqrt{\frac{E_t}{E}}$$

The advantage of this relation is that it leads to conservative results for any long plate, regardless of the boundary conditions, and that it can be used for shear as well as axial compression.

6.11 FINITE DEFLECTION THEORY OF PLATES

Introduction

Experience has indicated that plates, unlike columns, do not collapse when the critical load is reached. Instead, plates are usually able to resist increasing loads subsequent to the onset of buckling and may not fail until the applied load is considerably in excess of the critical load. It is thus obvious that the postbuckling behavior should be considered in formulating design criteria for plates. If one is solely interested in determining the critical load of a member, an analysis limited to infinitesimally small deformations suffices. However, if one desires to study the behavior of the member subsequent to the onset of buckling, as is the case with plates, it is necessary to consider deformations of finite magnitude.

If a plate is bent into a nondevelopable surface or if its edges are restrained from approaching one another during bending, membrane strains will be induced in the middle surface of the plate. As long as the transverse deflections of the plate are small compared to the plate thickness, these membrane strains may be safely neglected. However, once the transverse deflections become of the order of magnitude of the plate thickness, stretching of the middle surface is no longer negligible. The main difference between the finite-deflection theory to be developed in this article and the infinitesimal-deformation theory considered in the previous articles is that middle-surface strains, due to bending, that were neglected previously will now be considered.

A finite deflection is one that is of the same order of magnitude as the thickness of the member. It is, however, small compared to the other dimensions of the member. The assumptions regarding small angles, that is, $\sin \alpha = \tan \alpha = \alpha$ and $\cos \alpha = 1$, usually made in infinitesimal-deformation theory are therefore equally valid for finite deformations. Likewise, it is permissible to approximate the curvature with the second derivative when considering finite deflections.

Derivation of Equations

In deriving the equations governing the finite deformations of plates, all the idealizations made previously in the linear theory, except the one pertaining to membrane strains, will be assumed to be valid.

Equilibrium

A differential element of a laterally bent plate is acted on by two sets of forces: (1) The in-plane forces N_x, N_y, and N_{xy}, and (2) bending moments, twisting moments, and transverse shear forces. In going from infinitesimal to finite deformations no change occurs in the nature of the bending moments, twisting moments, and transverse shears. All equations pertaining to these forces derived in the linear analysis in Article 6.2 apply equally well to the finite-deflection theory. On the other hand the in-plane forces are effected significantly in going from infinitesimal to finite deformations. Whereas the externally applied middle-surface forces are the only in-plane forces that exist when the deflections are small, there are in-plane forces due to membrane action in addition to the forces applied along the edges of the plate when large deflections are considered.

The in-plane forces acting on a differential element of a laterally bent plate are shown in Fig. 6-20. It has been assumed that the deformations are small enough so that the cosines of the angles between the deflected surface and the horizontal are approximately equal to unity. The projections of the in-plane forces on the horizontal xy plane are therefore equal to the forces. Equating the sum of the forces in the x direction to zero gives

$$\frac{\partial N_x}{\partial x} + \frac{\partial N_{xy}}{\partial y} = 0 \tag{6.104}$$

Similarly, for the y direction

$$\frac{\partial N_y}{\partial y} + \frac{\partial N_{xy}}{\partial x} = 0 \tag{6.105}$$

Letting the sine of angles such as $\partial w/\partial x$ in Fig. 6-20 be approximated by $\partial w/\partial x$, one obtains for the z components of the N_x forces

$$-N_x \frac{\partial w}{\partial x}\, dy + \left(N_x + \frac{\partial N_x}{\partial x}\, dx \right)\left(\frac{\partial w}{\partial x} + \frac{\partial^2 w}{\partial x^2}\, dx \right) dy$$

which after simplifying and neglecting terms of higher order reduces to

$$N_x \frac{\partial^2 w}{\partial x^2}\, dx\, dy + \frac{\partial N_x}{\partial x} \frac{\partial w}{\partial x}\, dx\, dy \tag{6.106}$$

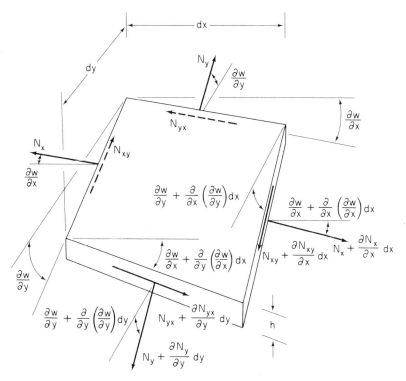

Fig. 6-20 In-plane forces acting on plate element—large deflections. (Adapted from Ref. 6.1.)

In a similar manner, the z components of the N_y forces are found to be

$$N_y \frac{\partial^2 w}{\partial y^2} dx\, dy + \frac{\partial N_y}{\partial y} \frac{\partial w}{\partial y} dx\, dy \qquad (6.107)$$

and the z components of the shear forces N_{xy} and N_{yx} are

$$N_{xy} \frac{\partial^2 w}{\partial x\, \partial y} dx\, dy + \frac{\partial N_{xy}}{\partial x} \frac{\partial w}{\partial y} dx\, dy \qquad (6.108)$$

and

$$N_{yx} \frac{\partial^2 w}{\partial x\, \partial y} dx\, dy + \frac{\partial N_{yx}}{\partial y} \frac{\partial w}{\partial x} dx\, dy \qquad (6.109)$$

By adding the terms in (6.106) through (6.109) and taking cognizance of Eqs. (6.104) and (6.105), one obtains for the z components of all the middle-surface forces

$$\left(N_x \frac{\partial^2 w}{\partial x^2} + N_y \frac{\partial^2 w}{\partial y^2} + 2N_{xy} \frac{\partial^2 w}{\partial x\, \partial y} \right) dx\, dy \qquad (6.110)$$

To write the equation of equilibrium in the z direction, the z components of the in-plane forces must be added to the transverse shear forces caused by bending. The latter were obtained in Article 6.2. They are given, according to Eqs. (6.4), (6.8), and (6.9), by

$$\left(\frac{\partial^2 M_x}{\partial x^2} - 2\frac{\partial^2 M_{xy}}{\partial x\,\partial y} + \frac{\partial^2 M_y}{\partial y^2}\right) dx\, dy \tag{6.111}$$

By using the moment–curvature relations in (6.33), (6.34), and (6.35), this expression can be rewritten in the form

$$-D\left(\frac{\partial^4 w}{\partial x^4} + 2\frac{\partial^4 w}{\partial x^2\,\partial y^2} + \frac{\partial^4 w}{\partial y^4}\right) \tag{6.112}$$

Combining (6.110) and (6.112), one obtains for the equation of equilibrium in the z direction

$$D\left(\frac{\partial^4 w}{\partial x^4} + 2\frac{\partial^4 w}{\partial x^2\,\partial y^2} + \frac{\partial^4 w}{\partial y^4}\right) - N_x\frac{\partial^2 w}{\partial x^2} - N_y\frac{\partial^2 w}{\partial y^2} - 2N_{xy}\frac{\partial^2 w}{\partial x\,\partial y} = 0 \tag{6.113}$$

At first glance, Eq. (6.113) appears to be identical to Eq. (6.37), the equation of equilibrium for small deformations. However, there is one all-important difference between the two equations. In Eq. (6.37) the terms N_x, N_y, and N_{xy} represent constant applied edge forces. The equation is thus a linear differential equation with constant coefficients, and it has only one dependent variable, w. By comparison, the terms N_x, N_y, and N_{xy} that appear in Eq. (6.113) are unknown functions of x and y. They represent both the variable membrane forces and the constant applied edge loads. Equation (6.113) is therefore nonlinear, and it contains four dependent variables, w and the three in-plane forces.

Compatibility

The equations of equilibrium, (6.104), (6.105), and (6.113) derived in the previous section contain four unknown functions N_x, N_y, N_{xy}, and w. To evaluate these functions, a fourth equation is obviously needed. The situation is similar to that encountered in an indeterminate structure, where the equations of equilibrium must be supplemented by one or more equations dealing with the deformation of the system in order to evaluate all the unknown forces and displacements. In the case of the plate, the additional equation is obtained by considering the middle-surface strain–displacement relationships.

As indicated in Article 6.2, the displacements u and v of a point (x, y, z) in the plate consist of two parts: (1) the displacement u_0 and v_0 of the corresponding point $(x, y, 0)$ in the middle plane and (2) the bending displacements u_b and v_b that the point (x, y, z) experiences relative to the point $(x, y, 0)$. In Article 6.2 we dealt with the relation of bending strains to bending displacements. We shall now concern ourselves with the relation between middle-surface strains and middle-surface displacements.

Consider a linear element AB of the middle surface of the plate, as shown in Fig. 6-21. Due to bending of the plate, the element assumes the configura-

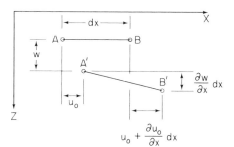

Fig. 6-21 Axial strain in plate—large deflections.

tion $A'B'$. The length of the element is changed due to the in-plane displacement in the x direction and due to the transverse displacement in the z direction. As a result of the u_0 displacement, the elongation of the element is

$$\frac{\partial u_0}{\partial x}\, dx \qquad (6.114)$$

The change in length of the element due to the w displacement is equal to the difference in length between the curved element $A'B'$ and its projection on the horizontal plane. According to Eq. (2.2), this is given by

$$\frac{1}{2}\left(\frac{\partial w}{\partial x}\right)^2 dx \qquad (6.115)$$

Thus the middle-surface strain in the x direction, that is, the total change in length per unit length, is

$$\epsilon_{x_0} = \frac{\partial u_0}{\partial x} + \frac{1}{2}\left(\frac{\partial w}{\partial x}\right)^2 \qquad (6.116)$$

Similarly, the middle-surface strain in the y direction is

$$\epsilon_{y_0} = \frac{\partial v_0}{\partial y} + \frac{1}{2}\left(\frac{\partial w}{\partial y}\right)^2 \qquad (6.117)$$

The shear strain is the change in the angle between two perpendicular lines, such as OB and OA in Fig. 6-22, that occurs as the plate deforms. Like

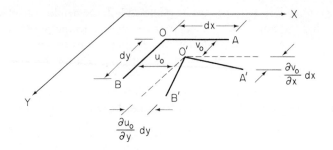

(a) Shear strain due to u_0 and v_0

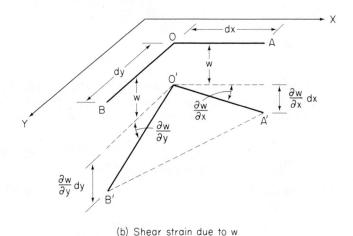

(b) Shear strain due to w

Fig. 6-22   Shear strain in plate—large deflections.

the normal strains, the shear strain consists of two parts, one due to the in-plane deformations u_0 and v_0 and the other due to the transverse deflection w. As is evident from Fig. 6-22a, the shear strain due to u_0 and v_0 is

$$\frac{\partial u_0}{\partial y} + \frac{\partial v_0}{\partial x} \tag{6.118}$$

The shear strain due to w (Fig. 6-22b) is equal to the difference between angle BOA and angle $B'O'A'$. Accordingly, angle $B'O'A'$ can be written as $(\pi/2) - \gamma$, and $A'B'$ is given by

$$(A'B')^2 = (O'A')^2 + (O'B')^2 - 2(O'A')(O'B') \cos\left(\frac{\pi}{2} - \gamma\right) \tag{6.119}$$

in which

$$(O'A')^2 = dx^2 + \left(dx\,\frac{\partial w}{\partial x}\right)^2$$

$$(O'B')^2 = dy^2 + \left(dy\,\frac{\partial w}{\partial y}\right)^2$$

$$(A'B')^2 = dx^2 + dy^2 + \left(\frac{\partial w}{\partial y}\,dy - \frac{\partial w}{\partial x}\,dx\right)^2 \qquad (6.120)$$

$$(O'A')(O'B') = dx\,dy$$

Recognizing that $\cos[(\pi/2) - \gamma] = \gamma$ for small angles γ, Eq. (6.119) reduces to

$$\gamma = \frac{\partial w}{\partial x}\frac{\partial w}{\partial y} \qquad (6.121)$$

Thus the total middle-surface shear strain is

$$\gamma_{xy_0} = \frac{\partial u_0}{\partial y} + \frac{\partial v_0}{\partial x} + \frac{\partial w}{\partial x}\frac{\partial w}{\partial y} \qquad (6.122)$$

Equations (6.116), (6.117), and (6.122) relate the middle-surface strains to the middle-surface displacements and the transverse displacement w. The middle-surface strains can also be expressed in terms of the corresponding middle-surface forces. That is,

$$\epsilon_{x_0} = \frac{1}{Eh}(N_x - \mu N_y) \qquad (6.123)$$

$$\epsilon_{y_0} = \frac{1}{Eh}(N_y - \mu N_x) \qquad (6.124)$$

$$\gamma_{xy_0} = \frac{2(1+\mu)}{Eh}N_{xy} \qquad (6.125)$$

Expressions (6.123), (6.124), and (6.125), the three strain–displacement relations (6.116), (6.117), and (6.122), and the equilibrium equations (6.104), (6.105), and (6.113) constitute a set of nine equations in nine unknowns. These equations completely describe the behavior of the plate and could be used to solve for all the unknown forces and displacements. The equations as they stand are, however, cumbersome to deal with. It is therefore desirable to uncouple some of the unknowns and thus reduce the number of equations that must be solved simultaneously.

One can eliminate the variables u and v by differentiating Eq. (6.116) twice with respect to y, Eq. (6.117) twice with respect to x, and Eq. (6.122) successively with respect to x and y. The resulting expressions are then combined to give

$$\frac{\partial^2 \epsilon_{x_0}}{\partial y^2} + \frac{\partial^2 \epsilon_{y_0}}{\partial x^2} - \frac{\partial^2 \gamma_{xy_0}}{\partial x\, \partial y} = \left(\frac{\partial^2 w}{\partial x\, \partial y}\right)^2 - \frac{\partial^2 w}{\partial x^2}\frac{\partial^2 w}{\partial y^2} \tag{6.126}$$

Equation (6.126) is a deformation compatibility equation. There are many solutions for the in-plane forces that satisfy the equilibrium equations. However, only the one that satisfies Eq. (6.126) in addition to equilibrium leads to continuous displacements that are compatible with the physical constraints of the system.

To further reduce the number of equations that must be solved simultaneously, a stress function is introduced. Equations (6.104) and (6.105) will be satisfied if the in-plane forces are defined, in terms of a function $F(x, y)$, as follows:

$$N_x = h\frac{\partial^2 F}{\partial y^2} \tag{6.127}$$

$$N_y = h\frac{\partial^2 F}{\partial x^2} \tag{6.128}$$

$$N_{xy} = -h\frac{\partial^2 F}{\partial x\, \partial y} \tag{6.129}$$

Making use of these expressions, Eqs. (6.123), (6.124), and (6.125) can be rewritten as

$$\epsilon_{x_0} = \frac{1}{E}\left(\frac{\partial^2 F}{\partial y^2} - \mu\frac{\partial^2 F}{\partial x^2}\right) \tag{6.130}$$

$$\epsilon_{y_0} = \frac{1}{E}\left(\frac{\partial^2 F}{\partial x^2} - \mu\frac{\partial^2 F}{\partial y^2}\right) \tag{6.131}$$

$$\gamma_{xy_0} = -\frac{2(1 + \mu)}{E}\frac{\partial^2 F}{\partial x\, \partial y} \tag{6.132}$$

Finally, by substituting the relations in (6.130), (6.131), and (6.132) into Eq. (6.126) and those in (6.127), (6.128), and (6.129) into Eq. (6.113), one obtains

$$\frac{\partial^4 F}{\partial x^4} + 2\frac{\partial^4 F}{\partial x^2\, \partial y^2} + \frac{\partial^4 F}{\partial y^4} = E\left[\left(\frac{\partial^2 w}{\partial x\, \partial y}\right)^2 - \frac{\partial^2 w}{\partial x^2}\frac{\partial^2 w}{\partial y^2}\right] \tag{6.133}$$

and

$$\frac{\partial^4 w}{\partial x^4} + 2\frac{\partial^4 w}{\partial x^2\, \partial y^2} + \frac{\partial^4 w}{\partial y^4} - \frac{h}{D}\left(\frac{\partial^2 F}{\partial y^2}\frac{\partial^2 w}{\partial x^2} + \frac{\partial^2 F}{\partial x^2}\frac{\partial^2 w}{\partial y^2}\right.$$
$$\left. - 2\frac{\partial^2 F}{\partial x\, \partial y}\frac{\partial^2 w}{\partial x\, \partial y}\right) = 0 \tag{6.134}$$

We have thus reduced the number of equations that must be solved simultaneously to two. Equations (6.133) and (6.134) were first derived by von Kármán, and they are accordingly referred to as the von Kármán large-deflection plate equations. These equations are very useful. They are, however, by no means the only set of equations that can be used for describing the finite-deflection behavior of plates. As long as electronic computers were unavailable and it was necessary to have equations as compact as possible, the von Kármán equations were used almost exclusively. This is, however, no longer the case. The availability of the computer makes it possible to deal effectively with almost any set of equations, and plate equations other than the von Kármán equations are now in general use. For example, if the boundary conditions are specified in terms of displacements, it is advantageous to use equations in u, v, and w. Starting with the equations of equilibrium (6.104), (6.105), and (6.113), a set of equations in u, v, and w can be obtained by expressing the middle-surface stresses in terms of strains and then using relations (6.116), (6.117), and (6.122) to express the strains in terms of displacements.

6.12 POSTBUCKLING BEHAVIOR OF AXIALLY COMPRESSED PLATES

Introduction

The finite-deflection plate equations derived in Article 6.11 do not have an exact closed-form solution. To study the postbuckling behavior of plates, one must therefore employ approximate methods of analysis. If a high order of accuracy is required, a numerical procedure must be used. The disadvantages of this type of solution are that it usually involves lengthy computations, and because no explicit relation among the variables is obtained, it is difficult to generalize the results. Solutions of this sort have been obtained by Levy (Ref. 6.7), Cheng (Ref. 6.8), and Hsueh (Ref. 6.9).

Another type of solution, less accurate than the numerical analysis, but also without the latter's shortcomings, has been employed by Timoshenko and Gere (Ref. 1.2), Marguerre (Ref. 6.10), and Volmir (Ref. 6.11). Timoshenko's analysis is based on a straightforward application of the minimum-energy principle. He assumes simple functions for u, v, and w, expresses the total potential energy of the system in terms of these functions, and then evaluates the arbitrary constants in u, v, and w by minimizing the energy with respect to them. A somewhat more accurate procedure is employed by Marguerre. Like Timoshenko he assumes a simple expression for w, but instead of also assuming the form of u and v, he solves Eq. (6.133) for F in terms of the assumed w. Having F and w, he then writes an expression for the strain energy, which he minimizes to obtain the arbitrary constant in w. The analysis used by Volmir is very similar to that employed by Marguerre. A suitable expression is chosen for w and Eq. (6.133) is used to express F in terms of w. However, the arbitrary coefficient in w is evaluated by using the Galerkin method instead of by minimizing the energy of the system. The results obtained by Volmir are identical with those of Marguerre.

The three methods have one important characteristic in common: they all lead to a closed-form solution. In other words, each analysis produces an explicit expression for the lateral deflection and in-plane stresses of the plate in terms of the applied loading. The solutions are not of a very high order of accuracy. They do, however, entail a minimum amount of numerical work, and they give a fairly good picture of the essential characteristics of the postbuckling process.

In this article we shall consider in detail the solution obtained by Volmir. As indicated before, the method of approach is to assume a simple function for w, solve Eq. (6.133) for F in terms of w, and then evaluate the arbitrary constant in w by means of the Galerkin method.

Analysis

Let us consider the simply supported square plate subjected to a uniaxial compression force N_x shown in Fig. 6-23. The origin of the coordinate system

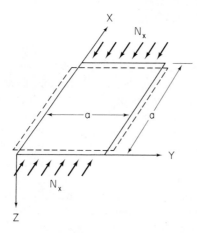

Fig. **6-23** Simply supported plate compressed in x direction.

is assumed to be located in the lower left-hand corner of the plate. Since a finite-deflection analysis involves the deformations in the plane of the middle surface as well as transverse bending deflections, both in-plane and transverse boundary conditions must be specified. The transverse boundary conditions corresponding to simply supported edges are

$$w = \frac{\partial^2 w}{\partial x^2} = 0 \quad \text{at } x = 0, a \tag{6.135}$$

$$w = \frac{\partial^2 w}{\partial y^2} = 0 \quad \text{at } y = 0, a$$

With regard to the in-plane boundary conditions, the following assumptions are made:

1. All edges remain straight and the plate retains its rectangular outline during bending, as indicated by the dashed lines in Fig. 6-23.
2. The shear forces N_{xy} vanish along the four edges of the plate.
3. The edges $y = 0, a$ are free to move in the y direction.

The restraint assumed to exist along the edges $y = 0, a$ represents an intermediary condition between the case of total fixety and the case of zero restraint. For total fixety to exist there can be no movement whatsoever, that is, $v = 0$, and for zero restraint there cannot be any stress, that is, $N_y = 0$. In our case the edges are permitted to move, provided that they remain straight. Thus only the average value of N_y and not N_y itself must be equal to zero. As far as the loaded edges, $x = 0, a$, are concerned, nothing is assumed regarding the distribution of the applied load, only that the displacement u remain constant in the y direction. This condition is realized if the plate is compressed in a controlled deformation type of testing machine.

For convenience we denote the average value of the applied compression stress by σ_{xa}. Thus

$$\sigma_{xa} = -\frac{1}{ah} \int_0^a N_x \, dy \tag{6.136}$$

Since N_x has already been defined as positive when tension, the negative sign in Eq. (6.136) denotes that σ_{xa} is positive when compression.

The first step in the analysis is the choosing of a suitable function for the lateral deflection. Thus we assume that

$$w = f \sin \frac{\pi x}{a} \sin \frac{\pi y}{a} \tag{6.137}$$

This expression represents the exact deflection at the instant of buckling, and should therefore be a fairly good approximation of the deflection in the postbuckling range. Having assumed the form of w, we next solve Eq. (6.133) for the stress function F. Substitution of the expression in (6.137) into Eq. (6.133) gives

$$\frac{\partial^4 F}{\partial x^4} + \frac{2 \partial^4 F}{\partial x^2 \partial y^2} + \frac{\partial^4 F}{\partial y^4} = f^2 \frac{E\pi^4}{a^4} \left(\cos^2 \frac{\pi x}{a} \cos^2 \frac{\pi y}{a} - \sin^2 \frac{\pi x}{a} \sin^2 \frac{\pi y}{a} \right) \tag{6.138}$$

which, in view of the identities

$$\cos^2 \alpha = \tfrac{1}{2}(1 + \cos 2\alpha), \qquad \sin^2 \alpha = \tfrac{1}{2}(1 - \cos 2\alpha)$$

can be reduced to

$$\frac{\partial^4 F}{\partial x^4} + 2\frac{\partial^4 F}{\partial x^2 \partial y^2} + \frac{\partial^4 F}{\partial y^4} = f^2 \frac{E\pi^4}{2a^4}\left(\cos\frac{2\pi x}{a} + \cos\frac{2\pi y}{a}\right) \quad (6.139)$$

The solution of this equation consists of a complementary and a particular part. That is,

$$F = F_c + F_p$$

To obtain the complementary solution of Eq. (6.139), one sets the right-hand side of the equation equal to zero. But this is equivalent to letting $w = 0$. Thus the complementary solution of (6.139) corresponds to the in-plane stress distribution that exists in the plate just prior to buckling. At that instant the in-plane stresses are known to consist of a uniform stress N_x and $N_y = N_{xy} = 0$. Hence a complementary solution of (6.139) is

$$F_c = Ay^2 \quad (6.140)$$

In view of Eq. (6.127) and the fact that $N_x = -\sigma_{xa}h$, Eq. (6.140) can be re-written as

$$F_c = -\frac{\sigma_{xa}y^2}{2} \quad (6.141)$$

Having established that the complementary solution represents the in-plane stress distribution that exists prior to buckling, it is obvious that the particular solution corresponds to the changes in the in-plane stress distribution that result from buckling. Considering the form of the right-hand side of Eq. (6.139), the particular solution can be written as

$$F_p = B\cos\frac{2\pi x}{a} + C\cos\frac{2\pi y}{a} \quad (6.142)$$

Substituting this expression into (6.139) and equating coefficients of like terms, one obtains

$$B = C = \frac{Ef^2}{32} \quad (6.143)$$

Thus
$$F_p = \frac{Ef^2}{32}\left(\cos\frac{2\pi x}{a} + \cos\frac{2\pi y}{a}\right) \quad (6.144)$$

and the complete solution of Eq. (6.139) is

$$F = \frac{Ef^2}{32}\left(\cos\frac{2\pi x}{a} + \cos\frac{2\pi y}{a}\right) - \frac{\sigma_{xa}y^2}{2} \quad (6.145)$$

Up to this point, two steps in the analysis have been completed. We have assumed an expression for w, and by satisfying Eq. (6.133) we have obtained a corresponding expression for F. There remains one final calculation, the evaluation of the coefficient f in accordance with Eq. (6.134). A relatively simple and direct way of carrying out this last step is to solve Eq. (6.134) by means of the Galerkin method outlined in Article 2.8. For the problem under consideration the Galerkin equation takes the form

$$\int_0^a \int_0^a Q(f)g(x, y)\, dx\, dy = 0 \tag{6.146}$$

where $Q(f)$ is the left-hand side of Eq. (6.134) and $g(x, y)$ is the variable part of w. Substituting (6.137) for w and (6.145) for F, $Q(f)$ can be written as

$$Q(f) = \left[\frac{4f D\pi^4}{a^4} - \frac{Ehf^3\pi^4}{8a^4}\left(\cos\frac{2\pi x}{a} + \cos\frac{2\pi y}{a}\right)\right.$$
$$\left. - \sigma_{xa}hf\frac{\pi^2}{a^2}\right]\sin\frac{\pi x}{a}\sin\frac{\pi y}{a} \tag{6.147}$$

and the Galerkin equation takes the form

$$\int_0^a \int_0^a \left[\left(\frac{4f D\pi^4}{a^4} - \sigma_{xa}hf\frac{\pi^2}{a^2}\right)\left(\sin^2\frac{\pi x}{a}\sin^2\frac{\pi y}{a}\right)\right.$$
$$- \frac{Ehf^3\pi^4}{8a^4}\left(\cos\frac{2\pi x}{a}\sin^2\frac{\pi x}{a}\sin^2\frac{\pi y}{a}\right. \tag{6.148}$$
$$\left.\left. + \cos\frac{2\pi y}{a}\sin^2\frac{\pi x}{a}\sin^2\frac{\pi y}{a}\right)\right]dx\, dy = 0$$

Making use of the definite integral

$$\int_0^a \sin^2\frac{\pi x}{a}\, dx = \frac{a}{2}$$

we can reduce Eq. (6.148) to

$$\left(\frac{4f D\pi^4}{a^4} - \sigma_{xa}hf\frac{\pi^2}{a^2}\right)\frac{a^2}{4} - \frac{Ehf^3\pi^4}{8a^4}\frac{a}{2}\left(\int_0^a \cos\frac{2\pi x}{a}\sin^2\frac{\pi x}{a}\, dx\right.$$
$$\left. + \int_0^a \cos\frac{2\pi y}{a}\sin^2\frac{\pi y}{a}\, dy\right) = 0$$

To further simplify, we note that

$$\cos\frac{2\pi x}{a}\sin^2\frac{\pi x}{a} = \frac{1}{2}\left(\cos\frac{2\pi x}{a} - \cos^2\frac{2\pi x}{a}\right)$$

and

$$\int_0^a \cos^2\frac{2\pi x}{a}\, dx = \frac{a}{2}, \qquad \int_0^a \cos\frac{2\pi x}{a}\, dx = 0$$

Thus we obtain

$$\frac{f D \pi^4}{a^2} - \sigma_{xa} h f \frac{\pi^2}{4} + \frac{E h f^3 \pi^4}{32 a^2} = 0$$

from which

$$\sigma_{xa} = \frac{4 D \pi^2}{h a^2} + \frac{E \pi^2 f^2}{8 a^2}$$

or

$$\sigma_{xa} = \sigma_{cr} + \frac{E \pi^2 f^2}{8 a^2} \qquad (6.149)$$

since $4 D \pi^2 / h a^2$ is the critical stress of the plate.

Equation (6.149) gives the relationship between the average applied stress σ_{xa} and the maximum lateral deflection f subsequent to the onset of buckling. A graphical representation of the relationship is shown in Fig. 6-24. As one

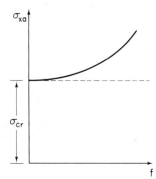

Fig. 6-24 Load–deflection curve for postbuckling region.

would expect, the plate begins to deflect laterally at the critical load predicted by the linear theory. Beyond that point, as long as the lateral deflection is infinitesimally small, the stiffness of the plate is zero; that is, the load–deflection curve has a zero slope. However, as soon as the lateral deflection becomes finite, the stiffness starts to increase and continues to do so as the deflection grows. It is thus possible for the plate to resist axial loads in excess of the critical load subsequent to buckling. This characteristic of the plate, known as postbuckling strength, is of extreme importance in thin-walled structures. Because of it, thin plates, even though they may buckle at very small stresses, are able to resist sizeable loads without collapsing. The post-buckling behavior of the plate is thus completely different from that of the column. Whereas the column collapses as soon as the critical load is reached, the plate continues to resist load subsequent to the onset of buckling, and failure may not occur until the applied load is considerably in excess of the critical load.

To understand why the plate exhibits postbuckling strength, it is necessary to consider the middle-surface stresses that exist subsequent to buckling. The longitudinal stress σ_x is

$$\sigma_x = -\frac{\partial^2 F}{\partial y^2} = \frac{E\pi^2 f^2}{8a^2} \cos \frac{2\pi y}{a} + \sigma_{xa} \tag{6.150}$$

From (6.149)

$$f^2 = \frac{8a^2}{E\pi^2}(\sigma_{xa} - \sigma_{cr})$$

Thus

$$\sigma_x = \sigma_{xa} + (\sigma_{xa} - \sigma_{cr}) \cos \frac{2\pi y}{a} \tag{6.151}$$

Similarly, the transverse stress σ_y is found to be

$$\sigma_y = (\sigma_{xa} \quad \sigma_{cr}) \cos \frac{2\pi x}{a} \tag{6.152}$$

The stress distributions given in (6.151) and (6.152) are shown plotted in Fig. 6-25. If one compares these stresses with the longitudinal and transverse

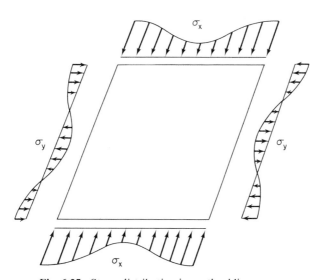

Fig. 6-25   Stress distribution in postbuckling range.

stresses that existed prior to buckling, two essential differences are apparent. There are transverse stresses, σ_y, present subsequent to buckling, whereas none existed prior to buckling; and the longitudinal stress, σ_x, which was constant up to the onset of buckling, varies across the width of the plate after

buckling has begun. The transverse stresses that are present in the postbuckling range vary from a maximum compression stress at the edges $x = 0, a$ to
a maximum tension stress at the center of the plate. Of these the tension stress
is by far the more important. Its presence tends to stiffen the plate against
lateral deflection and to prevent collapse from occurring after the critical load
has been reached. The postbuckling strength exhibited by the plate can thus
be attributed to the middle-surface tensile stress, σ_y, that arises subsequent to
the onset of buckling.

Prior to buckling, all longitudinal fibers have the same stiffness, and the
applied stress is uniformly distributed across the width of the plate. However,
in the deformed configuration subsequent to buckling, the fibers near the supported edges have a greater resistance to lateral deflection than do those in
the center of the plate. The longitudinal stresses in the postbuckling range are
therefore distributed across the width of the plate, as indicated in Fig. 6-25.
They vary from a maximum at the edges $y = 0, a$ to a minimum at the center
of the plate. A major portion of the increase in load that takes place subsequent to buckling is thus resisted by the relatively stiff portion of the plate
adjacent to the longitudinal edges.

The foregoing results are based on an approximate analysis and therefore
contain some minor inaccuracies. For example, a precise investigation would
indicate that in-plane shear stresses exist in addition to transverse tensile
stresses after buckling has begun. A very accurate analysis would also show
variations in σ_x and σ_y that the simplified analysis was unable to detect.
However, regarding the basic aspects of the postbuckling process, nothing
new would be learned by carrying out a more refined study than that
presented here. The main conclusions would still be that

1. Plates can continue to carry increasing load subsequent to reaching the
    critical stress; that is, they exhibit postbuckling strength.
2. Transverse tensile stresses that arise subsequent to the start of buckling
    are primarily responsible for the presence of postbuckling strength in
    plates.
3. The material near the longitudinal edges of the plate resists most of the
    increase in load that occurs in the postbuckling range.

6.13   ULTIMATE STRENGTH OF AXIALLY COMPRESSED PLATES

In Article 6.12 it was shown that plates do not fail when the critical load is
reached. Instead, they are able to support increasing axial load well beyond
the instant at which buckling begins. To make use of this postbuckling
strength in the design of plates, it is necessary to know at what load collapse

actually occurs. A theoretical investigation of the ultimate strength of plates is possible. However, it would have to include both the nonlinearities of inelastic behavior and those resulting from finite deflections, and would be extremely complex. As a consequence, the collapse load of plates is usually determined by a semiempirical method.

It has been observed, in theoretical as well as in experimental investigations, that failure of a plate usually occurs very soon after the maximum longitudinal stress at the edge of the plate reaches the yield strength of the material. Accordingly, it is customary in determining the failure load to assume that collapse coincides with the onset of yielding. In the approximate analysis presented in the previous article the maximum longitudinal stress at the edge of the plate was found to be

$$\sigma_{x(\max)} = 2\sigma_{xa} - \sigma_{cr} \tag{6.153}$$

Substitution of σ_y, the yield strength of the material, for $\sigma_{x(\max)}$ in this relation gives

$$\sigma_{fa} = \frac{1}{2}(\sigma_y + \sigma_{cr}) \tag{6.154}$$

where σ_{fa} is the average longitudinal stress at failure.

It is useful to rewrite Eq. (6.154) in the form

$$\frac{\sigma_{fa}}{\sigma_{cr}} = \frac{1}{2}\left(\frac{1}{\sigma_{cr}/\sigma_y} + 1\right) \tag{6.155}$$

and plot the variation of σ_{fa}/σ_{cr} with σ_{cr}/σ_y. Such a curve is shown in Fig. 6-26, and it indicates that the ratio σ_{fa}/σ_{cr}, which is a measure of the amount

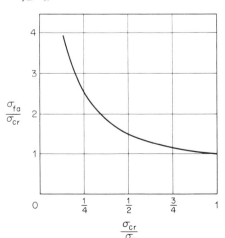

Fig. 6-26 Variation of postbuckling strength with ratio of σ_{cr} to σ_y.

of postbuckling strength present in a plate, increases as the ratio σ_{cr}/σ_y decreases. In other words, relatively thick plates that buckle at a high stress and begin to yield very soon thereafter do not exhibit a significant amount of postbuckling strength, whereas relatively thin plates that buckle at a low stress and do not yield until much later can be expected to have considerable postbuckling strength.

The approximate relation given in (6.155) is adequate for providing us with a general picture of postbuckling strength in plates. However, a more refined expression is needed for design purposes. To develop such a relation from the actual nonuniform stress distribution that exists in a plate, as was done above, is usually not practical. Instead, it is customary to employ the concept of an *effective width* introduced by von Kármán, Sechler, and Donnell (Ref. 6.12) in 1932. As shown in Fig. 6-27, the actual nonuniform stress that

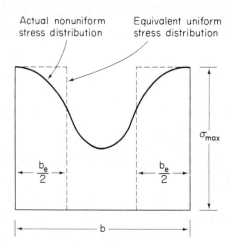

Fig. 6-27 Effective-width concept for determining postbuckling strength.

acts over the entire width of the plate, b, is replaced by an equivalent uniform stress distributed over a reduced effective width, b_e. The magnitude of the uniform stress is assumed to be equal to the actual stress existing at the edge of the plate, and the two rectangles of width $b_e/2$ are assumed to have the same area as the actual stress distribution. Thus the ultimate load carried by the plate is

$$P_u = b_e t \sigma_y \qquad (6.156)$$

To evaluate P by means of Eq. (6.156), an expression for b_e is needed. Von Kármán suggested the following approximate relation for simply supported plates:

$$b_e = b \sqrt{\frac{\sigma_{cr}}{\sigma_y}} \qquad (6.157)$$

Comparing this expression with (6.155), the approximate relation obtained in Article 6.12, it is seen that in both instances the ultimate load depends on the parameter σ_{cr}/σ_y. A slightly different expression has been proposed by Winter (Ref. 6.13). Based on extensive test results he suggests using the expression

$$b_e = b\sqrt{\frac{\sigma_{cr}}{\sigma_y}}\left(1 - 0.25\sqrt{\frac{\sigma_{cr}}{\sigma_y}}\right) \qquad (6.158)$$

This relation is similar to the one suggested by von Kármán except that an additional term accounting for initial imperfections has been added.

If the expression in (6.158) is substituted into Eq. (6.156) and the buckling stress coefficient in σ_{cr} is taken as 4.0, one obtains for the ultimate load

$$P_u = 1.90\sigma_y t^2 \sqrt{\frac{E}{\sigma_y}}\left(1 - \frac{0.475}{b/t}\sqrt{\frac{E}{\sigma_y}}\right) \qquad (6.159)$$

6.14 DESIGN PROVISIONS FOR LOCAL BUCKLING

In designing hot-rolled structural-steel shapes consisting of flat plate elements, it is common to proportion the member so that overall failure occurs prior to local buckling. Beams designed in accordance with allowable-stress theory are proportioned so that the yield stress is reached prior to the local buckling stress. Similarly, columns can be designed so that their resistance to Euler buckling is less than their local buckling strength. In the AISC specifications the local buckling stress is kept above the yield stress for columns as well as beams, thereby making it possible to have a single design provision for both types of members.

If local buckling is not to occur at a stress smaller than the yield stress

$$F_{cr} > F_y$$

where F_{cr} is the critical plate buckling stress and F_y is the yield strength of the material. Substitution of Eq. (6.102) into this relation gives

$$\frac{k\pi^2 E}{12(1 - \mu^2)}\left(\frac{t}{b}\right)^2 > F_y$$

For $E = 29 \times 10^3$ ksi and $\mu = 0.3$, one obtains

$$\frac{b}{t} < 161\sqrt{\frac{k}{F_y}} \qquad (6.160)$$

The limit on the width-to-thickness ratio necessary to prevent local buckling is thus seen to depend on the plate-buckling coefficient and on the yield strength. For a flange of an angle it is customary to assume one edge to be simply supported and one free. Thus $k = 0.425$, and the limiting expression for b/t becomes

$$\frac{b}{t} < \frac{106}{\sqrt{F_y}}$$

To ensure that failure of an actual member containing initial imperfections and residual stresses is overall and not local, the preceding requirement for b/t is reduced in the 1969 AISC specifications (Ref. 1.17) to

$$\frac{b}{t} < \frac{76}{\sqrt{F_y}} \tag{6.161}$$

To obtain the corresponding design criteria for the flange of a box section, one substitutes the plate-buckling coefficient for simple supports along both unloaded edges, $k = 4.0$, into Eq. (6.160). Thus

$$\frac{b}{t} < \frac{322}{\sqrt{F_y}}$$

which is reduced in the AISC specifications to

$$\frac{b}{t} < \frac{238}{\sqrt{F_y}} \tag{6.162}$$

The small b/t ratios commonly found in hot-rolled sections make it feasible to ensure that overall failure occurs prior to local buckling in most of these shapes. However, thin-walled sections like those used in cold-formed steel construction and aircraft framing are composed of elements with relatively large width-to-thickness ratios. In these shapes it is well nigh impossible to prevent local buckling from taking place prior to overall failure, and the allowable stress is accordingly based on the local buckling stress and on the postbuckling strength.

Depending on the manner in which the plate elements of a section are supported along their longitudinal edges, two types of elements are distinguished. Plates supported along both edges are referred to as *stiffened elements* and plates supported along only one edge are called *unstiffened elements*. A distinction between unstiffened and stiffened elements is made because unstiffened elements exhibit considerably less postbuckling strength than stiffened elements. Accordingly, the allowable stress of unstiffened elements is obtained by dividing the local buckling stress by a suitable safety factor, whereas the allowable load of a stiffened element is based on the ultimate load of the element. The calculation of the allowable load for both stiffened and unstiffened elements is illustrated in Ref. 3.8.

References

6.1   G. GERARD, *Introduction to Structural Stability Theory* (New York: McGraw-Hill Book Company, Inc., 1962).

6.2   G. H. BRYAN, "On the Stability of a Plane Plate Under Thrusts in Its Own Plane with Applications to the Buckling of the Sides of a Ship," *Proceedings London Mathematical Society*, Vol. 22, 1891.

6.3   S. LEVY, "Buckling of Rectangular Plates with Built-in Edges." *Journal of Applied Mechanics, ASME*, Vol. 9, 1942.

6.4   M. STEIN and J. NEFF, "Buckling Stresses of Simply Supported Rectangular Plates in Shear," *NACA Technical Note, No. 1222*, Washington, D.C., 1947.

6.5   G. GERARD, "Handbook of Structural Stability, Part I—Buckling of Flat Plates," *NACA, Technical Note, No. 3781*, Washington, D.C., July 1957.

6.6   E. Z. STOWELL, G. J. HEIMERL, C. LIBOVE, and E. E. LUNDQUIST, "Buckling Stresses for Flat Plates and Sections," *Transactions, ASCE*, Vol. 117, 1952.

6.7   S. LEVY, "Bending of Rectangular Plates with Large Deflections," *NACA, Technical Report, No. 737*, Washington, D.C., 1942.

6.8   T. CHENG, "Large Deflection Analysis of Rectangular Plate" (Ph.D. Thesis, University of Massachusetts, 1971).

6.9   P. S. HSUEH, "Large Deflection of Orthotropic Rectangular Panels" (Ph.D. Thesis, University of Massachusetts, 1969).

6.10 K. MARGUERRE, "Effective Width of Plates in Compression," *NACA, Technical Note, No. 833*, Washington, D.C., 1937.

6.11 A. S. VOLMIR, "A Translation of Flexible Plates and Shells," *Air Force Flight Dynamics Laboratory, Technical Report No. 66-216* (Ohio: Wright-Patterson Air Force Base, 1967).

6.12 T. VON KÁRMÁN, E. E. SECHLER, and L. H. DONNELL, "The Strength of Thin Plates in Compression," *Transactions, ASME*, Vol. 54, 1932.

6.13 G. WINTER, "Strength of Thin Steel Compression Flanges," *Transactions, ASCE*, Vol. 112, 1947.

6.14 K. K. KAPUR and B. J. HARTZ, "Stability of Plates Using the Finite Element Method," *Journal of the Engineering Mechanics Division, ASCE*, Vol. 92, No. EM2, 1966.

6.15 J. L. TOCHER and K. K. KAPUR, "Comment on Basis for Derivation of Matrices for the Direct Stiffness Method," *Journal of the A.I.A.A.*, Vol. 3, No. 6, 1965.

6.16 W. E. HASKELL, "Geometric Nonlinear Analysis of Thin Plates by Finite Elements" (Ph. D. Thesis, University of Massachusetts, 1970).

6.17 E. Z. STOWELL, "A Unified Theory of Plastic Buckling of Columns and Plates," *NACA Report. No. 898*, Washington, D.C., 1948.

Problems

6.1 Determine the critical loading for a simply supported, square plate loaded in two perpendicular directions by uniformly distributed loads as shown in Fig. P6-1. Obtain an exact solution by solving the governing differential equation ($N_{cr} = 2\pi^2 D/a^2$).

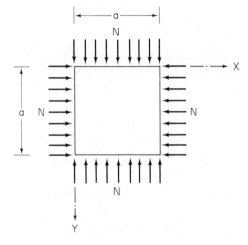

Fig. P6-1

6.2 Using the energy method, determine the critical loading of a simply supported, square plate loaded in the x direction by a linearly varying distributed load, as shown in Fig. P6-2.

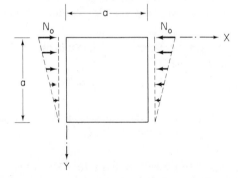

Fig. P6-2

6.3 Using the method of finite differences, determine the critical loading of a square plate, simply supported along two opposite edges and clamped along the other two edges. The plate is loaded by a uniformly distributed load N_x

along the simply supported edges, as shown in Fig. P6-3. Divide the plate into nine elements yielding four interior points. Compare the result obtained with the exact solution $N_{cr} = 7.69\pi^2 D/a^2$.

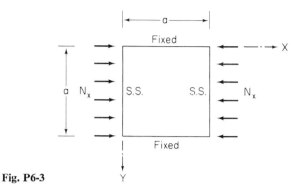

Fig. P6-3

6.4 Using the finite-element method, determine the critical loading of a square plate clamped along all four edges and uniformly compressed in one direction. Divide the plate into 16 elements and consider a quarter of the plate, as was done in Article 6.8. Compare the solution obtained with the result given in Article 6.5.

6.5 Using the energy method, determine the critical load for the one-degree-of-freedom model of a flat plate shown in Fig. P6-4. The model consists of four

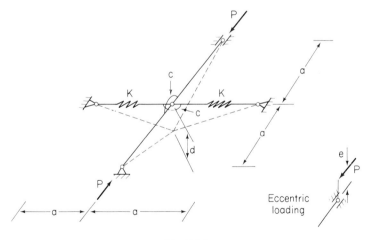

Fig. P6-4

rigid bars pin connected to each other and to the supports. At the center of the model two linear rotational springs of stiffness $C = M/\theta$ connect opposite bars to each other. Also, each of the two transverse bars contains a linear extensional spring of stiffness K. For small lateral deflections the energy in the extensional springs can be neglected. ($P_{cr} = 4C/a$)

6.6 Using the model in Fig. P6-4, obtain and plot relationships for the load P versus the lateral deflection d when
(a) the lateral deflection is large,
(b) the lateral deflection is large and the loads are applied eccentrically to the plane of the undeformed model.
Which fundamental buckling characteristics of an actual plate are demonstrated by these models? (Note: For large deflections the energy in the extensional springs must be considered.)

7
BUCKLING OF AXIALLY COMPRESSED CYLINDRICAL SHELLS

7.1 INTRODUCTION

A thorough treatment of shell stability should include a study of spherical shells under external pressure as well as cylindrical shells subject to axial compression, external pressure, and torsion. However, due to the introductory nature of this book, only axially compressed cylindrical shells will be considered. Axially compressed cylindrical shells have been singled out for study because their buckling characteristics differ radically from those of the columns and plates studied heretofore. Whereas real, slightly imperfect columns and plates do buckle at the critical stress predicted by the linear theory, real imperfect axially compressed cylindrical shells buckle at a stress significantly below that given by the linear theory. It is this aspect of the behavior of axially compressed cylinders that makes them especially worthy of our attention.

Before considering the stability of axially compressed thin cylindrical shells, a few words regarding the behavior of thin shells in general are in order. The primary difference between a shell and a plate is that the former has a curvature in the unstressed state, whereas the latter is assumed to be initially flat. As far as flexure is concerned, the presence of initial curvature is of little consequence. However, the curvature does affect the membrane behavior of the surface significantly.

Membrane action in a surface is caused by in-plane forces. These forces may be primary forces caused by applied edge loads or edge deformations, or they may be secondary forces resulting from flexural deformations. In a stability analysis, primary middle-surface forces must be considered regardless of whether initial curvature exists or not. However, the same cannot be said regarding secondary middle-surface forces. If the surface is initially flat, secondary in-plane forces do not give rise to appreciable membrane action unless the bending deformations are fairly large. It was for this reason that membrane action due to secondary forces was neglected in the small-deflection plate theory, but not in the large-deflection plate analysis. On the other hand, if the surface has an initial curvature, membrane action caused by secondary in-plane forces will be significant regardless of the magnitude of the bending deformations. Membrane action resulting from secondary middle-surface forces is therefore accounted for in both small- and large-deflection studies of shells.

7.2 LINEAR THEORY OF CYLINDRICAL SHELLS—DONNELL EQUATIONS

In the derivation of the shell equations, one encounters several terms of relatively small magnitude. If these terms are all retained, the solution of the equations becomes so involved that the equations are of little practical use. Most investigators have therefore decided to omit some of these terms. There is, however, no firm agreement as to which terms one should neglect. The result of the situation is that there have been developed various shell equations each based on a different set of simplifications.

In our investigation of the behavior of shells, we shall make use of the Donnell equations (Ref. 7.1). These equations are relatively uncomplicated, and they have been shown to give satisfactory results when used to deal with buckling problems. It has been demonstrated by Donnell that a simple way of developing the theory of thin shells is to start with relationships already obtained for thin plates and to revise these wherever necessary. We shall make use of this approach here. Both small- and large-deflection plate relationships will be referred to in developing the shell equations. It is necessary to do this because secondary membrane forces must be considered in a linear shell theory, and these are included only in the large-deformation plate theory.

In deriving the shell equations we shall make the following assumptions:

1. The thickness of the shell is small compared to the other dimensions of the shell; that is, the shell is thin.
2. Lateral deflections are small compared to the thickness of the shell.
3. The material from which the shell is constructed is homogeneous, isotropic, and obeys Hooke's law.

4. Lines normal to the middle surface before bending remain straight and normal during bending.
5. The shell is initially a perfect cylinder, and it is loaded concentrically at every cross section.

Let us consider a differential shell element of thickness h and having a radius of curvature R, as shown in Fig. 7-1a. The coordinate system is chosen so that the origin is in the middle surface of the shell, the x axis is parallel to the axis of the cylinder, the y axis is tangent to a circular arc, and the z axis is

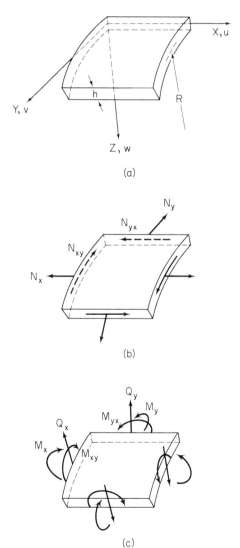

Fig. 7-1 Cylindrical shell displacements and forces.

normal to the median surface. Use of the circumferential coordinate y instead of an angular coordinate facilitates comparisons between the shell and the plate. Displacements of the shell are described by their components u, v, and w in the x, y, and z directions as indicated in the figure. The forces acting on the shell element consist of the in-plane forces depicted in Fig. 7-1b and the transverse shears, bending moments, and twisting moments shown in Fig. 7-1c.

Equilibrium

The equations of equilibrium in the x and y directions are considerably simplified if the curvature of the surface in these two directions, both initial and due to bending, is neglected. In other words, we assume that the transverse shear forces have negligible components in the x and y directions and that the components of the in-plane forces in these directions are equal to the forces themselves. Thus the equilibrium equations in the x and y directions for the shell are identical to those obtained for the plate [Eqs. (6.104) and (6.105)]. For convenience these equations are repeated here:

$$\frac{\partial N_x}{\partial x} + \frac{\partial N_{xy}}{\partial y} = 0 \tag{7.1}$$

$$\frac{\partial N_y}{\partial y} + \frac{\partial N_{yx}}{\partial x} = 0 \tag{7.2}$$

To obtain the equation of equilibrium in the z direction, it is necessary to take the curvature of the element into account. Both the initial curvature and the curvature due to bending must be considered. Due to the initial curvature of the shell, the N_y forces, as indicated in Fig. 7-2, have a component in the z

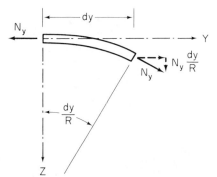

Fig. 7-2 Radial component of in-plane forces due to initial curvature.

direction equal to

$$N_y\left(\frac{1}{R}\right) dx\, dy \tag{7.3}$$

None of the other in-plane forces has components in the z direction due to the initial curvature. However, all the in-plane forces have z components due to the curvature that results from bending. These components are identical to the ones that exist for a bent plate element [Eq. (6.3)]. Thus the z components of the in-plane forces for a cylindrical shell element are obtained by adding the terms given in (6.3) to the term in (7.3). This leads to

$$\left[N_x \frac{\partial^2 w}{\partial x^2} + 2N_{xy} \frac{\partial^2 w}{\partial x \, \partial y} + N_y \left(\frac{\partial^2 w}{\partial y^2} + \frac{1}{R} \right) \right] dx \, dy \tag{7.4}$$

To the z components of the in-plane forces must be added the transverse shear forces given by

$$\left(\frac{\partial Q_x}{\partial x} + \frac{\partial Q_y}{\partial y} \right) dx \, dy \tag{7.5}$$

Since the equations of moment equilibrium about the x and y axes do not change in going from the plate to the shell element, Eqs. (6.6) and (6.7) are valid for the shell as well as the plate, and the shear forces in (7.5) can be rewritten in the form

$$\left(\frac{\partial^2 M_x}{\partial x^2} - 2 \frac{\partial^2 M_{xy}}{\partial x \, \partial y} + \frac{\partial^2 M_y}{\partial y^2} \right) dx \, dy \tag{7.6}$$

Combining the terms in (7.4) and (7.6), one obtains for the equation of equilibrium in the z direction

$$\frac{\partial^2 M_x}{\partial x^2} - 2 \frac{\partial^2 M_{xy}}{\partial x \, \partial y} + \frac{\partial^2 M_y}{\partial y^2} + N_x \frac{\partial^2 w}{\partial x^2} + 2N_{xy} \frac{\partial^2 w}{\partial x \, \partial y} + N_y \left(\frac{1}{R} + \frac{\partial^2 w}{\partial y^2} \right) = 0 \tag{7.7}$$

Force–Deformation Relations

As was done when analyzing a plate, the displacements and strains are separated into middle-surface and bending terms. Thus

$$u = u_0 + u_b$$
$$v = v_0 + v_b$$
$$\epsilon_x = \epsilon_{x_0} + \epsilon_{x_b}$$
$$\epsilon_y = \epsilon_{y_0} + \epsilon_{y_b}$$
$$\gamma_{xy} = \gamma_{xy_0} + \gamma_{xy_b}$$

where the subscript 0 denotes middle-surface terms and the subscript b refers to bending terms. Since ϵ_z is assumed to be negligible, $w = w_0$.

Moment–Curvature Relations

The relationships between bending moments and curvatures in the shell can be assumed to be the same as those existing between these quantities in a plate. Thus

$$M_x = -D\left(\frac{\partial^2 w}{\partial x^2} + \mu \frac{\partial^2 w}{\partial y^2}\right) \tag{7.8}$$

$$M_y = -D\left(\frac{\partial^2 w}{\partial y^2} + \mu \frac{\partial^2 w}{\partial x^2}\right) \tag{7.9}$$

$$M_{xy} = D(1 - \mu)\frac{\partial^2 w}{\partial x\,\partial y} \tag{7.10}$$

These expressions were derived in Article 6.2, where they appear as Eqs. (6.33), (6.34), and (6.35).

Middle-Surface Force–Deformation Relations

The middle-surface force–deformation relations for a shell differ somewhat from those in the plate, and we shall therefore need to revise the plate expressions wherever necessary in order to obtain the desired shell expressions. A shell fiber oriented in the x direction is initially straight. Its behavior is therefore similar to that of a corresponding plate fiber. The middle-surface strain ϵ_{x_0} for a plate is given by Eq. (6.116). For large deflections, both of the terms in this expression must be considered. However, when the deflections and consequently the slopes are very small, as in our case, the second term is negligible compared to the first. Thus we conclude that for shells with small deformations

$$\epsilon_{x_0} = \frac{\partial u_0}{\partial x} \tag{7.11}$$

In the y direction the shell has an initial curvature not present in the plate. To obtain the strain ϵ_{y_0} for the shell, we must therefore add to the first term of the plate strain, given by (6.117), the strain due to transverse bending when initial curvature is present. As shown in Fig. 7-3, element AB is displaced to

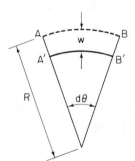

Fig. 7-3 Tangential strain due to radial displacement.

$A'B'$ due to the radial deformation w. The resulting strain in the element is

$$\epsilon = -\frac{AB - A'B'}{AB} = -\frac{R\,d\theta - (R - w)\,d\theta}{R\,d\theta}$$

$$= -\frac{w}{R}$$

(7.12)

in which the negative sign denotes that positive displacements w lead to negative strains. The total strain in the y direction is the sum of the first term in (6.117) and the expression in (7.12). Thus

$$\epsilon_{y_0} = \frac{\partial v_0}{\partial y} - \frac{w}{R}$$

(7.13)

The initial curvature of the shell has no influence on the middle-surface shear strain. Hence γ_{xy_0} is obtained from the corresponding plate strain [Eq. (6.122)] by dropping the higher-order term. That is,

$$\gamma_{xy_0} = \frac{\partial u_0}{\partial y} + \frac{\partial v_0}{\partial x}$$

(7.14)

Since the two-dimensional stress–strain relations used for thin plates [Eqs. (6.17), (6.18), and (6.19)] apply equally well to thin shells, the middle-surface shell forces are given by

$$N_x = \sigma_{x_0} h = \frac{Eh}{1 - \mu^2}(\epsilon_{x_0} + \mu\epsilon_{y_0})$$

(7.15)

$$N_y = \sigma_{y_0} h = \frac{Eh}{1 - \mu^2}(\epsilon_{y_0} + \mu\epsilon_{x_0})$$

(7.16)

$$N_{xy} = \tau_{xy_0} h = \frac{Eh}{2(1 + \mu)}\gamma_{xy_0}$$

(7.17)

Substitution of (7.11), (7.13), and (7.14) into these relations gives

$$N_x = \frac{Eh}{1 - \mu^2}\left(\frac{\partial u_0}{\partial x} + \mu\frac{\partial v_0}{\partial y} - \mu\frac{w}{R}\right)$$

(7.18)

$$N_y = \frac{Eh}{1 - \mu^2}\left(\frac{\partial v_0}{\partial y} - \frac{w}{R} + \mu\frac{\partial u_0}{\partial x}\right)$$

(7.19)

$$N_{xy} = \frac{Eh(1 - \mu)}{2(1 - \mu^2)}\left(\frac{\partial u_0}{\partial y} + \frac{\partial v_0}{\partial x}\right)$$

(7.20)

The middle-surface forces in the shell consist of two parts: (1) primary forces caused by the applied loads, which are present prior to buckling, and (2) secondary forces, which arise as a result of buckling, Since the latter are much smaller in magnitude than the former, it is essential that we distinguish between the two. The simplest way of accomplishing this is to assume that the middle-surface displacements appearing in the foregoing calculations are solely the secondary deformations resulting from buckling. Accordingly, the forces in (7.18), (7.19), and (7.20) are the secondary middle-surface forces caused by buckling and not the total middle-surface forces. Letting the primary middle-surface forces that are present prior to buckling be given by

$$N_x = P_x \qquad (7.21)$$

$$N_y = P_y \qquad (7.22)$$

$$N_{xy} = S_{xy} \qquad (7.23)$$

the total middle-surface forces are

$$N_x = \frac{Eh}{1 - \mu^2}\left(\frac{\partial u_0}{\partial x} + \mu \frac{\partial v_0}{\partial y} - \mu \frac{w}{R}\right) + P_x \qquad (7.24)$$

$$N_y = \frac{Eh}{1 - \mu^2}\left(\frac{\partial v_0}{\partial y} - \frac{w}{R} + \mu \frac{\partial u_0}{\partial x}\right) + P_y \qquad (7.25)$$

$$N_{xy} = \frac{Eh(1 - \mu)}{2(1 - \mu^2)}\left(\frac{\partial u_0}{\partial y} + \frac{\partial v_0}{\partial x}\right) + S_{xy} \qquad (7.26)$$

Differential Equations

The equilibrium equations will now be expressed in terms of displacements. Substitution of the appropriate derivatives of (7.8) through (7.10) and (7.24) through (7.26) into Eqs. (7.1), (7.2), and (7.7) gives

$$\frac{\partial^2 u_0}{\partial x^2} + \frac{1 - \mu}{2}\frac{\partial^2 u_0}{\partial y^2} + \frac{1 + \mu}{2}\frac{\partial^2 v_0}{\partial x \partial y} - \frac{\mu}{R}\frac{\partial w}{\partial x} = 0 \qquad (7.27)$$

$$\frac{\partial^2 v_0}{\partial y^2} + \frac{1 - \mu}{2}\frac{\partial^2 v_0}{\partial x^2} + \frac{1 + \mu}{2}\frac{\partial^2 u_0}{\partial x \partial y} - \frac{1}{R}\frac{\partial w}{\partial y} = 0 \qquad (7.28)$$

$$-D\left(\frac{\partial^4 w}{\partial x^4} + 2\frac{\partial^4 w}{\partial x^2 \partial y^2} + \frac{\partial^4 w}{\partial y^4}\right) + (N'_x + P_x)\frac{\partial^2 w}{\partial x^2}$$
$$+ (N'_y + P_y)\left(\frac{1}{R} + \frac{\partial^2 w}{\partial y^2}\right) + 2(N'_{xy} + S_{xy})\frac{\partial^2 w}{\partial x \partial y} = 0 \qquad (7.29)$$

where N'_x, N'_y, and N'_{xy} stand for the secondary middle-surface forces.

In Eq. (7.29) the initial curvature and the primary middle-surface forces are quantities of finite magnitude. By comparison, the curvatures due to bending and the secondary middle-surface forces are infinitesimally small. It is therefore possible to neglect some of the terms in Eq. (7.29) and reduce it to the form

$$-D\left(\frac{\partial^4 w}{\partial x^4} + 2\frac{\partial^4 w}{\partial x^2\,\partial y^2} + \frac{\partial^4 w}{\partial y^4}\right) + P_x\frac{\partial^2 w}{\partial x^2} + P_y\frac{\partial^2 w}{\partial y^2} + \frac{P_y}{R}$$

$$+ \frac{1}{R}\frac{Eh}{1-\mu^2}\left(\frac{\partial v_0}{\partial y} - \frac{w}{R} + \mu\frac{\partial u_0}{\partial x}\right) + 2S_{xy}\frac{\partial^2 w}{\partial x\,\partial y} = 0 \tag{7.30}$$

Equation (7.30) together with Eqs. (7.27) and (7.28) constitutes a set of three equations in three unknowns that can be used to obtain the critical load of a cylindrical shell. Because secondary membrane forces are not negligible in linear shell theory as they are in linear plate theory, the in-plane equilibrium equations are coupled to the equation of transverse equilibrium for the shell, and all three must be solved simultaneously. By comparison, the equation of equilibrium in the z direction is independent of the in-plane equilibrium equations for the plate, and the critical load can be obtained simply by considering the z-direction equation.

For certain types of solutions it is easier to deal with one than three equations. Accordingly, Donnell (Ref. 7.1) has reduced Eqs. (7.27), (7.28), and (7.30) to a single equation in w. The transformation is carried out as follows. Operating with $\partial^2/\partial x\,\partial y$ on (7.28), and with $\partial^2/\partial x^2$ and $\partial^2/\partial y^2$ on (7.27), one obtains three equations, which can be reduced to

$$\nabla^4 u = \frac{\mu}{R}\frac{\partial^3 w}{\partial x^3} - \frac{1}{R}\frac{\partial^3 w}{\partial y^2\,\partial x} \tag{7.31}$$

where ∇^4 denotes two successive applications of Laplace's operator in two dimensions. Similarly, operations with $\partial^2/\partial x\,\partial y$ on (7.27) and with $\partial^2/\partial x^2$ and $\partial^2/\partial y^2$ on (7.28) gives three equations that lead to

$$\nabla^4 v = \frac{\mu + 2}{R}\frac{\partial^3 w}{\partial x^2\,\partial y} + \frac{1}{R}\frac{\partial^3 w}{\partial y^3} \tag{7.32}$$

The operator ∇^4 is now applied to (7.30), which gives

$$-D\nabla^8 w + \nabla^4\left(P_x\frac{\partial^2 w}{\partial x^2} + P_y\frac{\partial^2 w}{\partial y^2} + 2S_{xy}\frac{\partial^2 w}{\partial x\,\partial y}\right)$$

$$+ \frac{1}{R}\frac{Eh}{1-\mu^2}\left(\nabla^4\frac{\partial v}{\partial y} + \mu\nabla^4\frac{\partial u}{\partial x} - \frac{1}{R}\nabla^4 w\right) = 0 \tag{7.33}$$

If (7.31) is operated on with $\partial/\partial x$ and (7.32) with $\partial/\partial y$ and the resulting expressions are substituted into (7.33), one finally obtains

$$D\nabla^8 w - \nabla^4\left(P_x\frac{\partial^2 w}{\partial x^2} + P_y\frac{\partial^2 w}{\partial y^2} + 2S_{xy}\frac{\partial^2 w}{\partial x\,\partial y}\right) + \frac{Eh}{R^2}\frac{\partial^4 w}{\partial x^4} = 0 \tag{7.34}$$

This linear eight-order equation in w is known as the Donnell equation. By letting $P_y = S_{xy} = 0$, it can be used to obtain the critical load of a cylinder subjected to axial compression. Similarly, by letting S_{xy} equal the applied shear force or by letting P_y equal the hoop force caused by pressure, one can use the equation to obtain the critical load for cylinders subjected to torsion or external pressure.

7.3 CRITICAL LOAD OF AN AXIALLY LOADED CYLINDER

Classical Solution

Let us consider an axially loaded cylinder of length l and radius R whose ends are simply supported, and determine its critical load by solving the Donnell equation in the manner outlined by Batdorf (Ref. 7.2). When axial compression is the only primary middle-surface stress present, Donnell's equation, Eq. (7.34), reduces to

$$D\nabla^8 w + \frac{Eh}{R^2}\frac{\partial^4 w}{\partial x^4} + \sigma_x h \nabla^4 \frac{\partial^2 w}{\partial x^2} = 0 \tag{7.35}$$

The boundary conditions corresponding to simply supported ends are

$$w = \frac{\partial^2 w}{\partial x^2} = 0 \quad \text{at } x = 0, l \tag{7.36}$$

These conditions are satisfied if the lateral displacement is of the form

$$w = w_0 \sin\frac{m\pi x}{l}\sin\frac{n\pi y}{\pi R} \tag{7.37}$$

where m is the number of half-waves in the longitudinal direction and n the number of half-waves in the circumferential direction. To simplify the calculations, we let

$$\beta = \frac{nl}{\pi R} \tag{7.38}$$

and rewrite (7.37) as

$$w = w_0 \sin\frac{m\pi x}{l}\sin\frac{\beta\pi y}{l} \tag{7.39}$$

Substitution of (7.39) into (7.35) gives

$$D\left(\frac{\pi}{l}\right)^8(m^2 + \beta^2)^4 + \frac{Eh}{R^2}m^4\left(\frac{\pi}{l}\right)^4 - \sigma_x h\left(\frac{\pi}{l}\right)^6 m^2(m^2 + \beta^2)^2 = 0 \tag{7.40}$$

If we divide Eq. (7.40) by $D(\pi/l)^8$ and introduce two new parameters, we obtain

$$(m^2 + \beta^2)^4 + \frac{12m^4 Z^2}{\pi^4} - k_x m^2(m^2 + \beta^2)^2 = 0 \qquad (7.41)$$

where

$$Z = \frac{l^2}{Rh}(1 - \mu^2)^{1/2} \qquad (7.42)$$

$$k_x = \frac{\sigma_x h l^2}{D\pi^2} \qquad (7.43)$$

The nondimensional parameter Z is a shape factor. It is a measure of the ratio of length to radius and is useful for distinguishing between short and long cylinders. The other parameter, k_x, is a buckling stress coefficient similar to the one that appears in the plate-buckling equation, [Eq. (6.49)].

Solving Eq. (7.41) for k_x, one obtains

$$k_x = \frac{(m^2 + \beta^2)^2}{m^2} + \frac{12Z^2 m^2}{\pi^4(m^2 + \beta^2)^2} \qquad (7.44)$$

Differentiating this expression with respect to $(m^2 + \beta^2)^2/m^2$ and setting the result equal to zero shows that k_x has a minimum value when

$$\frac{(m^2 + \beta^2)^2}{m^2} = \left(\frac{12Z^2}{\pi^4}\right)^{1/2} \qquad (7.45)$$

Substitution of (7.45) into (7.44) gives

$$k_x = \frac{4\sqrt{3}}{\pi^2} Z \qquad (7.46)$$

from which

$$\sigma_{cr} = \frac{1}{\sqrt{3(1 - \mu^2)}} \frac{Eh}{R} \qquad (7.47)$$

or, if μ is taken equal to 0.3,

$$\sigma_{cr} = 0.6 \frac{Eh}{R} \qquad (7.48)$$

Since Eq. (7.46) is not valid for all values of Z, the critical stress given by (7.48) does not apply to all cylinders. Solving (7.45) for β gives

$$\beta = \left[\frac{(12Z^2)^{1/4}}{\pi} m - m^2\right]^{1/2} \qquad (7.49)$$

which indicates that Z can be smaller than 2.85 only if either $m < 1$ or β is imaginary. Since neither of these conditions can be satisfied, we conclude that (7.46) and (7.48) apply only to cylinders for which $Z > 2.85$.

If $Z < 2.85$, the critical stress coefficient is determined by setting $m = 1$ and $\beta = 0$ in Eq. (7.44). This leads to

$$k_x = 1 + \frac{12Z^2}{\pi^4} \tag{7.50}$$

The critical stress for cylinders with $Z < 2.85$ is thus given by

$$\sigma_{cr} = \frac{k_x D \pi^2}{h l^2} \tag{7.51}$$

where k_x is defined by Eq. (7.50). The expression in (7.51) indicates that the critical stress of a short cylinder approaches that of a wide laterally unsupported plate as Z approaches zero.

In the foregoing analysis it was tacitly assumed that failure would occur as a result of local surface buckling. This assumption is valid only as long as the cylinder is not extremely slender. Long narrow cylinders may become unstable as a result of Euler column buckling before the local surface buckling stress is reached and must therefore be checked for both modes of failure.

It has thus been shown that the buckling mode of an axially loaded cylinder depends on the ratio of its length to its radius. Short and wide cylinders behave like plates that are supported along their loaded edges. They buckle into a single half-wave in the longitudinal direction and no waves in the circumferential direction. By comparison, the buckling of very long cylinders does not involve surface distortion at all. Instead the member simply behaves like an Euler column. In between these two extremes fall the cylinders that are of intermediate length. Since this category includes the majority of actual cylinders, it is the most important of the three. Cylinders of this type buckle by developing surface distortion in both the longitudinal and circumferential direction, and their critical stress is given by Eq. (7.48). By far the most important observation that one can make regarding cylinders of moderate length is that actual tests do not verify the results obtained from the linear theory. Experimentally observed buckling loads are usually much smaller than the critical load given by Eq. (7.48). It will be demonstrated in Article 7.4 that the linear theory is inadequate for describing the behavior of axially compressed cylinders and that a nonlinear large-deflection analysis is required instead.

New Solutions of Small-Deflection Equations

Recent investigations of simply supported, axially loaded cylindrical shells of moderate length have shown that there exist solutions to the linear, small-deflection equations other than the classical solution given by Eq. (7.48). It has been demonstrated that the in-plane edge conditions have a significant effect on the critical load, and that the conditions on u and v assumed to exist in the classical solution constitute only one of several possible alternatives for simple supports.

In the classical solution, boundary conditions appear to be stipulated only for the transverse deformations, that is, it is explicitly stated that $w = \partial^2 w/\partial x^2 = 0$ along the edges, but nothing is mentioned regarding the in-plane displacements. However, in the linear theory of shells, in-plane displacements are coupled to transverse displacements, and hence in-plane edge conditions arc implicit in the assumption that the lateral displacement, w, is a double sine function. The conditions that this approximation implies are (1) no tangential motion along the edges, that is, $v = 0$, and (2) a constant axial stress σ_x along the loaded edges during buckling. The solution given by (7.48) thus corresponds to a definite set of in-plane boundary conditions as well as simple supports in the transverse direction. Once the foregoing conclusion is reached, it becomes obvious that the in-plane edge conditions assumed in the classical solution are not the only possibilities for a simply supported edge, and that the critical load given by Eq. (7.48) is therefore not the only possible solution to the linear equations for simply supported moderately long shells. For example, the edges of the cylinder instead of being prevented from moving tangentially may be free to move in this direction, and instead of stipulating that the axial stress remain constant along the edges, the in-plane displacement u may be required to remain uniform.

Several extensive investigations into the effect of in-plane boundary conditions on the critical load of simply supported shells have been carried out (Refs. 7.3 and 7.4), and it has been concluded that critical stress is reduced drastically if the edges are permitted to move freely in the tangential direction. The critical stress obtained for simply supported edges that are free to move tangentially is roughly one half the critical stress given by the classical solution for edges that are restrained from moving tangentially. However, freeing the edges in the tangential direction is the only change in the in-plane conditions of the classical solution that produces a significant change in the critical load. For all other variations in the in-plane edge conditions from those assumed in the classical solution there is no significant change in the critical load.

In most experimental investigations of cylinders the edges are not free to move tangentially. The aforementioned findings concerning the effects of boundary conditions, although extremely interesting, are therefore not believed to explain the discrepancy that exists between the classical theory and test results.

7.4   FAILURE OF AXIALLY COMPRESSED CYLINDRICAL SHELLS

Historical Survey of the Problem*

The classical solution to the linear small-deflection equations for axially loaded cylinders was first obtained by Lorenz in 1908 (Ref. 7.6). It was later independently arrived at by Timoshenko in 1910 (Ref. 7.7), Southwell in 1913 (Ref. 7.8), and Flügge in 1932 (Ref. 7.9). The critical stress given by this solution could, however, not be substantiated by tests. Experiments made to verify the theoretical results inevitably indicated that actual cylinders buckle at loads considerably below that given by the classical theory. Buckling loads as small as 30 % of the load given by the classical solution were not unusual. Furthermore, the test results exhibited an unusually large degree of scatter.

The first progress toward an understanding of the problem and toward an explanation of the discrepancy between the theoretical and experimental results was achieved by Donnell in 1934 (Ref. 7.10) when he proposed that a nonlinear finite-deflection theory was required. In other words, Donnell realized that it was not sufficient to determine the load at bifurcation, but that an investigation of the postbuckling behavior of the shell was required as well.

To his now well-known small-deflection equations, Donnell added the same nonlinear terms that von Kàrmàn had already used in formulating the nonlinear plate equations, and thus arrived at the von Kármán–Donnell large-displacement shell equations. In addition to sensing the need for a large-displacement theory, Donnell was aware of the fact that the buckling pattern observed to exist during tests differed radically from the one assumed to exist in the classical theory. The latter consists of sinusoidal waves in both the axial and circumferential direction. By comparison, the actual buckle pattern consists of deep diamond-shaped bulges directed primarily toward the center of curvature. Using the large-displacement equations and attempting to take into account the actual buckled shape of the cylinder, Donnell proceeded to obtain a solution. However, his analysis was over-simplified and did not lead to satisfactory results.

It was not until 1941 that the first meaningful solution to the problem was obtained by von Kármán and Tsien (Ref. 7.11). Using essentially the same large-deflection equations as were used by Donnell and approximating the lateral deflection with a function that adequately represented the actual buckle pattern of the shell, von Kármán and Tsien obtained the first accurate picture of the postbuckling behavior of an axially compressed cylinder. Their

---

*The brief summary of the development of cylindrical shell stability theory presented here is taken from a more detailed account of the subject by Hoff (Ref. 7.5).

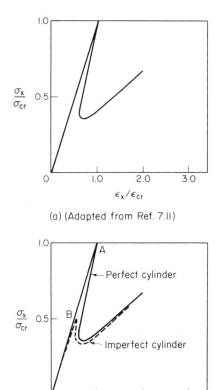

(a) (Adapted from Ref. 7.11)

(b) (Adapted from Ref. 7.16)

Fig. 7-4 Postbuckling of axially compressed cylinder.

results are best summarized by the curve of axial shortening versus axial compression depicted in Fig. 7-4a. The most significant aspect of this curve is that the axial load required to maintain equilibrium drops sharply as the cylinder bends subsequent to reaching the critical load. As a consequence, there exist equilibrium configurations at finite deflections that can be maintained by loads considerably below the critical load. Based on these results and in an attempt to explain the discrepancy between the theoretically obtained critical load and the experimentally observed buckling load, von Kármán and Tsien put forth the following hypothesis. They conjectured that it was possible for the cylinder to jump from the unbuckled state to the adjacent buckled configuration at a load far below the critical load, and that any slight disturbance, such as the vibration of the testing machine, would suffice to trigger such a jump. The maximum load that a real cylinder could support would thus be much smaller than the critical load.

Although the work of von Kármán and Tsien was far from complete, it proved to be the cornerstone of the large-displacement theory of axially loaded cylindrical shells. In the years that followed several investigators, including Legget and Jones (Ref. 7.12), Michielsen (Ref. 7.13), Kempner (Ref. 7.14), and Hoff, Madsen, and Mayers (Ref. 7.15), enlarged and improved von Kármán's theory. By including more terms in both the nonlinear equations and in the assumed deflection function, they obtained more and more accurate postbuckling curves.

The next step forward in the study of axially loaded cylindrical shells was made when Donnell and Wan (Ref. 7.16) in 1950 introduced initial imperfections into the analysis. The results of this investigation are summarized by the curves of axial shortening versus applied stress given in Fig. 7-4b. The solid curve corresponds to an initially perfect shell and the dashed one to a shell with a very small initial imperfection. It is evident from these curves that the maximum load reached by a slightly imperfect cylinder, point *B*, is much lower than the classically obtained critical load of the perfect cylinder, point *A*. While the possibility of a jump occurring before point *B* is reached cannot be ruled out, the incentive for adopting the jump theory is greatly lessened in the light of what initial imperfections do to the load–deformation curve. However, regardless of whether a jump does or does not occur, it can be concluded that initial imperfections can appreciably reduce the maximum load that an axially compressed cylinder can support.

As a consequence of the work of Donnell and Wan, initial imperfections are now generally believed to be the principal reason for the discrepancy between the classical buckling stress and the experimentally observed failure stress. Until recently this conclusion was based solely on theoretical investigations. However, in the last decade experimental verification of the imperfection theory has been obtained as well. Tennyson (Ref. 7.17), as well as several other investigators (7.18), by exercising extreme care, have for the first time been able to manufacture near-perfect shell specimens and thus minimize the effects of initial imperfections. For these near-perfect specimens the observed buckling load was very close to the theoretically obtained critical load. The test results also indicated that any small departures from the straightness in the perfect specimens resulted in a significant lowering of the buckling load. The belief that initial imperfections are the major reason for the discrepancy between the classical theory and test results thus appears at present to be more well founded than ever.

Large-Deflection Equations

All the idealizations previously made in the linear theory are assumed to remain valid, except that transverse deflections are no longer required to remain infinitesimally small. As a consequence of allowing deflections to become finite, terms that are quadratic functions of the deformations and their derivatives are no longer negligible when formulating the governing differential equations. Since no such terms were omitted in the derivation of the equilibrium equations, these equations are valid for the large-deflection theory as well as the small-deformation theory. They are

$$\frac{\partial N_x}{\partial x} + \frac{\partial N_{xy}}{\partial y} = 0 \tag{7.52}$$

$$\frac{\partial N_y}{\partial y} + \frac{\partial N_{yx}}{\partial x} = 0 \tag{7.53}$$

$$\frac{\partial^2 M_x}{\partial x^2} - 2\frac{\partial^2 M_{xy}}{\partial x\, \partial y} + \frac{\partial^2 M_y}{\partial y^2} + N_x \frac{\partial^2 w}{\partial x^2} + 2N_{xy}\frac{\partial^2 w}{\partial x\, \partial y} + N_y\left(\frac{1}{R} + \frac{\partial^2 w}{\partial y^2}\right) = 0 \tag{7.54}$$

Transverse deflections are no longer small compared to the thickness of the surface. They are, however, still assumed to be small in comparison with the other shell dimensions. Hence no change takes place in the moment–curvature equations in going from small to large deformations. These relations are still given by Eqs. (7.8), (7.9), and (7.10), and Eq. (7.54) can therefore be rewritten in the form

$$-D\left(\frac{\partial^4 w}{\partial x^4} + 2\frac{\partial^4 w}{\partial x^2\, \partial y^2} + \frac{\partial^4 w}{\partial y^4}\right) + N_x\frac{\partial^2 w}{\partial x^2}$$
$$+ 2N_{xy}\frac{\partial^2 w}{\partial x\, \partial y} + N_y\left(\frac{1}{R} + \frac{\partial^2 w}{\partial y^2}\right) = 0 \tag{7.55}$$

The middle-surface strain–displacement relations do, however, change as deformations become finite. As in large-deflection plate theory, the terms

$$\epsilon_{x_0} = \frac{1}{2}\left(\frac{\partial w}{\partial x}\right)^2, \qquad \epsilon_{y_0} = \frac{1}{2}\left(\frac{\partial w}{\partial y}\right)^2, \qquad \gamma_{xy_0} = \frac{\partial w}{\partial x}\frac{\partial w}{\partial y}$$

neglected in the linear equations, must now be included. Thus the strain–displacement equations become

$$\epsilon_{x_0} = \frac{\partial u_0}{\partial x} + \frac{1}{2}\left(\frac{\partial w}{\partial x}\right)^2 \tag{7.56}$$

$$\epsilon_{y_0} = \frac{\partial v_0}{\partial y} - \frac{w}{R} + \frac{1}{2}\left(\frac{\partial w}{\partial y}\right)^2 \tag{7.57}$$

$$\gamma_{xy_0} = \frac{\partial u_0}{\partial y} + \frac{\partial v_0}{\partial x} + \frac{\partial w}{\partial x}\frac{\partial w}{\partial y} \tag{7.58}$$

The relations between middle-surface forces and strains do not change in going from small to large displacements. However, the secondary as well as the primary forces are now finite, and no distinction similar to the one drawn in the linear theory can now be made between these two quantities. These relations are

$$\epsilon_{x_0} = \frac{1}{Eh}(N_x - \mu N_y) \tag{7.59}$$

$$\epsilon_{y_0} = \frac{1}{Eh}(N_y - \mu N_x) \tag{7.60}$$

$$\gamma_{xy_0} = \frac{2}{Eh}(1 + \mu)N_{xy} \tag{7.61}$$

Equations (7.52), (7.53), (7.55), and (7.56) through (7.61) are sufficient for investigating the postbuckling behavior of cylindrical shells. They can also be transformed into a more compact form. Differentiating (7.56) twice with respect to y, (7.57) twice with respect to x, and (7.58) successively with respect to x and y, one obtains the compatibility relation

$$\frac{\partial^2 \epsilon_{x_0}}{\partial y^2} + \frac{\partial^2 \epsilon_{y_0}}{\partial x^2} - \frac{\partial^2 \gamma_{xy_0}}{\partial x\, \partial y} = \left(\frac{\partial^2 w}{\partial x\, \partial y}\right)^2 - \frac{\partial^2 w}{\partial x^2}\frac{\partial^2 w}{\partial y^2} - \frac{1}{R}\frac{\partial^2 w}{\partial x^2} \tag{7.62}$$

A further simplification is obtained by introducing a stress function that satisfies (7.52) and (7.53). Thus we let

$$N_x = h\frac{\partial^2 F}{\partial y^2}, \qquad N_y = h\frac{\partial^2 F}{\partial x^2}, \qquad N_{xy} = -h\frac{\partial^2 F}{\partial x\, \partial y} \tag{7.63}$$

and rewrite (7.59), (7.60), and (7.61) in the form

$$\epsilon_{x_0} = \frac{1}{E}\left(\frac{\partial^2 F}{\partial y^2} - \mu\frac{\partial^2 F}{\partial x^2}\right) \tag{7.64}$$

$$\epsilon_{y_0} = \frac{1}{E}\left(\frac{\partial^2 F}{\partial x^2} - \mu\frac{\partial^2 F}{\partial y^2}\right) \tag{7.65}$$

$$\gamma_{xy_0} = -\frac{2(1 + \mu)}{E}\frac{\partial^2 F}{\partial x\, \partial y} \tag{7.66}$$

Making use of these relations and of the expressions in (7.63), Eqs. (7.55) and (7.62) become

$$\frac{\partial^4 w}{\partial x^4} + 2\frac{\partial^4 w}{\partial x^2\, \partial y^2} + \frac{\partial^4 w}{\partial y^4}$$
$$- \frac{h}{D}\left[\frac{\partial^2 F}{\partial y^2}\frac{\partial^2 w}{\partial x^2} - 2\frac{\partial^2 F}{\partial x\, \partial y}\frac{\partial^2 w}{\partial x\, \partial y} + \frac{\partial^2 F}{\partial x^2}\left(\frac{1}{R} + \frac{\partial^2 w}{\partial y^2}\right)\right] = 0 \tag{7.67}$$

$$\frac{\partial^4 F}{\partial x^4} + 2\frac{\partial^4 F}{\partial x^2\, \partial y^2} + \frac{\partial^4 F}{\partial y^4} = E\left[\left(\frac{\partial^2 w}{\partial x\, \partial y}\right)^2 - \frac{\partial^2 w}{\partial x^2}\frac{\partial^2 w}{\partial y^2} - \frac{1}{R}\frac{\partial^2 w}{\partial x^2}\right] \tag{7.68}$$

These equations were first derived by Donnell in 1934 when he combined the strain–displacement relations contained in the von Kármán large-deflection plate theory with his own linear shell theory. The equations are accordingly called the von Kármán–Donnell large-displacement shell equations.

Equations (7.67) and (7.68) are applicable only to an initially perfect cylinder. To make the equations valid for a shell with initial imperfections of shape as well, several minor modifications must be made. First, we assume that the lateral deflection consists of an initial distortion w_0 in addition to the deflection w produced by the applied loads. Next we consider the changes brought about by the initial distortion in Eq. (7.67). This is an equation of equilibrium in the radial direction. The first three terms are shear forces that depend only on the curvature caused by bending. The initial distortion does not affect them. The remaining terms are components of middle-surface forces obtained by multiplying the forces by the surface curvature. Since the total curvature applies here, w must be replaced with $w + w_0$ in these terms. The equation of equilibrium for the initially imperfect shell thus takes the form

$$
\frac{\partial^4 w}{\partial x^4} + 2\frac{\partial^4 w}{\partial x^2\,\partial y^2} + \frac{\partial^4 w}{\partial y^4} - \frac{h}{D}\left[\frac{\partial^2 F}{\partial y^2}\left(\frac{\partial^2 w}{\partial x^2} + \frac{\partial^2 w_0}{\partial x^2}\right)\right.
$$
$$
\left. - 2\frac{\partial^2 F}{\partial x\,\partial y}\left(\frac{\partial^2 w}{\partial x\,\partial y} + \frac{\partial^2 w_0}{\partial x\,\partial y}\right) + \frac{\partial^2 F}{\partial x^2}\left(\frac{1}{R} + \frac{\partial^2 w}{\partial y^2} + \frac{\partial^2 w_0}{\partial y^2}\right)\right] = 0
$$

(7.69)

To obtain the compatibility equation for an initially distorted shell, we must first rewrite the strain–displacement relations to include the effects of an initial imperfection. If in the derivation of these expressions in Article 6.11 the lateral deflection w is replaced with $w + w_0$ it can be shown that

$$
\epsilon_x = \frac{\partial u}{\partial x} + \frac{1}{2}\left(\frac{\partial w}{\partial x}\right)^2 + \frac{\partial w}{\partial x}\frac{\partial w_0}{\partial x}
$$
$$
\epsilon_y = \frac{\partial v}{\partial y} - \frac{w}{R} + \frac{1}{2}\left(\frac{\partial w}{\partial y}\right)^2 + \frac{\partial w}{\partial y}\frac{\partial w_0}{\partial y}
$$

(7.70)

$$
\gamma_{xy} = \frac{\partial u}{\partial y} + \frac{\partial v}{\partial x} + \frac{\partial w}{\partial x}\frac{\partial w}{\partial y} + \frac{\partial w_0}{\partial x}\frac{\partial w}{\partial y} + \frac{\partial w}{\partial x}\frac{\partial w_0}{\partial y}
$$

Differentiating, as in the case of the initially perfect shell, we obtain

$$
\frac{\partial^2 \epsilon_x}{\partial y^2} + \frac{\partial^2 \epsilon_y}{\partial x^2} - \frac{\partial^2 \gamma_{xy}}{\partial x\,\partial y} = \left(\frac{\partial^2 w}{\partial x\,\partial y}\right)^2 + 2\frac{\partial^2 w_0}{\partial x\,\partial y}\frac{\partial^2 w}{\partial x\,\partial y}
$$
$$
- \frac{\partial^2 w}{\partial x^2}\frac{\partial^2 w}{\partial y^2} - \frac{\partial^2 w_0}{\partial x^2}\frac{\partial^2 w}{\partial y^2} - \frac{\partial^2 w_0}{\partial y^2}\frac{\partial^2 w}{\partial x^2} - \frac{1}{R}\frac{\partial^2 w}{\partial x^2}
$$

(7.71)

which, after the stress function F is introduced, leads to

$$
\begin{aligned}
\frac{\partial^4 F}{\partial y^4} + \frac{\partial^4 F}{\partial x^4} + 2\frac{\partial^4 F}{\partial x^2\,\partial y^2} = E\bigg[\bigg(\frac{\partial^2 w}{\partial x\,\partial y}\bigg)^2 + 2\frac{\partial^2 w_0}{\partial x\,\partial y}\frac{\partial^2 w}{\partial x\,\partial y} \\
- \frac{\partial^2 w}{\partial x^2}\frac{\partial^2 w}{\partial y^2} - \frac{\partial^2 w_0}{\partial x^2}\frac{\partial^2 w}{\partial y^2} - \frac{\partial^2 w_0}{\partial y^2}\frac{\partial^2 w}{\partial x^2} - \frac{1}{R}\frac{\partial^2 w}{\partial x^2}\bigg]
\end{aligned}
\tag{7.72}
$$

Equations (7.69) and (7.72) are the governing differential equations for an initially imperfect cylindrical shell.

Postbuckling Behavior of Cylindrical Panel

The postbuckling behavior of a rectangular cylindrical panel is very similar to that of an entire cylinder. We shall therefore limit our considerations to such a panel and thus avoid the lengthy and complex calculations that an investigation of the entire cylinder entails. The analysis presented here follows the general outline of that given by Volmir (Ref. 6.11). It consists of solving the compatibility equation for F in terms of w and then using the Galerkin method to solve the equilibrium equation for the coefficient of w.

A cylindrical panel is essentially a section of an entire cylinder bounded by two generators and two circular arcs. Let us consider such a panel subjected to a uniform axial compression stress p_x as shown in Fig. 7-5. The radius of

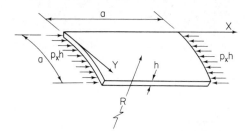

Fig. 7-5 Axially compressed cylindrical panel.

curvature of the panel is R, its thickness is h, and the length of each edge is a. The x and y coordinate axes are taken along the generator and arc, as shown in the figure.

As far as the boundary conditions are concerned, it is assumed that (1) the edges are simply supported, (2) the shear force N_{xy} vanishes along each edge, (3) the edges $y = 0$, a are free to move in the y direction, and (4) the panel retains its rectangular shape during buckling. These conditions are satisfied if we let

$$
w = f\sin\frac{\pi x}{a}\sin\frac{\pi y}{a}
\tag{7.73}
$$

The panel is also assumed to have an initial distortion given by

$$w_0 = f_0 \sin \frac{\pi x}{a} \sin \frac{\pi y}{a} \qquad (7.74)$$

The first step in the anlaysis consists of evaluating F in Eq. (7.72) in terms of the assumed deformation functions. Substitution of the expressions in (7.73) and (7.74) into (7.72) leads to

$$\frac{\partial^4 F}{\partial x^4} + \frac{2\partial^4 F}{\partial x^2 \partial y^2} + \frac{\partial^4 F}{\partial y^4} = E \left[(f^2 + 2ff_0)\frac{\pi^4}{2a^4}\left(\cos \frac{2\pi x}{a} + \cos \frac{2\pi y}{a} \right) \right.$$
$$\left. + \frac{f\pi^2}{Ra^2} \sin \frac{\pi x}{a} \sin \frac{\pi y}{a} \right] \qquad (7.75)$$

A particular solution to this equation, obtained by using the method of undetermined coefficients, is

$$F_p = \frac{E(f^2 + 2ff_0)}{32}\left(\cos \frac{2\pi x}{a} \cos \frac{2\pi y}{a} \right) + \frac{Efa^2}{4R\pi^2}\left(\sin \frac{\pi x}{a} \sin \frac{\pi y}{a} \right) \qquad (7.76)$$

The complementary solution is any function that satisfies both the homogeneous equation $\nabla^4 F = 0$ and the boundary conditions on F. It also corresponds to the primary middle-surface stress that exists prior to buckling, that is, a uniform compression stress, p_x, in the x direction and $N_{xy} = N_y = 0$. Noting that $N_x = -p_x h$ and taking cognizance of Eq. (7.63), one obtains for the complementary function

$$F_c = \frac{-p_x y^2}{2} \qquad (7.77)$$

Thus the entire solution of (7.75) is

$$F = \frac{E(f^2 + 2ff_0)}{32}\left(\cos \frac{2\pi x}{a} + \cos \frac{2\pi y}{a} \right)$$
$$+ \frac{Efa^2}{4R\pi^2}\left(\sin \frac{\pi x}{a} \sin \frac{\pi y}{a} \right) - \frac{p_x y^2}{2} \qquad (7.78)$$

By means of the Galerkin method a relation between f, f_0, and p_x will now be obtained from Eq. (7.69). For the problem being considered the Galerkin equation is of the form

$$\int_0^a \int_0^a Q(f)g(x, y) \, dx \, dy = 0 \qquad (7.79)$$

where $Q(f)$ is the left-hand side of Eq. (7.69) and $g(x, y) = \sin (\pi x/a)$ $\cdot \sin (\pi y/a)$. Substituting the expressions in (7.73), (7.74), and (7.78) for w,

w_0, and F, Eq. (7.79) becomes

$$\int_0^a \int_0^a \left\{ \left[4Df\frac{\pi^4}{a^4} - p_x\frac{h\pi^2}{a^2}(f+f_0) + \frac{Ehf}{4R^2} \right] \sin^2\frac{\pi x}{a} \sin^2\frac{\pi y}{a} \right.$$
$$- \frac{Eh\pi^4}{8a^4}(f+f_0)(f^2+2ff_0)\left(\cos\frac{2\pi x}{a} \sin^2\frac{\pi x}{a} \sin^2\frac{\pi y}{a} \right.$$
$$+ \cos\frac{2\pi y}{a} \sin^2\frac{\pi x}{a} \sin^2\frac{\pi y}{a} \right) - \frac{Ehf\pi^2}{2Ra^2}(f+f_0)\left(\sin^3\frac{\pi x}{a} \sin^3\frac{\pi y}{a} \right) \qquad (7.80)$$
$$+ \frac{Eh\pi^2}{8a^2R}(f^2+2ff_0)\left(\cos\frac{2\pi x}{a} \sin\frac{\pi x}{a} \sin\frac{\pi y}{a} \right)$$
$$\left. + \frac{Ehf_1\pi^2}{2Ra^2}(f+f_0)\left(\cos^2\frac{\pi x}{a} \sin\frac{\pi x}{a} \cos^2\frac{\pi y}{a} \sin\frac{\pi y}{a} \right) \right\} dx\,dy = 0$$

Making use of the identities

$$\cos\frac{2\pi x}{a} \sin^2\frac{\pi x}{a} = \frac{1}{2}\left(\cos\frac{2\pi x}{a} - \cos^2\frac{2\pi x}{a} \right)$$

$$\cos\frac{2\pi x}{a} \sin\frac{\pi x}{a} = \sin\frac{\pi x}{a} - 2\sin^3\frac{\pi x}{a}$$

$$\cos^2\frac{\pi x}{a} \sin\frac{\pi x}{a} = \sin\frac{\pi x}{a} - \sin^3\frac{\pi x}{a}$$

and carrying out the indicated integrations, Eq. (7.80) reduces to

$$\frac{Df\pi^4}{a^2} - \frac{p_x h\pi^2}{4}(f+f_0) + \frac{Ehfa^2}{16R^2}$$
$$- \frac{Eh}{R}\left(\frac{5}{6}f^2 + f_0 f \right) + \frac{Eh\pi^4}{32a^2}(f^3 + 3f^2f_0 + 2f_0^2f) = 0 \qquad (7.81)$$

from which

$$p_x = \left[\frac{4D\pi^2}{ha^2} + \frac{Ea^2}{4R^2\pi^2} + \frac{E\pi^2}{8a^2}(f^2 + 3ff_0 + 2f_0^2) \right.$$
$$\left. - \frac{4E}{\pi^2R}\left(\frac{5}{6}f + f_0 \right) \right]\frac{f}{f+f_0} \qquad (7.82)$$

To simplify this expression and make it more meaningful, we introduce the following nondimensional parameters:

$$\bar{p}_x = \frac{p_x a^2}{Eh^2}$$

$$k = \frac{a^2}{Rh}$$

$$\delta = \frac{f}{h} \qquad (7.83)$$

$$\delta_0 = \frac{f_0}{h}$$

These parameters are measures of the loading of the curvature and the deflection. Substituting them in (7.82) leads to

$$\bar{p}_x = \left[\frac{\pi^2}{3(1-\mu^2)} + \frac{k^2}{4\pi^2} + \frac{\pi^2}{8}(\delta^2 + 3\delta\delta_0 + 2\delta_0^2) \right. $$
$$\left. - \frac{4k}{\pi^2}\left(\frac{5}{6}\delta + \delta_0\right) \right] \frac{\delta}{\delta + \delta_0} \tag{7.84}$$

or, if $\mu = 0.3$,

$$\bar{p}_x = \left[3.6 + \frac{k^2}{39.5} + 1.23(\delta^2 + 3\delta\delta_0 + 2\delta_0^2) \right. $$
$$\left. - 0.405k(0.83\delta + \delta_0) \right] \frac{\delta}{\delta + \delta_0} \tag{7.85}$$

The load–deflection relationship given by (7.85) is shown plotted in Figs. 7-6 and 7-7. Figure 7-6 pertains to a panel with $k = 0$, that is, a flat plate, and

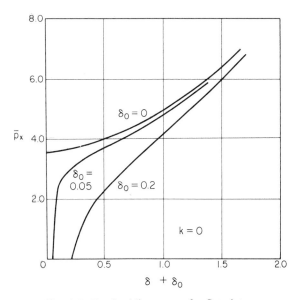

Fig. 7-6 Postbuckling curves for flat plates.

Fig. 7-7 to a cylindrical panel with $k = 24$. The curves in each figure depict the variation of the load parameter $\bar{p}_x$ with the total lateral deflection parameter $\delta + \delta_0$. Curves for several different values of the initial imperfection δ_0 are presented. Let us consider first the effect that initial imperfections have on the behavior of flat plates. As shown in Fig. 7-6, bending of an initially deformed plate begins as soon as the load is applied. The deflections increase

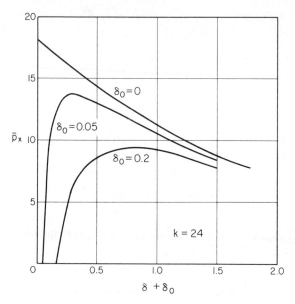

Fig. 7-7   Postbuckling curves for cylindrical shells.

slowly at first and then more rapidly in the neighborhood of the critical load. As in the case of the perfect plate, the critical load does not represent the maximum carrying capacity of the imperfect plate. Instead, as the deflections continue to grow, the imperfect plate is able to resist ever-increasing loads. Furthermore, as the deflections increase in magnitude, the curve of the initially imperfect plate approaches that of the perfect plate. Thus one can conclude that small initial deformations do not materially affect the buckling behavior of flat plates, and that the results obtained for the perfect plate are valid for actual plates with their unavoidable minor imperfections. In this respect the behavior of the flat plate is similar to that of the column. It will, however, immediately become apparent that the same is not true for cylindrical panels.

With regard to curved panels, whose behavior is described in Fig. 7-7, the following observations can be made. As long as the axial load is small, bending increases very gradually with an increase in the load. Then, suddenly, at a certain load whose magnitude appears to depend on the size of the initial imperfections, bending deflections begin to grow rapidly and the load drops. As the deflection continues to increase, the curve of the imperfect panel approaches that of the perfect panel. The all-important conclusion that can be drawn from these results is that the maximum load that an initially imperfect panel can support is considerably less than the critical load given by the classical theory. Even for a very small initial deformation, such as $\delta_0 = 0.05$, the maximum load is only 75% of the critical load. Contrary to what has been observed for columns and flat plates, small initial imperfections thus have a very significant effect on the buckling characteristics of cylindrical panels.

If the curves obtained here for a cylindrical panel are compared with those for an entire cylinder obtained by Donnell and Wan (Ref. 7.16), it will be seen that the conclusions reached for the panel are equally valid for the entire cylinder.

Interestingly enough, the postbuckling characteristics of axially compressed cylinders, described in the previous pages, are not typical of the behavior of either cylinders under external pressure or cylinders loaded in torsion. For both of these latter cases small initial imperfections do not affect the buckling characteristics appreciably, and the failure stress is fairly close to the critical stress predicted by the linear theory. One can thus surmise that the behavior of circular cylinders loaded in torsion or subject to external pressure is similar to that of axially loaded columns.

Design of Axially Compressed Cylindrical Shells

The design of axially compressed cylindrical shells can be based on the classical buckling stress, $\sigma_{cr} = 0.6Eh/R$, provided one accounts for the reduction in strength resulting from initial imperfections and inelastic behavior. Regarding the effect of initial imperfections, it has been shown, both theoretically and experimentally, that the reduction in the buckling stress increases as the ratio of radius to shell thickness increases. In other words, the thinner the shell, the greater the reduction in strength due to initial imperfections. The aforementioned investigations indicate that the classical buckling stress can be used to predict the strength of initially imperfect cylindrical shells, provided it is written in the form

$$\sigma_{cr} = CE\frac{h}{R} \tag{7.86}$$

in which C is a parameter that varies with R/h, as indicated in Fig. 7-8.

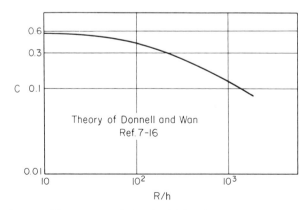

Fig. 7-8 Buckling stress coefficient for initially imperfect circular cylinder.

For aluminum-alloy cylinders the reduction in strength caused by inelastic behavior can be accounted for by a plasticity reduction factor. Thus Gerard (Ref. 6.1) recommends that the buckling stress be given by

$$\sigma_{cr} = \eta C E \frac{h}{R} \tag{7.87}$$

in which $\eta = \sqrt{E_t E_s / E}$, E_t and E_s being the tangent and secant modulii of the material.

For structural-steel cylinders inelastic buckling cannot be readily dealt with using a plasticity reduction factor. Instead, it is customary to use empirical formulas such as those listed in the CRC Guide (Ref. 1.20).

References

7.1   L. H. Donnell, "Stability of Thin-Walled Tubes Under Torsion," *NACA, Technical Report, No. 479*, Washington, D.C., 1933.

7.2   S. B. Batdorf, "A Simplified Method of Elastic-Stability Analysis for Thin Cylindrical Shells," *NACA, Technical Report, No. 874*, Washington, D.C., 1947.

7.3   N. J. Hoff and L. W. Rehfield, "Buckling of Axially Compressed Circular Cylindrical Shells at Stresses Smaller than the Classical Critical Value," *Stanford University Department of Aeronautics and Astronautics, Report SUDAER No. 191*, May 1964.

7.4   B. O. Almroth, "Influence of Edge Conditions on the Stability of Axially Compressed Cylindrical Shells," *Journal of the American Institute of Aeronautics and Astronautics*, Vol. 4, No. 1, 1966.

7.5   N. J. Hoff, "The Perplexing Behavior of Thin Circular Cylindrical Shells in Axial Compression," *Israel Journal of Technology*, Vol. 4, No. 1, 1966.

7.6   R. Lorenz, "Achsensymmetrische Verzerrungen in dünnwandigen Hohlzylindern," *Zeitschrift des Vereines Deutscher Ingenieure*, Vol. 52, No. 43, 1908.

7.7   S. Timoshenko, "Einige Stabilitätsprobleme der Elastizitäts-theorie," *Zeitschrift für Mathematik und Physik*, Vol. 58, No. 4, 1910.

7.8   R. V. Southwell, "On the General Theory of Elastic Stability," *Philosophical Transactions of the Royal Society of London*, Series A, Vol. 213, 1914.

7.9   W. Flügge, "Die Stabilität der Kreiszylinderschale," *Ingenieurarchiv*, Vol. 3, 1932.

7.10   L. H. Donnell, "A New Theory for the Buckling of Thin Cylinders Under Axial Compression and Bending," *Transactions, ASME*, Vol. 56, 1934.

7.11   T. von Kármán and H. S. Tsien, "The Buckling of Thin Cylindrical Shells Under Axial Compression," *Journal of the Aeronautical Sciences*, Vol. 8, No. 8, 1941.

7.12   D. M. A. LEGGETT and R. P. N. JONES, "The Behavior of a Cylindrical Shell Under Axial Compression When the Buckling Load Has Been Exceeded," *Aeronautical Research Council Memorandum, No. 2190*, 1942.

7.13   H. F. MICHIELSEN, "The Behavior of Thin Cylindrical Shells After Buckling Under Axial Compression," *Journal of the Aeronautical Sciences*, Vol. 15, 1948.

7.14   J. KEMPNER, "Postbuckling Behavior of Axially Compressed Circular Cylindrical Sheels," *Journal of the Aeronautical Sciences*, Vol. 21, No. 5, 1954.

7.15   N. J. HOFF, W. A. MADSEN, and J. MAYERS, "The Postbuckling Equilibrium of Axially Compressed Circular Cylindrical Shells," *Stanford University Department of Aeronautics and Astronautics, Report SUDAER No. 221*, Feb. 1965.

7.16   L. H. DONNELL and C. C. WAN, "Effect of Imperfections on Buckling of Thin Cylinders and Columns Under Axial Compression," *Journal of Applied Mechanics, ASME*, Vol. 17, No. 1, March 1950.

7.17   R. C. TENNYSON, "An Experimental Investigation of the Buckling of Circular Cylindrical Shells in Axial Compression Using the Photoelastic Technique," *Institute of Aerospace Sciences, University of Toronto, Report No. 102*, Nov. 1964.

7.18   M. STEIN, "Some Recent Advances in the Investigation of Shell Buckling," *Journal of the American Institute of Aeronautics and Astronautics*, Vol. 6, No. 12, 1968.

Problems

7.1   Using the energy method, investigate the behavior of the one-degree-of-freedom model of a curved plate shown in Fig. P7-1. The model consists of four rigid bars pin connected to each other and to the supports. At the center of the model two linear rotational springs of stiffness $C = M/\theta$ connect opposite bars to each other. Also, each of the two transverse bars contains a linear extensional spring of stiffness K. Determine the load-deflection relation for finite deflections when the load P is applied

(a) concentric with the axis of the longitudinal bars,

(b) eccentric to the axis of the longitudinal bars.

Which buckling characteristics of a curved plate do these models demonstrate?

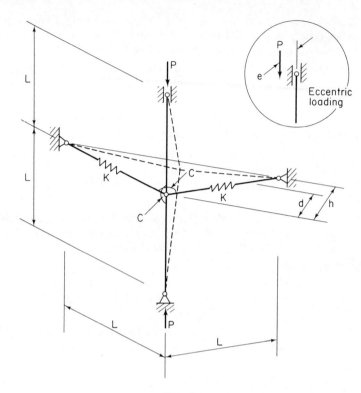

Fig. P7-1

APPENDIX
STABILITY FUNCTIONS
(From Ref. 3.2)

kl	α_n	α_f
0.00	4.0000	2.0000
0.20	3.9946	2.0024
0.40	3.9786	2.0057
0.60	3.9524	2.0119
0.80	3.9136	2.0201
1.00	3.8650	2.0345
1.20	3.8042	2.0502
1.40	3.7317	2.0696
1.60	3.6466	2.0927
1.80	3.5483	2.1199
2.00	3.4364	2.1523
2.04	3.4119	2.1589
2.08	3.3872	2.1662
2.12	3.3617	2.1737
2.16	3.3358	2.1814
2.20	3.3090	2.1893
2.24	3.2814	2.1975
2.28	3.2538	2.2059
2.32	3.2252	2.2146
2.36	3.1959	2.2236
2.40	3.1659	2.2328
2.44	3.1352	2.2424

kl	α_n	α_f
2.48	3.1039	2.2522
2.52	3.0717	2.2623
2.56	3.0389	2.2728
2.60	3.0052	2.2834
2.64	2.9710	2.2946
2.68	2.9357	2.3060
2.72	2.8997	2.3177
2.76	2.8631	2.3300
2.80	2.8255	2.3425
2.84	2.7870	2.3555
2.88	2.7476	2.3688
2.92	2.7073	2.3825
2.96	2.6662	2.3967
3.00	2.6243	2.4115
3.10	2.5144	2.4499
3.15	2.4549	2.4681
3.20	2.3987	2.4922
3.25	2.3385	2.5148
3.30	2.2763	2.5382
3.40	2.1463	2.5881
3.50	2.0084	2.6424
3.60	1.8619	2.7017
3.70	1.7060	2.7668
3.80	1.5400	2.8382
3.90	1.3627	2.9168
4.00	1.1731	3.0037
4.20	0.7510	3.2074
4.40	0.2592	3.4619
4.60	−0.3234	3.7866
4.80	−1.0289	4.2111
5.00	−1.9087	4.7845
5.25	−3.3951	5.8469
5.50	−5.6726	7.6472
5.75	−9.8097	11.2438
6.00	−20.6370	21.4534
6.25	−188.3751	188.4783
2π		
6.50	29.4999	−30.2318

INDEX